STORM CHASING HANDBOOK

TIM VASQUEZ

STORM CHASING HANDBOOK
Second edition

November 2008 / January 2009

ISBN 0-9706840-8-8

Printed in the United States of America

Weather Graphics Technologies
P.O. Box 450211, Garland TX 75045
(800) 840-6280 fax (206) 279-3282
Web site: www.weathergraphics.com
servicedesk@weathergraphics.com

Contents

FOREWORD

by Dave Hoadley, storm chasing pioneer

I have been chasing storms and tornadoes for 52 years, longer than anyone else. One other enthusiast, Roger Jensen, a Minnesota photographer, began taking storm pictures a few years before I did, but he has since passed on. That leaves me as the last of the "really old timers".

Like a few others, I had a significant early experience with a severe storm that damaged my home town. I was a teenager fresh out of high school and could have cared less about a few dumb, boring clouds. After that seminal moment, my life turned around, and every year thereafter was spent anticipating the start of the next storm season. Of course, each spring also brought its share of frustration as the learning curve was just beginning, and I missed many, many tornadoes. There was no National Severe Storms Lab (NSSL), no university chase programs, and I couldn't even imagine a storm chasing book that would answer my every question. After all, as far as I knew, I was the only one doing this.

I began in 1956, before there were weather satellites, cell phones, laptops, or Interstate highways. My earliest photography was on an 8mm Kodak Reliant movie camera, with a hand crank to wind the spring and move the film. My first stop each storm-morning was the local airport and "Weather Bureau" in Bismarck, North Dakota to look at facsimile weather maps, hand drawn and received at similar offices all over the country, based on data that was already hours old. The last stop was in front of a noisily clicking teletype machine, with clipboard in one hand and pencil in the other, rapidly entering hourly surface obs from dozens of local stations onto my own weather map. Where were the clues that would lead to a tornado?

Over the decades since then, satellites went up, radar improved, thousands of storms entered data-banks, and the most sophisticated computers in the world analyzed the atmosphere. Today, instantly accessible data and satellite imagery at every level of the atmosphere is constantly updated, as well as detailed computer projections and severe forecasts --available to anyone with a laptop or data-capable cell phone.

When I began in the 1950s, there was nothing like the publication in your hands to make sense of this rich bounty of information. Were it available then (along with the science), I would be storm chasing today with one prosthetic arm, since the other would have been gladly given for just a few hours to read these pages. If you want to learn how to chase storms, where and why they occur, and how to find tornadoes, then this is your quintessential source.

DAVID HOADLEY
co-founder of *Stormtrack*
November 2008

ACKNOWLEDGEMENT

Book writing is always alluring, but when you get down to the nuts and bolts of it, it's absolutely overwhelming to churn out new paragraphs while preserving quality and accuracy. Fortunately there are people to thank. First is my wife Shannon Key for her support during the final crunch weeks, including the free passes to sleep in late after a dusk-to-dawn writing session. Thanks also go to William Hark for detailed comments and criticisms, to Dave Hoadley for new artwork and suggestions, and to Gene Rhoden of Weatherpix for his support.

I thank the people who helped me with new photos, quotes, and suggestions in the second edition: Shane Adams, Greg Ansel, Paul Austin, Brian Barnes, Dean Baron, Cheryl Chang, Danny Cheresnick, Dann Cianca, Dean Cosgrove, Shawna Davies, Lanny Dean, Charles Doswell, David Drummond, Laura Duchesne, Charles Edwards, Roger Edwards, Brian Emfinger, John Erwin, Mark Farnik, Jason Foster, Andy Gabrielson, Donald Giuliano, Mikey Gribble, Andrea Griffa, Paul Hadfield, Laura Hedien, Greg Higgins, Justin Hobson, Bryan Howell, Jody James, Joey Ketcham, Paul Knightley, George Kourounis, Chris Kridler, Jim LaDue, Tony Laubach, Jim Leonard, Thomas Levendusky, Stephen Levine, Adam Lucio, Tim Marshall, Jean-Francois Massicotte, Connor McCrorey, Ryan McGinnis, Dick McGowan, Steve Miller of Oklahoma, Steve Miller of Texas, Alan Moller, Joseph Nield, Angie Norris, Michael O'Keefe, Jayson Prentice, Andrew Pritchard, Doug Raflik, Ron Riemersma, Scott Roberts, Andrew Ryan, Chris Sanner, Rob Satkus, Mike Scantlin, Cris Schroeder, Mike Smith, Brian Stertz, Greg Stumpf, Brandon Sullivan, Rich Thompson, Rob Wadsworth, Scott Weberpal, John Wetter, Cliff Windham, Tommy Winning, and Jason Young. I greatly thank you all for your time and effort. If I've forgotten anyone, it's not intentional; it's been a real challenge keeping track of all the details of a project of this size. Fortunately we print in small batches and if you let me know I can make minor changes to the layout on the fly.

I want to thank the people who contributed to the First Edition in those busy autumn days of 2002. Their content still remains the backbone of this book. Daphne LaDue(Zaras) and Jim LaDue reviewed the draft and surprised me with many pages of suggestions and comments. David Hoadley helped contribute specially-drawn artwork, Gene Rhoden assisted with stock photos, and Karen Leszke contributed a couple of her photos. Jean Ward helped me fill in photos of chase pioneer Neil Ward and recounted his work decades ago. Bill Hark gave excellent pointers on the book content and the restaurant section. Other contributors to the first edition were Rob Satkus, John Monteverdi, Charles Doswell, Jim Johnson, Roger Edwards, Elke Ueblacker, Mike Hollingshead, Matt Hartman, Blake Naftel, Michael Peregrine, Scott Weberpal, Matt Sellers, Bill Hark, Jason Branz, Andrew Revering, Susan Strom, Jonathan Triggs, Mike Watts, Roger Hill, and Lon Curtis.

TIM VASQUEZ

INTRODUCTION

In March 1999, I produced the hour-long homebrew video *The Art of Storm Chasing* with the help of my then-girlfriend Shannon Key on her Apple G3 computer. The video quickly became a popular introduction to storm chasing but eventually the content aged due to changing technology and the changing nature of the chase. People wanted more, and in a portable form. Fortunately, writing is my strong suit, and work on a chasing book began in August 2002. It was released a few months later.

It didn't surprise me that by 2005 *Storm Chasing Handbook* became a gold standard for the chase community. Not only did I get re-orders for beat up books, but I heard of chasers bringing their copy out in the field so others could autograph their margin quotes. But technology has been on the march, and I've been feeling strongly that the original version is no longer up to snuff. For instance, mobile broadband offerings are completely different from the early days, and cheap digital cameras are no longer something to inspect with a stick and surgical gloves while at Best Buy. I've also wanted to make changes, expand certain sections, and improve the guide.

Work on the second edition started in January 2008 but was soon derailed by our move back to Norman, Oklahoma, summer travel, and several flu and cold bugs that went around in July. I was finally able to resume work in October. I'm glad to say that all the effort was worth it. This update is not perfect, though; it's been constrained by a need to make a December 2008 release date so I can meet other pressing obligations, and it's hard to give all 300 pages the attention they deserve. I feel there may still be some old information in the thunderstorm and forecasting chapters, given the advances in meteorology. However this will be treated lavishly in a separate severe weather book I have under production. The *Storm Chasing Handbook* book still serves its purpose as a friendly introduction to storm chasing in general.

My philosophy is that I always try to improve on my work, so there will doubtless be third and fourth editions of this book in the near future that will be even better. All feedback is important. The best way to send suggestions is to write an e-mail to the address shown on the edition notice page near the copyright. What do you want in a third edition?

That said, let's get on with the exciting subject of chasing and storms!

TIM VASQUEZ
November 2008
Norman, Oklahoma

DISCLAIMER

Storm chasing is a dangerous activity. The information presented throughout this book is not complete and may contain errors or inaccuracies. It is NOT a substitute for educating yourself using other resources and receiving mentoring from an experienced storm chaser. If you do not understand the risks of storm chasing and are not willing to accept all responsibility for your decisions, DO NOT engage in storm chasing.

Student: “Is there anything more miraculous than the wonders of nature?”

Master: “Yes. Your appreciation of those wonders.”

- Zen proverb

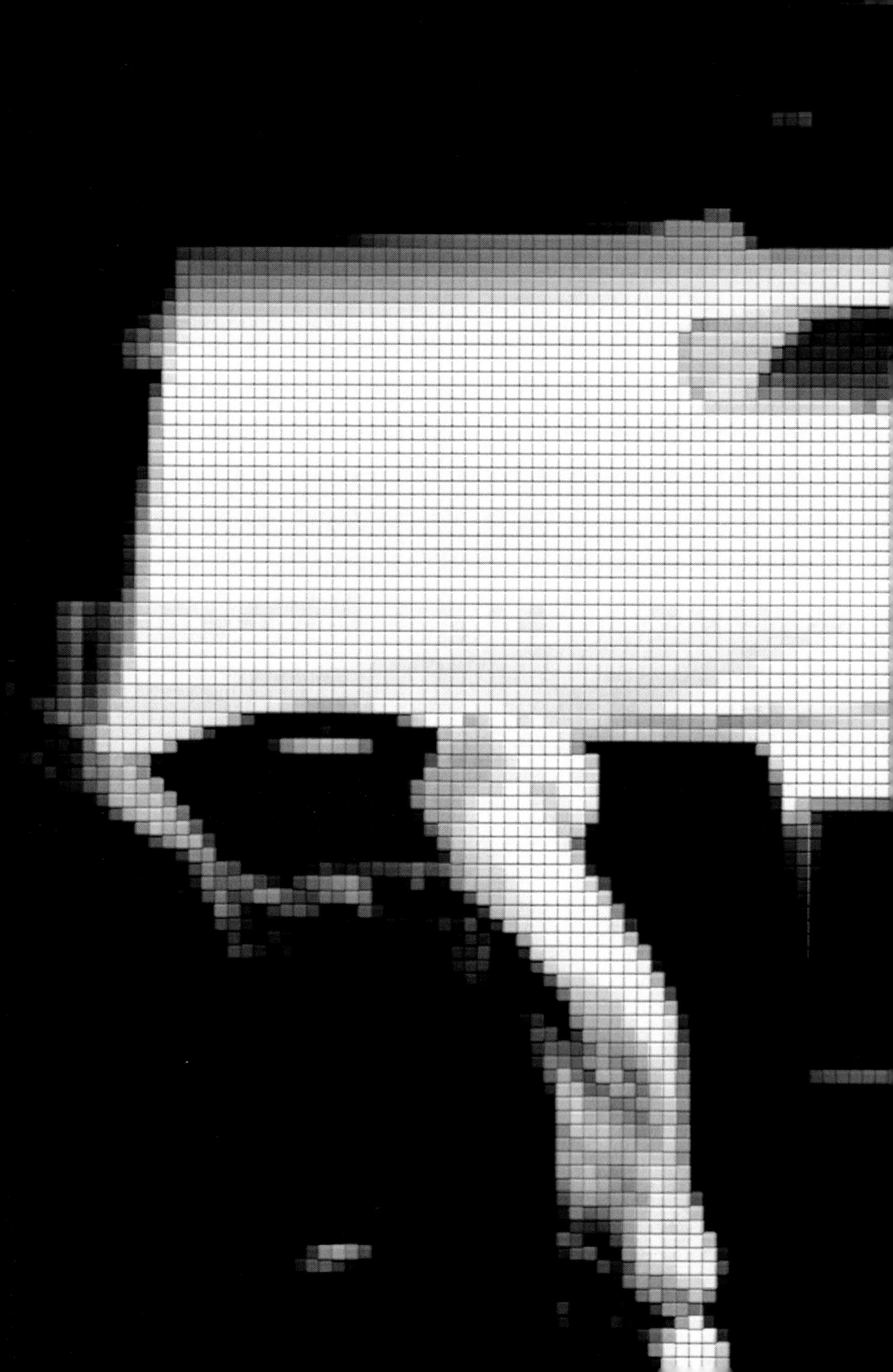

CHAPTER ONE
STORM CHASING

Storm chasing, in its simplest terms, is the art and science of meeting with a thunderstorm, for any reason. Tornadoes are widely regarded as the main target for storm chasing activity, but anything photogenic, unique in structure, or awe-inspiring fits the definition of a chase target. The photographers throughout Arizona and New Mexico who head to the foothills in pursuit of a perfect lightning shot are storm chasers, too, and many have just as much skill and experience as the Great Plains storm chasers.

The ultimate goal of storm chasing is incredibly multifaceted and varied. Some chasers focus on honing their photography skills. Some chase to supplement their income. Others see it as a great alternative to a dull beachfront vacation in Hawaii. Others are invested intellectually as part of a university research project. Regardless of the goal, a common thread binds all of these activities together: the need for an unrivalled degree of perseverance and a requirement for scientific understanding. Almost no chasers get very far before they have to turn to the books and to the latest scientific research to get a grasp of what they are seeing in the sky. This shapes field strategy and determines success.

Finally, a unique attribute of storm chasing is that it shares common roots with flying and computer gaming: it was made possible only by 20th century technological advances. Storm chasing requires a dense, efficient road network; reliable automobiles with low operating costs and fast speed; and an understanding of storm-scale meteorology and forecasting. The first two ingredients did not exist in the United States until the 1930s, and still do not exist in many parts of the world that get tornadic storms. The latter prerequisite, storm knowledge, did not appear until the 1950s, as the work of storm researchers Horace Byers, Roscoe Braham, and later Theodore Fujita slowly solidified into an primordial understanding of storm cell character. With this knowledge, storm chasing slowly began to flourish.

The essence of chasing

The whole chase experience is surreal. It's a nomadic existence for one or more weeks, never knowing where you'll lay your head that night. It's an excuse to live on junk food, eat at greasy spoon cafes, have bacon every day, and be blissfully unaware of slow service. It's the beauty of the endless flat prairie, which before I chased I saw as boring but have come to love. It's soothing, like being on a boat in the middle of an endless sea.

It's a refreshing feeling of freedom that makes the East Coast seem claustrophobic with its hills and trees. It's the tiny "blink-and-you-miss-it" towns. It's the way the sky, even on a fair-weather day, demands your attention. It's the pride of knowing the geography: the obscure towns and knowing its motels and restaurants.

And last but not least, it's the fellow chasers as well as the offbeat characters who call the Great Plains home.

JIM CARUSO
Pennington, NJ chaser

David Hoadley, one of the first recreational chasers.

Neil Ward, one of the first research chasers.

Roger Jensen, one of the first severe weather photographers.

The history of chasing

One of the first storm chasers is **David Hoadley** (1938-) who in 1956 began chasing storms in North Dakota. He was a prolific artist and later founded *Stormtrack* magazine. Further south in the late 1950's, Weather Bureau employee **Neil Ward** (1913-1972) unwittingly became the first scientific chaser. Initially he pursued Oklahoma storms out of curiosity but soon developed an interest in seeking visual correlation with radar signatures and forming conceptual models of storms. The late **Roger Jensen** (1933-2001), a published Minnesota photographer, is considered in some circles to be a storm chasing pioneer. Jensen was among the first storm photographers and had a great passion for weather which sustained him through his later years of declining health.

Though there were airbone storm chases in 1946 during the federally-operated Thunderstorm Project in Florida, the first research chases by car date back to the mid-1960s, in which various universities and research facilities fanned out to collect fresh hailstone specimens. Hurricane chasers were also becoming active, starting in the 1950s with **Arthur Pike** of the National Hurricane Research Laboratory and **Clarence Gibbons** of CBS News. Later in the 1960s chasers affiliated with Florida State University's weather department began chasing hurricanes.

The first full-scale thunderstorm research chase program began on 18 April 1972 in Oklahoma. The University of Oklahoma (OU), in cooperation with the National Severe Storms Laboratory (NSSL), created the Tornado Intercept Project (TIP). Designed to investigate characteristics of tornadic storms, this project was a turning point in the history of storm scale meteorology. Its core group created the first generation of storm chasers, some of whom are are still active today. The program also quickly paid off with rich documentation of the famous Union City, Oklahoma tornado in 1973.

Soon a fusion of storm chasing roots occurred. At an American Meteorological Society conference in October 1977, pioneer David Hoadley, chaser Randy Zipser, and TIP veterans Charles Doswell, Alan Moller, and Richard Anthony gathered in a hotel room and screened their thunderstorm slides. The group resolved to keep in touch, and that very night, Dave Hoadley began working on the first issue of

David Hoadley's self-portrait: the early years.

The Early Years of Chasing

David Hoadley

I began storm chasing in 1956, a few years after the late Roger Jensen blazed that first, brave trail on which we all now follow. My early range was from the Dakotas to western Minnesota, but usually centered on the eastern half of my home state: North Dakota.

My first chase car was the family "Olds 88," which we bought new in 1955 and to which I added many of the 163,000 miles. It was later traded for a Buick. I used it on weekends — a Saturday here, a Sunday there — when it wasn't needed at home and storms were brewing. My family was always very supportive, if a little apprehensive, and enjoyed my chase accounts after each return.

I saw my first tornado on August, 1958 near Wing, North Dakota — but that was mainly luck, since the next one didn't come for another four years near Leola, South Dakota. After another few years, my learning curve began to kick in and more were seen as skill added to luck.

My particular memories of those early Dakota chases, besides traveling many more graded farm roads than are found today, were the blizzard of bugs and carpet of frogs that followed many heavy storms. On warm summer nights, when returning from a chase, the Dakota ponds that dot the eastern half of the state quickly served up an instant generation of flying insects that swarmed to the only headlights for 20 miles and soon rendered my windshield a greasy mess.

On other nights, the insects took a break and the amphibians took over. Then my headlights showed a pavement covered with thousands of small, leaping frogs. I always slowed since traction quickly becomes a problem. The frogs were impossible to dodge. You just kept going, quietly saying to no one in particular, "Sorry. Sorry. Sorry."

One thing I especially miss from those Dakota years were the northern lights. That, plus the long drives across once-Indian country and the remembered history of pioneer settlements have etched that experience indelibly in the mind. It was a good place to hone both my patience and skills for the later, more abundant years in the heartland of "tornado alley."

Stormtrack, sent to a dozen individuals. It would be the first of many issues.

In the public arena, storm chasing emerged into the American conscience with the airing of *In Search Of...* (Alan Landsburg Productions) in 1978. This show profiled chase and research operations at NSSL. Years later, the PBS program *Nova: Tornado!* (WGBH) aired in November 1985, touching again on NSSL chase operations and the TOTO tornado observatory. The hour-long scientific documentary and publicity surrounding the program stirred interest among many weather enthusiasts and inspired future meteorologists, leading to drastic increases in the Stormtrack subscription roster. In May 1986, Dave Hoadley retired from *Stormtrack*, handing the enterprise to Tim Marshall, a damage engineer and meteorologist in Texas.

During the early 1990s, television once again seized on tornado chasing, though this time the dry educational content was replaced with the cocktail of unpredictable content from home video, which had recently exploded into popularity. Tornado clips showed frightened families, merry narrators, and reckless chasers. In spite of this content, the storm chasing hobby saw another generation of productive beginners who saw past the hype and took inspiration.

The final wave that sent ripples through the storm chasing community was the May 1996 release of the Warner Brothers film *Twister*, a scientifically-bankrupt blockbuster

Merits of *Twister*

I know most people look at this movie as nothing more than a big, dumb special effects movie, but I seem to get MUCH more out of it. I adore this film. Why is *Twister* something more then just your normal dumb summer movie? Well there are a few reasons. One that comes to mind is how gorgeous this film is. No other film I can think of so beautifully captures middle America as well as *Twister*. There are over a hundred shots in this film that could easily be made into a postcard — they are that gorgeous!

Anonymous reviewer
imdb.com

A long day's sunset. *(Tim Vasquez)*

film that promoted massive interest in storm chasing. In spite of the temporary chaos it brought to the hobby, including an overnight doubling of the *Stormtrack* ranks, countless *Twister* enthusiasts dropped out of sight by 2000, probably having discovered that chasing was nothing like the movie.

The storm chasing hobby saw its biggest revolution with the arrival of the Internet, which completely redefined how storm pictures and video gets published. Moving with the times, *Stormtrack* discontinued its paper magazine in 2002 and provided its followers with a discussion forum, currently the largest online community that caters to chasers. Many storm chasers maintain their own websites and post photo galleries, chase logs, and streaming video. Today's storm saturation is a far cry from that mild October night in 1977 when chasers were blessed with an unimaginable, rare chance to feast on amazing storm imagery and uncharted chase stories.

Not just the sky: the ground!

I took several geology classes in school and I often find myself searching the ground for unusual rocks and minerals. I've found several arrowheads and fossils over the years. I especially enjoy checking out the rocky, hilly terrain of southwest Oklahoma. Although I'm not particularly fond of botany or zoology, it is still interesting to see the different types of plants and animals across the region. Makes the bust days a little more interesting. Well, sometimes!

ROB SATKUS
Oklahoma City, OK chaser

What is a chaser?

Storm chasers are individuals who share a common interest in severe thunderstorms. They are not necessarily meteorologists or researchers; in fact the vast majority of them are engineers, cooks, salespeople, programmers, mechanics, and so forth. Storm chasing is largely a hobby, and nearly all storm chasers pay for their pursuits out of their own pockets. A sum of $50 per day for a chase is a typical expense, not counting lodging or car rental.

It's important at this point to make a distinction between *storm spotters* and *storm chasers*. Storm spotters are amateur radio operators who travel within or just outside of a city to observe and monitor severe weather as part of a local emergency management program. Spotters operate under the centralized guidance of a team leader at the base station, and operations focus entirely on interpreting existing storm structure. This is an important distinction, because storm chasers are free to travel anywhere

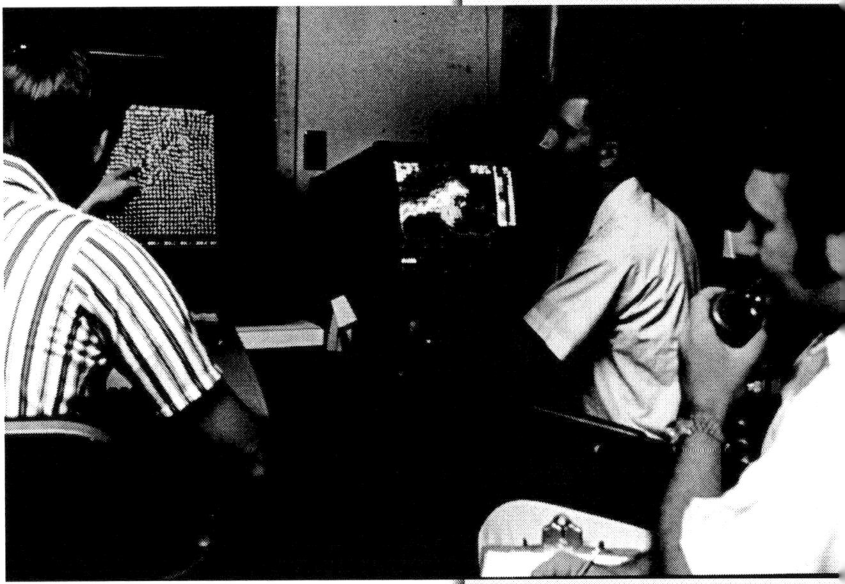

Storm chasing in the 1970s wasn't just about chase vehicles. It depended on a sophisticated nowcasting operation that used impressive legacy technology but relied on an assortment of coarse surface, satellite, and radar data and very limited forecast experience. *(NOAA)*

Great storm experiments

TIP (1972-1986) — *Tornado Intercept Project.* The first scientific field project on severe thunderstorms, undertaken by NSSL.

SESAME (1979) — *Severe Environmental Storms And Mesoscale Experiment.* Sampled southern plains storm activity at different scales of motion.

VORTEX (1994-95) — *Verification of the Origins of Rotation in Tornadoes Experiment.* Sought to understand the origins of tornado development.

SUB-VORTEX (1997) — Explored mobile mesonet systems.

ROTATE (1998-99) — *Radar Observations of Tornadoes And Thunderstorms Experiment.* A Doppler on Wheels field project conducted by OU.

IHOP (2002) — *International H_2O Project.* NCAR project studying water vapor evolution on the Plains.

VORTEX 2 (2009-2010) — An effort to study supercells and tornadoes with maximum density in surface, upper-air, and radar measurements.

they wish and do whatever they like near the storm. With freedom comes the burden of having to forecast for these broad areas using relatively little weather data. This book is specifically written for the storm chasers.

Another distinction needs to be made: *research chasers.* These individuals consist of meteorology students and faculty that participate as part of an institutional research program. For students and volunteers, there is no pay for this activity except for free lodging and food, as well as a small travel stipend. The group chases as a team, and important field decisions are made by a complement of team leaders. While this does take the guesswork out of the chase, the structured objectives make it difficult for participants to personally develop their own forecast methodologies and test their own tactics in the field. Therefore it's no surprise that a lot of research chasers head to the field by themselves, living and dying by their own decisions to see what fortune brings.

A meteorology degree is not any kind of prerequisite for being a chaser. However a formal education can help provide insight into forecasts and storm theory, as well as make sense of the latest research papers. No type of credentials, certification, or licensing is required to chase storms and there is no sanctioning body nor even a national storm chaser association. It is largely a loose-knit community. Storm chasing is in no way regulated by Federal, state, or

About research chasing

There are definite pros and cons to chasing with a major field project compared to chasing on your own. The advantages include low-cost chasing (gas and lodging is paid for, and sometimes a small stipend or per diem is even paid), meeting and networking with some of the leading meteorological scientists in the world, learning about the instrumentation and equipment used in the project, and being able to take part in a project with research goals designed to benefit all of society.

There are disadvantages. You do not have any control over the daily target area. Most people are not able to participate in the forecasting and decision making except for the core scientists, so most volunteers are basically a worker doing exactly the task they are assigned.

On individual chase vacations downtime can be used to go home briefly, visit friends, go to scenic or historics sites or any other number of entertaining ways to spend time. During a major project, they will likely be spent in an individual city, sometimes small and fairly rural, with a full workload on vehicles repairs, data backups, and analysis etc.

These programs can be difficult to get into, depending on the number of volunteers and the number of positions available. However, if an individual is interested in the scientific benefits from chasing, this can be an excellent opportunity to learn and lot in a fun environment, while meeting many people and observing high tech data collection methods.

DANNY CHERESNICK
Longmont, Colorado chaser

local laws. Chasers operate freely, and are simply expected to abide by all laws that apply to the general public.

There's a popular misconception, especially among school-age children, that a career can be made in storm chasing. The reality is that with rare exception there is no such thing as a storm chaser job. Getting paid any sizable sum to storm chase can only be accomplished through two avenues: either as a self-motivated entrepreneur such as a tour operator or photographer, or as a university researcher specializing in severe weather and having completed the right graduate work. With the former, the financial risks are high, and with the latter, research dollars are chronically scarce.

Some storm chasers have cultivated a business of selling their video and photographs to media companies and stock agencies. For decades this has been a favored way of increasing the chase budget, though in the 1990s a few chasers earned thousands of dollars for their pictures. The tide, however, is changing due to a glut of weather stock photos, amateur pictures, and freelancers, and the outlook for this line of work has already clouded.

Perhaps it's only fair that storm chasing remains primarily a hobby. A chaser becomes their own boss, going where they want to go rather than where a team member or agenda dictates, and success is measured not by how many tornadoes were logged but by whether it was a memorable, awe-inspiring day that taught us all something new.

Shooting for TV stations

If you shoot some great footage and the chase is still ongoing, you may be expected to stop your chase to send in the video. Also, on chase days where your target is out of the viewing area, there still may be a chance of severe weather in the viewing area.

On these days, you may be asked to stay in the area. This is not always a bad thing. On May 1, 2008, everyone was roaming around Kansas watching the storms line out, but I was in perfect position to intercept tornadoes from the surprise Stillwater storm. Chasing for a TV station paid off on this day. It's also a great way to get some easy gas money, even on non-chase days. In certain situations, being a member of the media will get you certain privileges that being a regular chaser will not.

MIKE SCANTLIN
Tulsa, Oklahoma chaser

Chase convergence. *(Tim Vasquez)*

Chasers upload storm video at an Arby's restaurant in Enid, Oklahoma to regional news stations. Chasers pictured are (left to right) Andrea Miller, Heather Briggs, and Matt Patterson. Selling chase footage is a sacrifice that sometimes requires breaking off from the chase to deliver the goods. *(Steve Miller, www.hamwx.com)*

Caution with the media

Storm chasers should be careful when dealing with the media since any off-color remark will be quoted and used out of context. When I give interviews, I emphasize the beauty of storms, the importance of calling in storm reports, and my hope that a storm will occur in an unpopulated area.

BILL HARK
Richmond, VA chaser

Philosophy and objectives

To some readers, it might appear that a section on philosophy is chasing abstracted into psychological babble. Perhaps so! But sooner or later, participants in nearly every type of human activity begin dwelling on our relationship with the activity itself. This yields intriguing insights on what we do, giving us more avenues for appreciation and even helping to sharpen our skills.

Consider the definition of philosophy: the study of how we think. Storm chasing is certainly a thinking, intellectual activity, and how we think during the culmination of a chase day shapes not only our result but also the notion of whether we've succeeded of failed. This is largely why there is such a tremendous range of attitudes in the hobby: negative and positive alike. *Philosophy is the framework that helps us clarify the definitions of success or failure.* Without having a philosophy, how can we define what chase success is and find real satisfaction in what we do?

The art of storm chasing is rooted deeply in the dualism between subjectivity and objectivity, probably more so than any other hobby. For example, to a journalist it seems quite simple: a chaser uses intellectual methods to pick out target areas, and then emotionally experiences the fruits of labor. It's certainly an acceptable perspective, but in a sense being pigeonholed into this method of thinking keeps a chaser from enjoying all aspects of the experience. In many cases, we have personalities that are "stuck" to one end of this spectrum throughout the entire chase!

Take the romantic storm chaser. His objectives are excitement, inspiration, and visual beauty. The contact with nature and with others humans is the essence of the experience. To reach the storm, however, the romantic chaser must grudgingly look at the underlying form using scientific tools: maps and data. Perusing these, he applies only sage experience and pattern recognition, rather than sound principles and logic. When omega diagnostic charts, thermodynamic diagrams, and journals are pulled out, the romantic chaser's eyes become glazed over. He says, "Those charts are ugly, dull, and complicated. Let's look outside! The atmosphere is something real, not expressed in these coarse abstractions!" Once out in the field, the romantic chaser fails to synthesize what he sees visually with actual data and conceptual models, and has a hard time in finding consistent chase success.

At the opposite extreme, there's the classical chaser. She focuses on the mechanics behind the storm. To her, the chase day is an incredible puzzle box. She enjoys perusing the morning data, and she makes use of the mobile mesonet on her SUV to fill in the data gaps. Seeing a tornado, she sees a dramatic example of structure and form. It evokes questions of, "How is it all linked together? What's going on above the tornado? How does this relate to the conceptual structures I remember from the journals?" The interplay of colors on the cloud surface and the rich smell of June on the Great Plains suggest unique combinations of sun angles, vegetation, and calendar date. The classical chaser looks at the spotters down the road and grows concerned over whether anyone is reporting the developing wall cloud. To simply go out and lie on the hood and soak up the experience would be hedonistic and shallow. The storm is objectified, so much to the point that subtle, beautiful features of the storm are filtered out — ones which might represent some sort of critical process taking place in the atmosphere. The tornado fascinates, but fails to make a deep, haunting impression that encourages the thirst for knowledge. The classical chaser might simply become bored and move on to other pursuits after a couple of years.

It can be seen that there's fantastic value and beauty in each of these mindsets: not just through the romantic perspective but in the classical form, too. How is it possible

The importance of receptivity

One of chase veteran Al Moller's favorite books is Gross & Shapiro's *The Tao of Photography*. In order to convey some of its potential application to chasing, Moller strung together several passages with his 30 years of experience to form the following pearl of wisdom:

"The Tao *sage* or wise man has an open mind. It is not an empty mind, but one that is uncluttered from constricted awareness and/or bloated sense of self. This is critical for achieving storm chase success. "Little thinking" has a chaser worried about yesterday's failures, rather than the beauty of being on the road and searching actively for today's environmental clues.

"Receptivity allows one's thoughts to balance properly the daily stream of observational data, model data, and environmental clues, while enjoying the process of determining which clues are most critical. Receptivity allows the chaser to accept what happens, and to maximize the event, whether during scientific data collection during a field experiment, or photography during an unstructured chase. And it allows the chaser to respond instantaneously to chance encounters.

"The more you love the forecasting, navigating, and ingestion of data and environmental clues, the greater the success you will have. Get lost in the joy of the process!"

for the chaser benefit from each of them? Should a chase philosophy be constructed in terms of the moment? Is it wrong to be stuck in one mental way of thinking or the other?

A much more prudent chase philosophy is to strive for a fusion of the two modes, not simply gravitating towards one perspective or the other but casting it aside completely. This is done through total awareness. Gusty southeast winds are noticed, enjoyed, savored, contemplated in the context of the forecast situation. The mesocyclone is obviously getting its act together above the widening cloud base, portending of imminent chase action yet evoking a sense of timelessness, this same scene conceivably unfolding on a Wednesday a billion years ago, man's presence just a speck within the Holocene sliver in which we live.

It's very likely that a chaser who is immersed in total awareness understands all the subtleties of the atmosphere and can enjoy enormous success rates. Robert Pirsig, in *Zen and the Art of Motorcycle Maintenance*, suggests that the fusion of classicism and romanticism in our culture is rare. It can probably never be achieved perfectly, but can be strived for. It's the mechanism that breeds quality through inspiration and moments of genius. Through this fusion, storm

The ideal chase

I see chasing in many ways a metaphor for how we do life. In both cases, we are pursuing a goal, and how we pursue that goal as well as how we react to it when we reach our intended target tells us alot about what we may learn about ourselves and where we still may grow.

For instance, what if that supercell that seemed certain to produce a tornado for you when it was 60 miles away and being the only storm anywhere on the horizon - collapses just as you arrive and you instead see a lightning show or full double rainbow instead? How do you handle this? Do you cuss and kick the ground, or do you say "thank you Creator for the opportunity to engage in this hunt today."?

When I chase, my most successful times include the attitude of gratitude.. On my way to a target region, if I see a beautiful pearly TCU towering into blue sky, I give thanks to Creator, and state that even if nothing else comes out of the chase today, this scene made the trip worth it.

When I have an attitude of gratitude, I seem to tap into the flow intuitively better. If I have an attitude of impatience or grouchiness, then I tend to make mistakes or in general forget the possibility of enjoying the journey in zen-like fashon.

STEPHEN LEVINE
Garland, Texas chaser

Gene Rhoden and Scott Peake check on a radar image to help fine-tune their position. *(Andrew Ryan / shearamazement.com)*

chasing becomes an art form, a philosophy, way of looking at life, and a source of inner happiness and contentment.

Pirsig suggests that the only way to reach this fusion is to cultivate an inner quietness. This allows one to be completely in tune with the surroundings. But there are three main requirements before this can actually occur. First, comfort is required. This means taking breaks for meals, suppressing distractions, and keeping the vehicle at a comfortable temperature. Second, adequate tools are needed. Carry in moderation the partners, gadgets, and equipment you need to chase successfully. A laptop or cell phone may not be such a bad idea.

Finally, and most important, avoid traps which make inner quiet elusive. These include destructive mindsets that result from anxiety, ego, boredom, impatience, and chase partner conflicts. If you sense a mental trap developing, learn to short circuit this way of thinking, figure out what *really* matters to you at the lowest common denominator, and work on finding happiness by living only in the moment. If you're delayed by one of the many Kansas Specials (50-mile construction zones), let go, enjoy the timeless scenery along the highway, and perhaps reflect on your good fortune not being stuck in an office building on this chase day.

A chaser who is pursuing a total-awareness approach to chasing exhibits both the classic and romantic aspects of chasing. By being in tune with all aspects of the chase and the brain freed from stress and frustration, storm chasing opens the mind, broadens the ability to process and sort knowledge to make a correct decision, and encourages a sense of delight no matter what the forecast brings.

Ethics

For a hypothetical chaser alone on a desert island and separated from other forms of life, ethics are meaningless. For the rest of us, however, chasing brings contact with other individuals, other chasers, local residents, and TV viewers, requiring a framework of respect to everyone involved. The opportunities for a chaser to embarrass or offend others are surprisingly numerous. This can harm the hobby over the long term through pervasive public attitudes, law enforcement harassment, a bad stigma precipitated by the media, and even the appearance of legislation. All of these are bad long-term investments for future chases. A measure making an emergency situation a national security

A British perspective

For me, the central Plains states have long held a place in my heart, having seen pictures of tornadoes at an early age in various books. For years before I came to the USA chasing, the most evocative image of states like Kansas, Oklahoma, and Texas was one of a road stretching into the far distance, with a line of telegraph/power poles down one side of the road. And far from being some kind of romantic personal vision of the region, my trips have yielded uncountable such scenes, each of which makes my desire to get back to the region the following year even stronger.

Also, it's very interesting to me to garner a fuller understanding of the history of the region, including that of the Native American people. I like to stop and look at historical markers, etc, when given the chance. The quieter days relaxing by the pool in a motel, and waiting for the next potential round of severe weather, is intoxicating. And quite apart from this, and, of course, the storms, I just love the massive skies, flat lands, and, above all, the empty roads - the latter only something we can dream of on our crowded British islands.

PAUL KNIGHTLEY
Reading, England chaser

Ten "Nevers" Of Storm Chasing

Never ignore the traffic, the road, and other drivers; they're the biggest danger.
Never ignore the lessons of the chase: the bad ones as well as the good ones.
Never talk about storms with unrestrained delight around local residents.
Never block lanes of traffic with your vehicle, equipment, or yourself.
Never follow another chaser on their chase except by permission.
Never frivolously core-punch or frivolously chase at night.
Never trespass on private land except by permission.
Never chase without a learning objective in mind.
Never put yourself or your passengers in danger.
Never chase without safety and courtesy.

area and prohibiting photography would not be a surprising development in today's political climate.

To help deal with issues like these, many hobbies and professions in similar predicaments have developed codes of ethics. Ethics are guiding philosophies which establish a moral code: a set of right and wrong choices. One of the first efforts to bring ethics to storm chasing occurred in 1992 when Alan Moller wrote "Ethics of Storm Chasing" for Stormtrack. It subdivided core ethics into two key points: safety and courtesy.

Safety is a topic so important that further discussion of it will be relegated to its own chapter here within this book. Not only does safety protect the chaser's life: it protects passengers and other drivers and sets an example for newcomers to the hobby.

Courtesy is defined as "respect for others". It's a way of channeling positive energy and goodwill into all interactions with fellow chasers and the general public, which in turn makes those facets of chasing easier and much more enjoyable. It's worth noting that many *dojos* stress that martial arts without courtesy demonstrates a lack of spirit, equated with chaos or violence. Lack of courtesy breeds ill will, and in chasing it sows the seeds for awkward, unpleasant encounters in the field.

One principle which has increased in importance during recent years is courtesy toward locals and respect for storm victims. A surprising number of individuals in the Great Plains have lost property, family, and friends in severe weather and tend to become fearful and irrational

An Italian viewpoint

I have to admit that when you chase in the United States, it's so fine the feeling to be part of the chase community. You find other chasers on the road and it's simple to make friends with them! You wait for convection and you meet someone that offers his congratulations on your hail dents! You speak about meteorology as if those guys were longtime friends. I mean you feel great and it's very funny.

Moreover when you speak with normal people as a chaser, they don't treat you as a crazy man. To them you are a man who helps people to defend their own safety, and that, believe me, is great. And about American people: it's incredible to see how a Greensburg survivor puts himself forward to rebuild his city, confident in the future and in his country. I love this positive spirit.

ANDREA GRIFFA
Cantù, Italy chaser

during severe weather outbreaks. They staff the gas stations and wait tables at the restaurants where chasers congregate, who might be innocently raving over storm chase success. Be aware of your conduct. Damage is another area where chasers can extend courtesy. Leave unless you're saving life or property.

A May 3 crowd

A chaser crowd gathers near Binger, Oklahoma on May 3, 1999 in central Oklahoma. This one was unexpectedly created by a roadblock. Many chasers turned around and picked alternate routes. *(Tim Vasquez)*

The yahoo

A yahoo is any individual chasing a storm who practices *harmful or unethical conduct.* Reckless driving is the prime example, as is blocking roads and trespassing onto private property. We all share the responsibility of not tolerating unsafe, unethical behavior and demonstrating good chasing by example.

Unfortunately, yahoos attract attention and bask in it. During the late 1990s, broadcasters capitalized on this to drive up ratings. Some yahoos became de-facto ambassadors for the hobby. Fortunately this perspective has run its course and media programming has drifted back to some semblance of quality. Some local news outlets and Internet video sites like YouTube, however, do play a part in perpetuating yahoo stereotypes.

It must also be pointed out while a few yahoos are indeed experienced chasers who have a fringe affiliation with the chasing community, *most of them are not part of the chaser community at all.* With only a local outlet for their weather interests (often just their own families or neighbors), they're known as "local yokels". One local yokel example is the truckload of teenagers driving into a storm, getting directions via cellphone from a girlfriend watching the local television weathercast. Most local yokels are completely unaware of storm chasing history and meteorology, aside from a few casual Internet searches, and have little understanding of how to chase safely.

For the experienced chaser, this makes defensive driving even more important. Yahoo behavior will probably never go away, but by recognizing it and understanding its roots, we can all give ourselves a better margin of safety and personal enjoyment when out in the field. For those who want to enjoy storms without the "circus" crowds, a common

---

The reward

You can't begin to imagine the struggle that I have to endure to achieve the proper outlook on chasing. When I achieve it I'm rewarded as my criteria for success broadens. No longer is a chase day consumed by worries that I might not get the right storm, or that someone else has a better view. In the right state, I live the moment, enjoy what the sky unfolds, and my intuition governs my decisions without distraction. The tornado is no longer the only requirement for satisfaction. Enjoyment and success are delivered in many ways including capturing a photogenic sky, meeting friends in the field, even the thought of letting the sky, instead of society, be in control.

JIM LADUE
Norman, OK chaser

strategy is to separate from the main show and take a risk on the long shots. Some amazing events have unfolded away from all the action.

How to start chasing

The very first thing a new chaser should do is, in the words of chase veteran Tim Marshall: "Read all you can." There is no way that a chaser can pursue storms, stay safe, and improve their skill without drawing on the rich body of meteorological knowledge that's blossomed during the past twenty years. A number of web sites offer links to excellent resources and can be found throughout this book. Also there is substantially more which is available in the form of books and publications. These are listed in the appendix. Check them out. After educating yourself on storm fundamentals, keep note of the angles that interest you. Use them as teasers to encourage yourself to learn more. The rest will fall in place.

Chasers must also spend time putting their knowledge into actual practice. Obviously you can't repair a Honda Accord by reading car manuals at bedtime every night — you have to put your knowledge to use by actually seeing the engine and trying your hand at making a few repairs. Likewise, there is a wealth of real-time weather information on the Internet. Seize every opportunity to use this information and prepare your own weather forecasts and chase predictions, even if you're not going anywhere. Chasing vicariously is done by many veterans when they can't make it out the door.

It pays dividends to go on a couple of chases with an experienced chaser. This allows you to get a firsthand look at the decisionmaking process. Unfortunately, many experienced chasers have grown weary of e-mail contacts with individuals who have no sense of what chasing really involves, who expect the chaser to fit their schedule, or are only participating for the thrill. To ride with an experienced chaser, you'll have to do your homework and demonstrate substantial amounts of flexibility, dedication, and commitment. The opportunities are there; a perusal of the Stormtrack web site or various E-mail lists will present many options for those with persistence.

One surefire way to get involved right away is to buy your seat on a chase. There are a handful of excellent commercial chase tour operators who are happy to take you

Who is the yahoo?

The "yahoo" is the chronically inconsiderate bonehead, the normally sane person who often loses his ability to think clearly and act safely in the heat of the moment — under pressure to catch up and get that intense footage — or the vacuum-brain who doesn't have that ability at all. These are the people who run others off the road, set up tripods in traffic lanes, drive 90 mph on a wet two-lane, and roar across private property. Then there are a few yahoo media crews, justifying all sorts of dangerous actions on the roadways to get the most extreme possible close-up footage of neighborhoods being shredded apart, all in the name of "serving the viewing public" and winning an Emmy.

Dangerous behavior crosses all experience levels in chasing. I do argue it is *less common* among the veterans. In some ways, the handful of guys who have many years of experience as unsafe, inconsiderate chase bozos do make things worse! By getting away with it for so long without either dying in a crash or being thrown in jail, they are setting a terrible example for others who may accompany them or observe the way they operate. Propagation of stupidity is indeed possible!

ROGER EDWARDS
Norman, OK chaser

along and teach you as you intercept spring storms. Always look for a tour operator who is recommended by other chasers and look for indicators of safety and quality rather than mere statistics. More tips are provided in the appendix.

And if you have to start chasing the hard way, as many of us do: start small! Don't head out the door hoping to see a wedge tornado your first season. Try your hand at intercepting even the smallest garden-variety storms, and enjoy the success that comes from simply making it to a given storm, holding an observing position, and correlating the storm structures to textbook conceptual models. These smaller, simpler storms serve as an important foundation for understanding bigger thunderstorms and offer many visual puzzles that will sharpen your skills. As you chase, pay careful attention to your mistakes and your errors, and make efforts to learn from them after the fact.

Finally, it's important to cultivate some interests that you can draw upon when storms fail to materialize or the weather patterns go bad. Geology, ornithology, photography, antique-hunting, hiking, and even local history are among some popular pursuits. Find some aspect of the Great Plains that captures your interest. The last half of this book contains an extensive description of various parts of the Great Plains, proving that there's much more than meets the eye!

A common thread?

The anecdotal evidence strongly suggests that while there might be a semblance of gender parity at the casual level, it fades away as one approaches the inner sanctum of [this] obsessive [activity]. The Nobel-prizewinning Dutch ethnologist Nikolaas Tinbergen speculated [this hobby] was some sort of sublimated expression of the ancient hunting instinct — an observation so screamingly true it seems rather petty of Tinbergen to have bothered to slap his name on it.

Every healthy, red-blooded man knows the experience of being jolted awake, sometimes at four in the morning, by an aching conviction that he really should be out there on his belly in the undergrowth stalking a fellow organism. If one happens to have binoculars at hand, [it] is a more than decent outlet for this atavistic hunger.

BRUNO MADDOX,
discussing birdwatching
Blinded by Science: Birding Brains
Discover Magazine, 2006

The agitation and pressure of making your own forecast is what creates skill and instills intuition. Never be afraid to think outside the box and live or die by your own forecast! *(David Hoadley)*

CHAPTER TWO
EQUIPMENT

The year 1988 was a season of drought and disappointment for storm chasing. Ironically, though, this was a time of significant optimism within the hobby. It marked the final year that chasers were marooned in primitive technology: namely the hefty VHS camcorders, pay phone cards, film cameras, and arguably even the poor auto worksmanship of the 1980s that occasionally left chasers stranded overnight.

In 1989 the revolutionary Canon A-1, the first Hi-8 camcorder, hit the market and was snapped up by chasers. The first PCS cellular phone network arrived in January 1989, a precedent that would sweep the nation with cheap digital technology during the coming decade, putting an end to static-filled phone calls. The first generation of notebook computers also arrived in 1989: the NEC UltraLite and the Compaq LTE. The FAA touchtone service IVRS came on the scene, allowing chasers to stop at any payphone and check surface observations. Even film photography got a facelift thanks to the 1990 introduction of Velvia slide film, the new talk of the town among chasers. Data distribution via the Internet would follow only a few years later.

Though equipment quality has reached amazing milestones, there is a real question whether this equipment drives some chasers to distraction. Equipment also has opportunity costs. An extra $500 for a data link setup might be better spent on building up a personal thunderstorm meteorology library and attending conferences to learn the latest findings and meet like-minded chasers. Equipment is *never* a substitute for skill and knowledge.

Furthermore it may be prudent to start slow and let your chase philosophies and specialty areas emerge. It's a sour experience to sell an HDV outfit at a loss when you're suddenly drawn to digital SLR photography. Heavy equipment purchases should come later as you build a relationship with chasing activities.

Parallels: Cycling

As an outdoors enthusiast, I first noticed a shift towards consumerism on a hiking trip in the early eighties. One of the hikers asked about camping, and the trip leaders began reciting a list of "things you must have", going so far as to give brand names. I thought, "This is crazy; there's nothing that's mandatory!" I had begun camping without a sleeping bag, tent, or pack. I used blankets, a plastic tarp, and a bed roll, and still had a wonderful time.

As an avid cyclist, I did not realize that, in the future, many cyclists would be more concerned about components than about riding. In the mid-80's, I saw a major shift. For the first time in my life, I found my town full of cyclists. They were all well-equipped with new bikes, helmets, shoes, and cycling shirts and shorts. I also discovered something else odd: none of these cyclists wanted to ride with me!

KEN KIFER
d. 2003 in collision with intoxicated motorist

First camcorder

My first camcorder was an RCA VHS. I had walked into a Sears one day in January of 1999. A salesman said he could make a 3-minute phone call and check my credit. It was free, so I said "what the hell."

After a few minutes he hung up and said "Ok Mr. Adams, you're approved for $3600." Unfortunately in my credit bliss, I failed to realize the camcorder I chose had no manual focus. This would plague me throughout the 1999 season.

I didn't really feel the burn of having an analog camcorder until the night of May 3, 1999, while I was waiting in line at KOCO to send video. The guy in front of me had this state-of-the-art digital camcorder and the picture was amazing. Then I put my tape in, and he stood there watching. He was impressed with my shots, but told me I would need to get a digital video camera if I wanted to sell and keep pace with the competition. Right then I realized my mistake.

SHANE ADAMS
Norman, OK chaser

Overall, there's nothing wrong with bringing a lot of equipment into the field. Some chasers find enjoyment in an externally-motivated chase, managing an array of equipment to help develop a field tactic or to document a storm in detail. At the other extreme, the art of introspective chasing still exists. It is the lure of the Great Plains and the mystery of the chase with nothing more than a few maps, some sandwiches, and an ice-cold Dr. Pepper, the same way Dave Hoadley and Roger Jensen did it in the 1960s.

Camcorders

During the 1980s, the video camera market was a headache for many storm chasers. The formats in use were VHS, VHS-C, S-VHS, S-VHS-C, and Betamax. Nearly everything under $2000 produced only 240 "lines", horizontal lines, of resolution. By 1990, Hi-8, a high-quality analog format, became the medium of choice, and finally it was possible to get 420 lines for under $1000.

The digital revolution arrived in 1995 with the Sony VX1000 camcorder, the first consumer camera to use the new DV format. The entry price was $3500, but by the year 2000, DV camcorders had become widespread with many models available for as low as $500. The "large" DV tape, with a shell measuring 4.7 inches wide, gained some initial acceptance, but was eclipsed by the miniDV tape with a smaller size of 2.6 inches. In its consumer camcorders, Sony used a variation of DV from the start called "Digital8". This format is still considered state-of-the-art and is exactly identical to DV at the bitstream level, but it uses a different

Techno-chasing is one style enjoyed by many chasers. *(David Hoadley)*

tape shell: 8 mm tapes (which have 3.7-inch wide shells). The only real downside of Digital8 is that the tapes are not compatible with rest of the DV universe and they are like the proverbial Betamax tapes of decades past, with no machines that can play them in commercial production facilities.

The high definition revolution

High-definition television (HDTV) is now slowly revolutionizing home video. The first TVs were sold in 1998, but it wasn't until late 2004 that consumer HD camcorders arrived on the market with the introduction of the Sony HDR-FX1. The resolution offered with high-definition cameras is at least 1080 vertical lines, quadrupling the video resolution compared to legacy 480-line (standard definition, or SD) television. Furthermore, the cost for an entry-level HDV has fallen below $1000.

HDTV cameras record onto standard DV and miniDV tapes, which combined produces a system known as HDV. An alternative solution is called AVCHD, which records video not to tape but to optical disc, a special video hard drive, or flash memory.

To HD or not to HD

If a chaser is in the market for a new camcorder, a decision needs to be made as to which type: Standard definition (SD) or High Definition (HD). SD has approximately 400-500 lines of resolution, and HD has 1080 lines of resolution-certainly a very notable difference. Each has its advantages, but I believe that having the higher resolution wins out over the common complaint of lower light sensitivity-which is typical of most consumer HD camcorders. If one considers that an HD camcorder is taking 30 high resolution 'pictures' per second, and each picture has enough quality to actually produce a good 5x7 print, the choice is clear.

TIM SAMARAS
Denver, CO chaser

Video resolution can best be illustrated by these examples. An image of the Winterset, Iowa house from the film *Bridges of Madison County* has been degraded to conform to the resolution of the three major video formats used in storm chasing. *(Tim Vasquez)*

Top left: Image at VHS/VHS-C/8 mm resolution.

Top right: Image at Hi-8/DV (480i) resolution.

Bottom left: Image at HDV 1080i resolution.

A clean lens

Make sure you clean the lens of the camcorder before each encounter. On vacation in Africa, I forgot to do this one or two times. In several shots and videos , there are some beads of water from condensation. The photos and videos still came out fine, but at certain times you can really see that water drop and it is a little annoying that it spoils some shots even though I think most don't notice. When in doubt, clean your lenses. While I wasn't chasing storms but chasing eclipses, this still pertains.

ERIC FLESCHER
Olathe, KS chaser

A word about time code

Before chasing, one should make sure the time-codes on video and digital cameras are accurate. This makes reviewing the event and comparison to other chasers easier. Accurate time codes also add to the scientific value of video since the images can be compared to radar data.

WILLIAM HARK
Richmond, VA chaser

Before you rush to buy HDV, consider that the video is compressed, using a lossy scheme that can, in certain situations, introduce noticeable artifacts into the video. One troublesome area is lightning shots, where illumination changes instantly. The compressed video scheme imposes a major technology barrier that makes it impractical to do on-the-fly editing in consumer equipment. A computer can be tasked, but this requires a lot of time, a robust computer, and several hundred dollars for editing software. Anyone contemplating serious HD work will need to graduate to DVCAM, which uses the same codec as DV except with more reliable tape transport, or DVCPRO, a broadcast standard with linear editing capabilities. Be advised: entry-level decks and cameras in 2008 were priced at $8999 for DVCAM and $29,995 for DVCPRO!

If you want to share your HDV masterpiece, count on buying a BluRay disc burner for your computer, which will set you back $200 and about $8 per blank disc — about what blank CDs cost in 1995! It's not possible to burn HD video to DVD for regular HD television viewing, though you can burn a WMV-HD file to any DVD or CD for viewing on another computer or on a feature-packed DVD player that supports the format.

Performance

There are several key performance qualities that a chaser will want in a camcorder: low light performance, color performance, image stabilization, and perhaps basic editing features.

Low-light performance is paramount. How does the camera perform at dusk, *without using any special features*? Most picturesque storm scenes occur under cloudy skies as evening approaches. Is the image gray and grainy, or does it hold rich color? This varies drastically between different models. Lux ratings are useless since there is no standardized method for arriving at a given number.

The true litmus test is in CCD chip size. The larger the CCD chip, the more light the camera can gather, which reduces the noise in low-light conditions. Many consumer cameras in the early 1990s used 1/2-inch CCD chips and gave surprisingly good night performance. They were close cousins to the 2/3-inch chip sizes used in broadcast cameras. Since the 1990s, there has been a cost-cutting trend, with marginal 1/4-inch chips becoming common, and some Sony units, particularly the DCR-PC line, even use 1/6-inch chips, which are considered garbage for storm photography. The rules get confusing with HDV cameras, which pack many more sensors in a given space to accommodate the larger screen geometry, but by recognizing that 480i chips are 720x480 and a true HDV chip is 1920x1080, it can be estimated that a 2/3" HDV chip will perform on par with a 1/4-inch 480i camera.

Color performance is also a consideration. Here, the discriminator is the 1-CCD chip versus the more expensive 3-CCD chip. The former design makes up the vast majority of consumer camcorders. The latter is a professional design that uses a prism to break the light into its color components, which are then processed individually to improve color accuracy. This avoids the slightly bleached look that affects 1-CCD models. Three chips alone does not improve low-light performance. Chip size still remains a critical consideration.

Does the camera have image stabilization? Smooth video footage is a major plus, and optical or electronic stabilization systems will compensate for the jerkiness of hand-held shots. There are two methods to accomplish this: through electronic and optical techniques, the latter of which is thought to have a slight edge over the other. If you plan to use a tripod most of the time, image stabilization is not particularly important.

Does the camera have IEEE1394 (i.e., Firewire or i.LINK) output? This makes it incredibly easy to offload full-motion video to your Firewire-equipped computer in pure digital form, without the need for a capture card. Once you offload the video, which usually appears on your computer as an AVI or MPEG file, you can then use software like ffmpeg, VirtualDub, or commercial editors to manipulate the video, make a DVD, post clips on YouTube, or even grab a screen capture for your website. Due to the popularity of Internet video, most DV consumer camcorders sold in 2000 or later offer this capability.

Finally, it must be mentioned that features thrown around to impress consumers such as digital zoom and large color screens are of surprisingly low importance to chasing activities, and should not be major considerations in a chase camera purchase. Shop for quality, not features, unless you have a specific need for that feature. Also consider the need

Tips from a pro

If at all possible, mount your camera on a tripod. However, be aware of outflow winds and other hazards that can damage your camcorder. When filming a storm do not use the camcorder as you would your eyes. Hold the shot for at least 10-15 seconds before changing it, and do not zoom in and out during the shot.

ROGER HILL
Denver, CO chaser

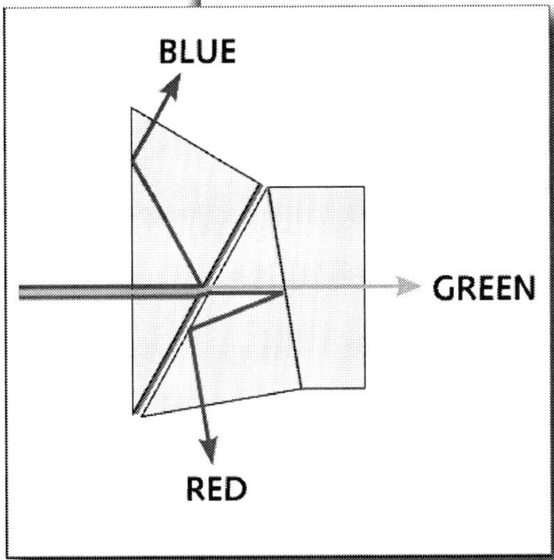

Explanation of 3-CCD color. The trichroic prism assembly uses two dichroic prisms to separate light into blue, green, and red. These channels are handled individually by the camcorder's chips and internal signal processors, providing higher quality.

Video camera tips

- **Install a microphone windscreen** to eliminates the noise of wind blowing against the microphone.
- **During excitement, keep calm and double-check the camera.** It's incredibly easy to forget details.
- **Avoid excessive use of zoom.** Frequent zoom-in/zoom-out techniques are disorienting.
- **Avoid autofocus.** Autofocus is unreliable, especially in dim conditions. Set the focus on "infinity" if practical.
- **Check the focus when turning the camera on.** Some camcorders with electronic focus have to be refocused.
- **Consider a wide-angle lens.** A wide angle lens sometimes has a magical effect on chase footage.
- **Use a tripod as much as possible.** Smoothness and stability are the hallmarks of professional footage.
- **Keep storm footage as condensed as possible.** Many chasers eventually find that less is better.
- **Don't forget to show chase partners and other chasers.** Human interest a big part of the chase story.
- **Avoid damage sightseeing.** The extra attention may be seen by residents as inappropriate and insensitive.

to buy a rain cover, an extra battery, and a wide-angle lens. A microphone windscreen can cut down unwanted noise from the breeze ripping past.

Makes and models

With many videographers flocking to HDV systems, the cost of 480i equipment is falling precipitously. Even with the smallest chase budget it's possible to buy a high-quality DV camera. At the low end of the scale, the Sony DCR-TRV520 (1/4" 1-CCD Digital8, $250 used) is the best starter camera available, has proven itself as a chasing workhorse, and even has Firewire capability. The Sony DCR-TRV730 (1/4" 1-CCD Digital8, $300 used) offers slightly better images. The Sony DCR-HC90 (1/3" 1-CCD miniDV, $350 used) makes the transition to larger CCD for improved low-light performance, and uses the more universal miniDV format instead of the Digital8 format used on the TRV line.

For over $500, the chaser enters the realm of entry-level 3-chip cameras with quarter-inch CCDs. The Sony DCR-TRV900 (1/4" 3-CCD Digital8) ($600 used) was the top dog of the prosumer market for awhile, even beating out its TRV950 cousin, and has been reported as being a rugged, reliable device. The Panasonic PV-GS400 (1/4" 3-CCD miniDV, $1000 used) is considered a good alternative to the TRV900.

The ultimate in 3-CCD models comes with the jump from 1/4" to 1/3" chips. The Sony DCR-VX2000 and DCR-VX2100 (1/3" 3-CCD, miniDV, $1300-1400 used) have been a longtime favorite of storm chasers. The Panasonic AG-DVX100A (1/3" 3-CCD, $1500 used) is a very highly rated camera. The Sony DSR-PD150 (1/3" 3-CCD miniDV/DVCAM, $1800 used) is probably as good as it gets at the 480i standard without going to broadcast equipment; it offers generous CCD chips and is a remarkable performer in high-contrast situations. Another choice is the Canon XL-1 (1/3" 3-CCD miniDV, $1000 used) but its lack of an infinity focus stop has troubled some chasers.

Then there is HDV. As of 2008, HDV equipment has entered the "affordable" range for most chasers and is now beginning to compete seriously with legacy 480i equipment. For instance, the Canon HV20 (1/3" 1-CMOS 1920x1080, $750 new) is a rock-solid storm chasing camera with a remarkably cheap price tag. There is the JVC GR-HD1 (1/3" 1-CCD 1280x960, $1500) . The Sony HDR-HC line (1/3" 1-CCD, $800 to $1400) and the identical shoulder-mount

"YOUR NEW EASY TO USE
DIGITAL CAMERA."
"Just correctly choose:
-- Pixel size
-- Diopter adjustment
-- JPEG Fine, Normal or Basic
-- AF Area Mode
-- Firmware version
-- AEL/AFL
-- ISO (10 choices)"
-- etc.

Cameras in the digital age. The first big chase in April is not the time to get familiar with your camera! *(David Hoadley)*

version HVR-HD1000 ($1599) have all been cited as having exceptionally poor performance in low light.

For those with bigger budgets, the three-chip models command a higher price tag. The Canon XH-A1 (1/3" 3-CCD, $3500 new) is widely regarded as the camera to have. The Sony HDR-FX1 (1/3" 3-CCD 960x1080, $3000 new) is the camera that ushered in the HDV revolution and is still available. Beyond this tier, the chaser gets into professional HDV gear and DVCAM equipment with time code, separate lens systems, and more.

For more information the website <*www.camcorderinfo.com*> and <*www.videomaker.com*> are recommended for thorough reviews and tests, vastly better than the sites that just recite the manufacturer's numbers.

Digital cameras

During much of the late 1990s, affordable digital cameras were scorned and suffered a poor reputation. Consumer cameras were not much better than camcorder screen captures. It wasn't until 2000 that consumer equipment reached a level of sophistication that seriously competed with film photography. Now they've become a mainstay of storm chasing. With a digital camera, there is no film in-

Camera mistakes

The most likely mistake a new chaser might make in selecting a digital camera for storm photography would be to buy a very expensive camera and then put a very low quality lens on it. It's better to buy a less expensive camera and a higher quality, more expensive lens than to buy an inexpensive lens and an expensive camera. The lenses that come bundled with most SLR cameras are generally fairly low in quality.

RYAN MCGINNIS
Lincoln, Nebraska chaser

volved. The photograph is held inside the camera in a flash card, and the contents can be transferred to a computer via a cable — or the card itself can be transferred to the computer. For those who own websites, digital cameras are the definitive way to go.

Digital cameras come in two main flavors: point-and-shoot and SLR (single lens reflex). The point & shoot is cheaper and good for beginners, and can actually provide some decent quality at the $200 to $300 range. Above $300 it becomes possible to buy SLR, which has most of the optics and mechanism of an actual modern camera, allowing interchangability of lenses for optimum photography.

With SLRs, a significant consideration is its *crop factor*, sometimes called *format factor*. This describes the CCD size and also gives insight into how the camera will behave with a given lens. A full-frame sensor measures 24 x 36 mm, an industry standard. But full-frame sensors are expensive and because of the wider image path, the camera body and lenses need to be larger, heavier, and more costly. A sensor with crop factor is smaller, described by a ratio that equals 36 mm divided by its actual width; thus a 16 x 24 mm sensor has a crop factor of 1.5. This is important because a scene projected through a given 35 mm lens will be captured in its entirety with a full-frame sensor, but a sensor with crop factor is smaller so only a portion of the projected image near the center is captured by the sensor. A sensor with crop factor does have advantages: cheaper prices, less bulk, and peripheral areas captured by the lens are ignored, which can be a good thing as cheap lenses have distortion at the edges. But smaller sensors have more noise and image quality is lower. Most consumer cameras have a 1.3 to 1.6 crop factor, but some Olympus cameras have as much as 2.0. By comparison, point-and-shoot cameras and many video cameras have crop factors of 4 to 10, though of course they don't accept 35 mm lens accessories.

Point-and-shoot cameras in the $200 to $400 range are the recommended starting point for outdoor photography. These models are cheap, but the lens options and exposures are limited, and they are unable to take lightning time exposures. The Pentax Optio A20 and A30 (about $250) models have a solid track record of excellent images, particularly in low light. When shopping for a point & shoot, the most important things to look for are battery consumption, reliability and sturdiness, and favorable user comments. The people to see for recommendations are the remote-control aerial

Mail order advice

Internet and mail-order equipment vendors offer some of the best opportunities for purchasing gear. You can avoid pushy salesmen and hefty sales tax charges, and shop from the comfort of your own home.

However the axiom "if it's too good to be true" most be taken to heart and cheap prices must never be the bottom line for an equipment purchase. The New York City metro area has established itself as a haven for dozens of mail-order electronics stores that use underhanded tactics like adding accessories and warranties without authorization, refusing to ship without an upsell, and falsely confirming an item is in stock then charging the card while the item makes its journey on the slow boat.

The Internet, fortunately, has made it easy for us all to rat out bad merchants. A visit to the website *www.reseller-ratings.com* is a good resource for sniffing out excellent stores and avoiding the bad apples. Amazon.com and Yahoo.com are large storefronts that have effective ratings systems for their merchants. There are also a number of trusted firms that are trusted for good service: namely Camera World of Oregon and B&H Photo/Video of New York City.

TIM VASQUEZ

photography hobbyists, who depend on point & shoots for their light weight but demand excellent performance in all outdoor illumination, in spite of the unexpected raindrop or rough drop. Head to <*www.rcgroups.com*> for good shopping advice.

The $500 price point places the chaser in the realm of DSLR (digital single-lens reflex) cameras. These offer interchangeable lenses, the ability to use various photographic filters, and tremendous flexibility. The image sensors are also generally larger and give better results. As of 2008 a popular entry-level DSLR was the Canon Digital Rebel XTi ($700 new, body only) and the Nikon D50 ($500 used, body only). Further up are the Nikon D70 and D80 (about $900, body only). This Nikon line carries a solid reputation among storm chasers.

Chasers with budgets of over $1500 and ideally past $5000 can obtain professional-grade digital cameras that deliver results nearly on par with slide film. The performance of these cameras are quite impressive, which makes them stand out in critical low-light situations. One model making waves at press time in late 2008 was the Nikon D3 <*www.nikonusa.com*, $4999>.

Documenting the storm. Chasers in eastern Colorado keep tabs on an outflow dominant storm on 31 May 2006. Photography is a core skill for a great many storm chasers. Like chasing, it's not all about becoming an expert; rather it's a skill and art form with endless opportunities for learning and improving. *(Laura Duchesne)*

For more information on the digital camera market, visit <*www.megapixel.net*> and <*www.shortcourses.com*>.

Film cameras

As of 2008, film photography was in steep decline, with sales of film stock declining over 75% from eight years earlier. Fueling the departure of film is the cost of consumables. While the cost of a digital picture is negligible, a slide film exposure may run as high as 40 cents a piece counting the cost of film and developing at a trusted lab. This is a serious price to pay in a storm's difficult lighting conditions. Also the results cannot easily be manipulated without scanning the pictures into digital form.

However, film still offers outstanding quality and there is no debate that even in 2008 *it has superior dynamic range and better exposure latitude* compared to the current crop of digital cameras. A $500 SLR camera loaded with Velvia deliver quality can theoretically outperform a $5000 digital camera. Another interesting advantage is that the decline of film photography means great bargains on 35 mm equipment. Cameras that were once only for the wealthy in 1990 can now be had for less than $200.

Finally, film photography produces a tangible, physical image that is difficult to destroy. It will never fall off the treadmill of changing digital formats, and if properly stored will degrade only slightly. The slightest degradation of a CD disc, by comparison, can destroy the contents. All these are dilemmas that deserves serious consideration.

Surprisingly, the easiest decision for a new photographer is picking out a camera. Canon EOS film cameras are still available, with the latest model being the EOS Elan 7N which was released in 2004. A cheap

STILL CAMERA TIPS

■ **Use a tripod**! This is guaranteed to make the biggest difference in your photography results. Avoid flimsy, cheap department store tripods. Lightweight models come with a compromise.

■ **Be prepared to shoot a lot of film.** You may want to bracket or play with different kinds of framing. The more pictures you shoot, the more you'll learn.

■ **Keep a notebook handy.** Use this to jot down brief comments about the kind of film you used and the exposures you used for each shot. It will help improve your future photographs.

■ **Use a polarizer on bright or hazy days.** This can help improve contrast, particularly when facing at perpendicular angles to the sun, by darkening the sky. It may improve color saturation slightly.

■ **Use a split neutral density filter with bright skies.** This allows you to match the sky brightness with that of the ground, eliminating a sihouetted or darkened foreground.

■ **Bracket your photos**. This is important for slide film, which is highly sensitive. Adjust the f-stop each way by half-notches and take extra photos. The more important the shot, the more you bracket.

■ **Don't rely on exposure meters or autoexposure.** Cloud exposures can be tricky, and autoexposures aren't designed to handle these compositions. Once again, bracket, bracket, and bracket!

■ **Be aware of the rule of thirds**. Your pictures will look best of the image is a third ground and two-thirds sky. This is particularly important when photographing for professional clients.

■ **Research photo magazines**. Many magazines list how the photographer went about taking the shot and what filters and exposures were used. Find shots you like and learn about them.

■ **Contrasts between warm and cool shades make great shots**. When a blue sky is dominant, for example, a field of yellow wildflowers will likely make a better foreground than a bluish pond.

■ **Be aware of shilled equipment reviews.** There is currently some suspicion that one or two photography mags are bestowing favors on advertisers. Seek opinions from fellow photographers.

■ **Be persistent**! Excellent photography comes with lots of practice and experience. If you don't like your photos, study them and decide what you don't like. Get comments from friends.

A Fuji Velvia slide film photograph taken in May 1997 in northeast New Mexico. The remarkable dynamic range of film has long held its own against digital. *(Tim Vasquez)*

classic starter camera with widespread support is the Pentax K1000, a model manufactured from 1976 to 1997. Complete kits are widely available used on eBay for $100.

Cheap "instamatics" and "point & shoot" cameras found in department stores should be avoided, since they're designed for use on the beach and at birthday parties, and not in the challenging, dim conditions found underneath storms. There are no threads for filters, the lens can't be changed, the workmanship of the cameras leaves a lot to be desired, the focus will rarely be crisp, and quite simply a cheap digital camera will give better results.

Camera film

If a film camera is selected, the toughest decision of all comes: do you shoot on slide or print film?

Print film is by far the most familiar format to the average person. A roll of film is exposed, and the negatives are used to produce paper prints. The leading benefit of prints is that they are cheap and easy to share, it's easy to find a store to develop your prints, and film labs can easily compensate for poorly-exposed photographs. The drawback is that you use reflected light when looking at the prints, so the images are definitely not as vibrant and lifelike as slide

Lightning photos

A light meter is totally useless when you photograph lightning. The extreme contrast between the brilliant bolt and the ambient light in the sky can't be read accurately with any kind of meter. Instead, you must lock the shutter open with a locking cable release and wait until another bolt of lightning strikes. When it does, close the shutter, advance the film, and open the shutter for another try. Based on tests that I've done, the standard aperture for distant lightning is f/4 to f/5.6 and f/8 to f/11 for a closer strike when you're using medium speed film.

JIM ZUCKERMAN

Techniques of Natural Light Photography, 1996

images. Also there are tremendous differences in printing quality from store to store.

Slide film saw tremendous use among storm chasers in the 1980s and 1990s. The advantage is that there is no "middleman" negative involved, removing a step that can diminish quality. The film is the print. Slide projectors also allow the photograph to become extremely vivid and true to life thanks to the use of projected light. Drawbacks are that there is less margin for error, requiring "bracketing" (a few extra photos at different exposures) to get the perfect shot. Also one has to find a lab that handles slides and buy a projector or a scanner. For more information on slide films, see Roger Edwards' film evaluations at <*www.stormeyes.org/tornado/stilfilm.htm*>.

Photographic accessories

Filters are often associated with still cameras, but they can also be used on video cameras. When used properly and sparingly, they can add just the right flavor to an exposure.

UV filters are by far the most common accessory. They produce almost no visible change in the photo so they are often added immediately to a lens system as a permanent fixture to protect it. A rising tide of opinion suggests that they may do more harm than good, and that a clear filter should specifically be used instead for this purpose. Functionally, a UV filter does reduce the haziness caused by excessive ultraviolet light, and in a digital camera it can reduce purple fringing along high-contrast zones. Since these are problems when photographing outdoors, the decision on whether to use a UV filter or a clear filter for default will probably remain a matter of personal opinion.

Polarizers are the next most favored item. They are handy in sunlit situations, as they add contrast to the sky at perpendicular angles to the sun. They tend to darken the sky and can also be used to eliminate reflections on glass panes, such as from car windshields.

Finally, a split neutral density filter is useful in scenic compositions. Inserted into a mount and properly used, it can dim down a bright sky while allowing the landscape to be fully exposed, reducing the harshness of the shot and bringing out the beauty of the landscape.

Dashboard-mounted cameras have become quite popular, yielding stable views out the front window instead of the

Techno-chasing

I've always been a "techno-chaser", enjoying the challenge of getting data in the field to make my own decisions. People enjoy this great hobby from different perspectives. Some go strictly "visual", chasing with just a car radio and perhaps a cellular phone. I feel that to get the biggest "bang for the buck" on my vacation days, I wish to be informed the best I can about the atmosphere.

TIM SAMARAS
Denver, CO chaser

Handheld anemometer. The Kestrel 4500 is considered the Rolls-Royce of pocket weather devices.

Project VORTEX vehicles, the original model for storm chaser instrument exposures. This photograph was taken in front of the old NSSL building in the mid 1990s. *(NOAA)*

traditional shaky handheld views from the passenger seat. This greatly supplements the tripod shots while parked and outside the vehicle. No dashboard camera mount kits exist, but it's possible to buy some metal L-brackets from hardware stores, attach a tripod head to this bracket, and screw them into the dashboard. A removable window-mount tripod might provide another similar alternative for views out the passenger windows and without glass in the way. They're available from photography and sports equipment stores and made for the bird watching hobbyist.

Finally, a tripod or monopod is essential to good photography. Shaky hand-held video is almost universally frowned upon, though some documentary producers may find that it enhances the fear factor of the video. Department store tripods are better than nothing, though they break quickly, they resist smooth panning and tilting movements, and a little wind can blur the shot or blow the entire tripod and camera over. A heavy metal tripod from a manufacturer like Bogen is the way to go.

For more information, check out Chuck Doswell's photo tips at <*www.cdoswell.com/tips.htm*>. Luminous Landscape is a great site that teaches principles of photography as it relates to the outdoors <*www.luminous-landscape.com*>. For suggestions on what to buy, see Photography Review's buying guides at <*www.photographyreview.com*>.

Instrumental inconvenience

You will often see mobile mesonets while chasing, whether it's a research group or someone's personal vehicle. One evening after a one of those long chase days I watched a guy pull into a hotel parking lot with his mobile mesonet on top of his vehicle. Of course it was raining thanks to some post-frontal storms and he didn't want to get wet now.

He pulled in as close to the door as he can get. Of course that means going under the hotel awning. Needless to say, there is definitely a clearance problem with mesonets and hotel awnings.

JAYSON PRENTICE
Ames, IA chaser

Weather stations

For those who have to know the exact temperature and wind speed, a mobile weather station may fill the bill. Though it's exceedingly rare that chasers actually use the

Atlases in the technology age

Although I am using GPS, I still regularly consult atlases. I keep individual state maps for most of Tornado Alley along with a Rand McNally national atlas. The problem with GPS is the loss of smaller roads as one goes to a wider view. With paper maps I can easier see the relationship between different points of interest or where a long but minor road ends.

Atlases are also good as backup when a GPS is not functioning or has wrong information. For long-range planning and targeting, I use paper maps. In the heat of the chase, I stick with a GPS. A GPS is great for determining location when surface features (crossroads, towns, and rivers) are scarce. I know when road options are approaching or if I missed a turnoff. I am less likely to get lost and head in the wrong direction with GPS. To effectively chase, one should have both paper maps and GPS.

BILL HARK
Richmond, VA

data for research projects, readings of dewpoint and wind direction can add critical information on what is taking place, and measurement of wind gusts can quantify how bad the outflow winds are.

A mobile weather station can be as simple as an anemometer on a metal pole attached to the back bumper with temperature sensors protected under the front grille. At the other end of the spectrum, some chasers construct elaborate stations made of PVC pipe, modelled after instrumented vehicles that participated in the VORTEX project. These setups are not without criticism, including the heightened risk of theft and vandalism, the added fuel mileage costs due to drag, the validity of temperature readings over road surfaces in light wind regimes, and the "magnet factor" for chase roaches. If such a station is what you need, complete design details can be found in *A Mobile Mesonet for Finescale Meteorological Observations*, by Jerry M. Straka, Erik N. Rasmussen, and Sherman E. Fredrickson, available as a PDF at <*ams.allenpress.com*>.

Most weather stations cannot calculate the actual wind speed and direction while the vehicle is moving, however if the vehicle's motion is known it is possible to estimate ground-relative wind by vector subtraction. A new line of weather stations built for boats accomplishes this with a built-in GPS: the Airmar Ultrasonic line <*www.airmar.com*>. It's easy to adapt the unit for road use. Models like the Airmar do have an upper measurement limit of only 92 mph, which is not a desirable attribute for those wanting maximum performance under the storm.

Chasers who prefer to keep a clean exterior will get a lot of use out of pocket devices. Furthermore these can be taken to shady areas to get accurate values of temperature and dewpoint for reliable cap forecasting. Kestrel <*www.kestrelmeters.com*> products are highly regarded for their accuracy. The Kestrel 4500 ($289) measures temperature, dewpoint, pressure, wind speed, and even the wind direction thanks to a built-in compass, while a basic wind meter is the Kestrel 2000 ($90). For a tight budget, eBay is filled with bargains on Chinese-made wind meters which may work adequately.

A sling psychrometer should not be overlooked, as it is the ultimate in accurate dewpoint measurement and remains the gold standard for official measurements. Since integrations of instability and instability indices are highly sensitive to low-level moisture changes, this can give ac-

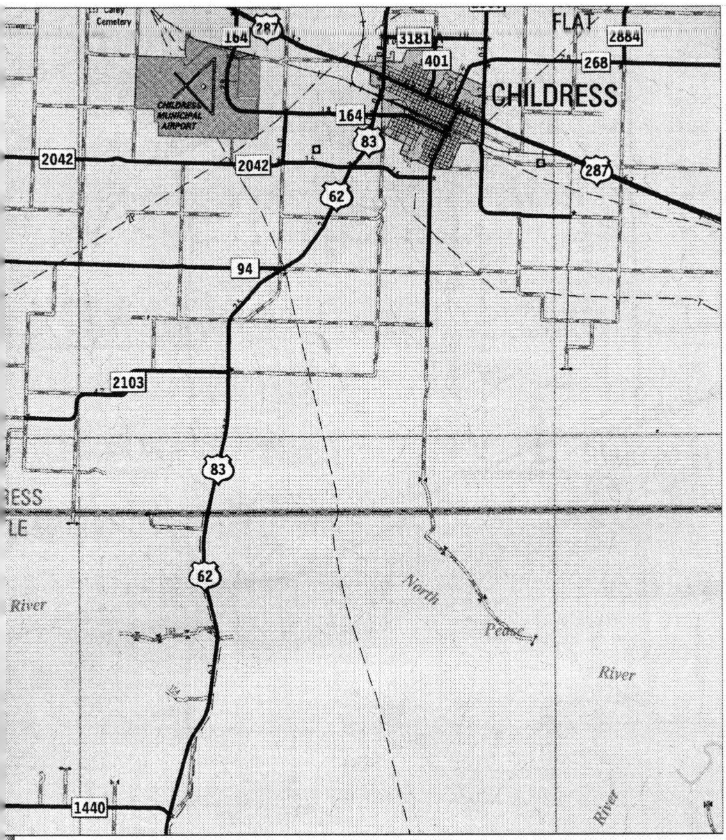

Roads of Texas

Shearer Publications

It's said to get to heaven or hell you have to connect through Atlanta. And for a chase career, Childress is that proverbial place. Here it is depicted on the *The Roads of Texas*. This series has been a prized possession of chasers since the late 1980s, expanding into neighboring states during the next several years. The Shearer maps are clean and readable. When you get lost in an unfamiliar town, Shearer's street symbology is easy to read. Note the industrial notations like airport runways and pipelines, which are omitted in the DeLorme guide.

Texas Atlas & Gazetteer

DeLorme

For a chaser, the true test of an atlas is not what it shows in Manhattan but in the remote areas of the Plains. Here the relief shading and coarse contours are fantastic additions, suggesting bluffs that might offer a good photo location. The depiction of all dirt roads yields an additional smorgasbord of valuable information. However, the line thickness between highways and town streets is not very well balanced, causing some obscuration and ambiguity of navigation details in towns. The DeLorme maps have been available since the early to mid 1990s.

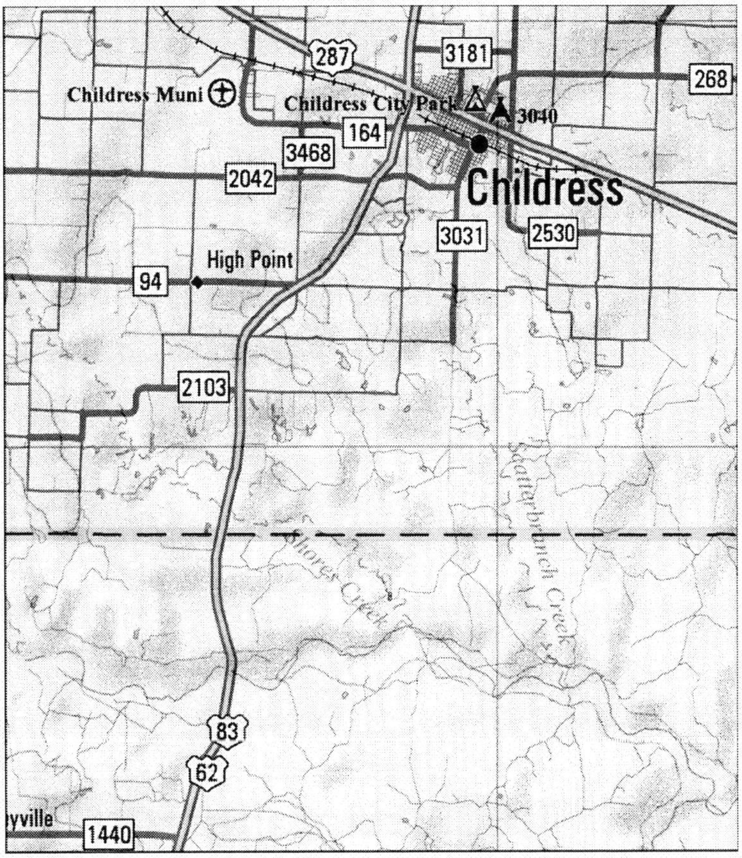

curate information on whether the air mass is becoming more potent or the moisture is mixing out. You will need a conversion table or a psychrometric calculator to convert wet-bulb and temperature figures to dewpoint. You'll also have to properly maintain the instrument by replacing the wick regularly and using distilled water as much as possible to prevent mineral buildup, which degrades the accuracy.

Navigation aids

Even with rapid advances in GPS technology and computer mapping, paper maps are important for "big picture" route planning, emergency maps, planning side trips, marking points of interest, and just for curling up with in bed to process the day's events. The detail in paper maps far surpasses anything stored in off-the-shelf GPS units and online road map sites.

The foundation of paper maps is the state-by-state road atlas. The most detailed atlas is the *AAA North American Road Atlas* ($11), though it is sometimes criticized for its tiny typefaces. Coming in a close second is the *Rand McNally Road Atlas* ($9). A favorite of the author is the *Michelin North America Road Atlas* ($13), which uses a

A navigation decision is made by chasers Jim Leonard, Bill Hark, and Dave Lewison with the help of a paper road atlas. In spite of the advantage of a computer-based road atlas, a paper atlas is perfect for team strategy. *(Chris Kridler/skydiary.com)*

section-by-section layout that helps road map use in border areas like the Sioux City area and the Arklatex region and mitigates having to flip back and forth.

Highly detailed single-state atlases are another tool, widely available in bookstores and on the Internet. Each book is published for an individual state and contains extremely detailed maps covering about 20 x 20 miles per page showing everything from freeways to the tiniest of dirt roads. This allows chasers to select obscure routes while near a storm and to plan escape routes. The two brands of atlases in widespread use are the DeLorme *"[STATE] Atlas and Gazetteer" series*, and the series by Shearer Publications titled *"Roads of [STATE]"*.

In general, the atlases are comparable. When shopping, it's a good idea to compare them side-by-side and check them for timeliness by looking for newly-constructed roads you're familiar with.

GPS navigation devices

The Global Positioning System (GPS) is a United-States operated navigation system that uses reference data from a network of U.S. Air Force satellites. The satellite orbits are measured by ground radar to the nearest centimeter and extrapolated mathematically, thus the exact *x-y-z* position of all GPS satellites are known at all times. If the satellites

Clash of cultures

We stopped at a small hole-in-the-wall Mexican restaurant in the Texas Panhandle. When ordering, one of our British tour guests ordered a chicken fajita. Except he pronounced the "j" as you would in "ajar". Needless to say, the [mostly Hispanic] restaurant staff got a good laugh out of the British word "fahd-jee-tah", occasionally looking into the dining area and chuckling.

SCOTT WEBERPAL
Janesville, WI chaser

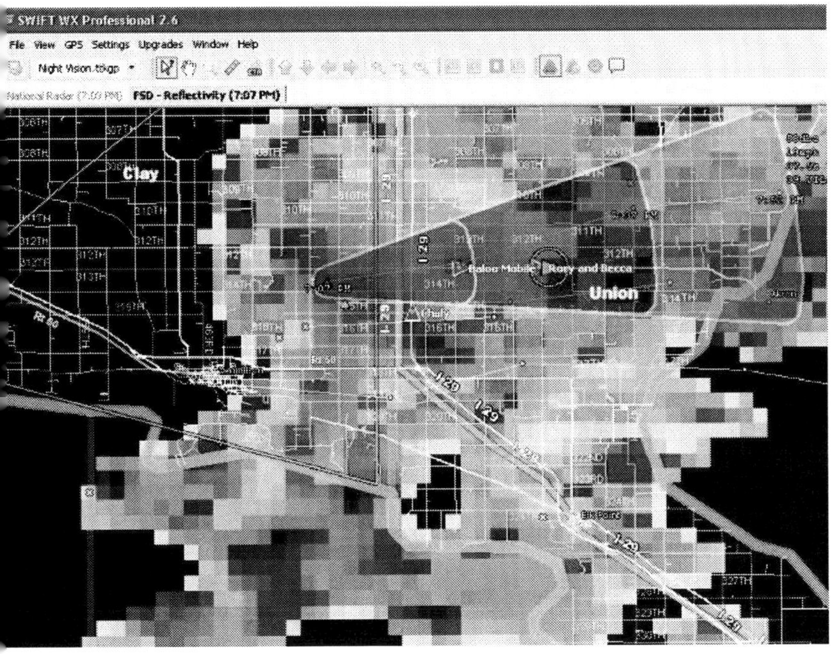

Swift Wx is a unique software program that marries GPS data and a mobile Internet connection to produce plots that superimpose the vehicle on a WSR-88D image.

Mammatus clouds above prototype Doppler radars at the National Severe Storms Laboratory in 1999. *(Tim Vasquez)*

broadcast a precisely synchronized time standard along with an almanac of these *x-y-z* positions, it's a simple matter for a device receiving this information to triangulate its own position based on the almanac data and the delays detected in the clock signals from each satellite. Each delay, of course, implies a certain distance to each satellite figured from the speed of light.

GPS receivers are sold in two basic flavors: the handheld GPS unit and the component GPS device, which requires a computer. The handheld device is somewhat more expensive since it includes a display screen. Automotive navigation systems are also rapidly coming onto the market, which are built into the dashboards of cars, but these systems are beyond the scope of this book.

All portable GPS units have long relied on the 9-pin serial cable, but USB units are becoming common. In 2002, the first Bluetooth GPS unit came on the market, offering a wireless solution supporting a tidy chase vehicle. There is still demand for serial GPS units since this type of connection is robust, reliable, and does not introduce the headache of fussy device drivers. When choosing an obscure GPS unit, it's wise to be sure it supports NMEA, which is the universal communication language between GPS units and computer mapping software.

It must be mentioned that DeLorme GPS devices are designed to use their own proprietary protocol, which is supported only by special mapping software. The devices can be forced to talk in NMEA, but chasers in 2008 reported erratic performance and lockups in doing so. An alternative solution for this problem is the Pharos iGPS ($55).

A *handheld GPS* displays its output on its own tiny screen and does not necessarily need to be connected to a computer. Older handhelds built before 1997 should be avoided as they have no mapping capability. Newer units, generally those built from 1997 onward, contain graphical displays with many U.S. and Interstate highways. This makes them well-suited for chase purposes. Secondary roads might not listed, but these units will leave breadcrumb trails to show the vehicle's path. The Garmin eTrex Legend and eTrex Venture are great starter handhelds with built-in maps. They cost about $160 in 2008.

Nearly all GPS units can be connected to a notebook computer running special mapping software. The mapping software contains an exhaustive atlas that contains almost every paved street and dirt road in existence. A classic example of popular mapmaking software is the affordable DeLorme Earthmate package. The primary advantage of computer-assisted GPS is that the computer is capable of showing a very clear, unambiguous format, providing unmatchable navigation capabilities that nearly eliminate the need for paper atlases. The drawback, of course, is that a notebook computer is required, and it takes up valuable space up front.

With a laptop connected to both the Internet and a GPS unit, software can be used that plots radar images, such as SwiftWx, showing the vehicle's position in relation to the storm. The GPS data can also be used to maintain a presence on mobile spotter networks.

Cellular phones

A mobile telephone is indispensable. It keeps travellers in contact with friends and family, helps with motel reservations, and provides a hotline in case of a vehicle breakdown or an emergency. It's truly a lifesaver, whether in terms of chase success or a car wreck, and at current prices every chaser should carry one.

During the 1970s and 1980s, chasers relied on pay phones. Many of them are being scrapped due to unprofitability, but most gas stations still have one. If one is used, avoid giving your credit card information to the pay phone company as you run the risk of surprise charges and overin-

Pioneer's view of technology

The older chasers, especially solitary ones like myself, remember when data was scarce, and the gift of our eyes made the world seem more magical. What was important then was the shape of a distant tower, the boiling energy in an updraft column, and sharpness to an anvil's edge. Also, what you felt in the warm, gusting wind and heard on the singing wires of a power line.

A forecast then was a blending of all the senses with the natural world. You were looking for the old-time "storms that granddad knew", and that only fate could understand, when uncertainty and luck prevailed. And glorious success, when it happened, was a soul-deep charge that passed all verbal understanding. Then, the sun touched the horizon and turned the receding storm to gold and red against a deep blue sky, and you didn't want it to end.

That was the kind of total experience that has been lost, when the great storm was a magnificent, mysterious and unpredictable wonder of nature. And the chaser — a lonely presence on the vast prairie, learning patience with infrequent success that led to a deeper understanding of the hawk gliding silently overhead and the antelope running free across a distant field.

DAVID HOADLEY
Falls Church, Virginia chaser

flated rates. Always know the access code for connecting to a long distance carrier of your choice, and use a calling card rather than a credit card to avoid getting bilked out of real money. Calling cards can be bought at most drugstores and department stores.

Fortunately, cellular phones have become extremely affordable and there is really no reason to use a pay phone anymore except as a last-ditch solution. The cheapest cell phone service is Tracfone, where it's possible to pay as little as $20 for a starter cell phone at a Wal-Mart, walk out, put $20 of funds on the account, and enjoy light use for weeks or months. Used with a lifetime double-minute card it's extremely economical for light use and works on all major cell phone towers.

Otherwise, a chaser can opt for standard cell phone service. This is usually with one of the "big three": AT&T, Verizon, or T-Mobile, though Alltel is a major regional service in the Great Plains and is highly regarded by many chasers. A standard cell phone plan is a good choice if any heavy use of the phone is anticipated, and unlike Tracfone allows tethering and other data solutions that will be covered in the next section.

Overall, the cellular phone network in the United States is extremely dense and chasers will have few problems. However there are still some areas without any cell towers.

A cellular phone primer

In the 1980s and 1990s, cellular phone systems ran on an analog FM-radio based standard known as AMPS. Anyone with a scanner could listen in, and users had to hold their phones just right to keep a good connection. This ancient system is now known as 1G.

The digital revolution called 2G, sometimes referred to as PCS, arrived in the mid-1990s, bringing three new solid voice technologies: TDMA (D-AMPS), CDMA, and GSM. It also brought the first Internet systems: GPRS, EDGE, and 1xRTT, the latter appearing in 2001 and still in widespread use.

Starting in 2006, the entire national network began a transition to 3G, integrating the CDMA2000 EV-DO standard that offers fast Internet service. It also adds a future Internet system called WiMax.

What's coverage like? As of 2008, most metropolitan areas and large towns receive 3G service. Rural areas are served by the 2G system. A few extremely remote areas of the Plains still have 1G, which is being phased out.

If a data plan is in your future, be certain that a cell phone you buy features EV-DO, which is the fast Internet 3G standard. If you buy cheap, you may end up stuck with 1xRTT Internet, part of the older, slower 2G standard. Most new phones pushed by the big providers will meet the EV-DO standard and can fall back on 1xRTT.

Tracfone prepaid phone that can be used in most parts of the Great Plains. *(Tim Vasquez)*

These include the Texas Big Bend, far southeast Colorado, and the Indian reservations of South Dakota. It's not uncommon for a chaser to be 20 miles from a cell phone tower. An external antenna might be a smart purchase. Wilson Electronics <*www.wilsonelectronics.com*> is one popular source of cell phone antennas. Amplifiers are also available but generally the antenna is what will provide the biggest gains.

Chasers with a big budget or who are physically disabled may want to consider a SPOT phone <*www.globalcomsat-phone.com/spot*> ($149, $99/year, limited use) for unforeseen emergencies. This ties directly to a satellite in the sky and is usable anywhere.

This leads us to cell phones and forecasts. How do you get forecast information with such a device? Talk to someone who's looking at data! This is called "having a nowcaster". With this scheme, the chaser calls a friend or a family member makes interpretations of Internet products.

In the 1970s and 1980s it was not unheard of for a chaser to call a National Weather Service office when they needed forecast assistance. While forecasters back then

Checking data. Chaser Bob Hall checks weather information just outside of Pratt, Kansas. Hall travels up to 15,000 miles in just three months in search of supercells. In an area where the only information is from NOAA weather radio, mobile Internet can be a fantastic resource. *(Steve Miller, hamwx.com)*

tolerated it with varying degrees of professional curiosity, it's now highly discouraged. With the growth of the NWS into clear-cut emergency preparedness roles and the increasing visibility of the agency by the general public, media, and government officials, there's now much less tolerance for outside distractions and added workload.

A more capable alternative is to use a paid forecasting service. At this time, the only such service in existence has been the author's own Chase Hotline <*www.chasehotline.com*>, which has shifted in recent years from a subscriber pool to an impromptu VIP chase consulting service. Chasers with a larger budget or mission-critical needs can hire a consulting service, many of which are listed by the American Meteorological Society <*www.ametsoc.org*>.

Another use of telephone service is give rather than get. Report severe weather! National Weather Service offices are highly dependent on severe weather reports. During the 1980s and much of the 1990s, many NWS offices relied on spotter radio networks and frowned on accepting direct calls. This has changed, and offices are now working to bring as much information into the office as staffing and technology can allow. Specific tips for reporting are found in the "Strategy" chapter, with a map of reporting phone numbers in the appendix.

Though many voice cell phones nowadays have the capability to run applications, including accessing the Internet through miniature browsers, such capabilities are limited. Cell phone Internet browsers tend to be clumsy and awkward. Going up to a higher price tier, the Apple iPhone has a much better interface for surfing the web. But even on cheap phones, it's possible, with fortitude and cooperative fingers, to view useful sites like WeatherTap and UCAR Weather.

A few alert services are targeted especially for cell phones. For example the Pilot My-Cast service <*www.digitalcyclone.com/products/pilot-my-cast*> for $13/mo delivers images with 1 km satellite, radar, surface data, and more directly to a cell phone. A large number of services allow you to receive e-mail weather alerts on your cell phone, and this works with almost any model, including the cheaper Tracfone phones. One experimental cell phone alert service introduced in September 2008 by the National Weather Service can be found at <*nwsmobile.wrh.noaa.gov*>.

Tune in or tune out?

Swimming in the pond of satellite and radar data may cause a chaser to tune out from what can be seen and felt, and can add a superficial sense of connection with what the atmosphere is doing. In my estimation, this disconnect is a profound loss.

Looking back on my 22 on-off years of chasing, I've noticed that my most rapid advances in skill came at times when I left home saturated with a thorough analysis and diagnosis, and then plunged myself into the unknown, with no data but the sky laid out before me. It made for agonizing, memorable chase decisions. Perhaps this disconnect sparks the same connections in the cerebral cortex that shaped the survival instincts of our hunter-gatherer ancestors: forcing one to open their eyes, ears, and sense of smell and become acutely attuned to the prey.

A vast amount of chasing was done in the 1970s and 1980s this way, with little or no afternoon data to go on. The stakes in terms of time, money, and sanity were much higher. Chasers rapidly developed sixth senses about what they saw and felt, and after the chase unfolded, mistakes were followed by an unquenchable thirst for knowledge.

All this seems to suggest that there's merit in avoiding the "data battleship" method from time to time and trying to take on a major chase visually. There is of course more chance for error, but I believe it can't be underemphasized what connections this makes in the brain and to one's way of thinking.

TIM VASQUEZ

Mobile Internet

Using a computer to obtain weather data on the road has been done regularly during the late 1980s and early 1990s using acoustic couplers hooked up to pay phones. By the mid 1990s, chasers learned how to connect laptops to analog cellular phones and get weather data. This method is sometimes used even today to reach the Internet.

Internet equipment options

Wi-Fi hotspots made a huge splash among storm chasers in 2001 as a form of high-speed mobile Internet. Chasers tapped into public hotspots located at rest areas, cafes, hotels, and even in neighborhoods to collect the latest weather data. This scheme of data access is still very much in existence today, though some businesses and many homes have closed off their ports from public access. If you choose to rely on Wi-Fi, you may want to invest $50 in a Wi-Fi detector, available at most electronics stores. They'll alert you to hotspots as you drive through a town, saving the trouble of monitoring the computer.

Another development occurred in 2001: the appearance of the first true mobile Internet network, a system known as 1xRTT ("NationalAccess", 2G). This was run by cell phone companies and piggybacked on their signal. Unfortunately

Changes in technology

The biggest change I've seen that's revolutionized chasing is the mobile technology that allows us to obtain data directly from our vehicles. I remember the days of going into a library and seeing herds of chasers at the computer looking over data. Now I can't even recall the last time I've seen that.

We've entered an era where everything is becoming wireless, so we are starting to see more and more mobile devices being designed with WiFi capabilities. This has been a huge step in technology since I've been chasing. If you have a palm pilot with WiFi, you can pull up to one of the many hotels with WiFi with wireless Internet, or any other public place that allows wireless, and connect. You can literally get data right at your fingertips without even leaving your vehicle.

JOEY KETCHAM
Pittsburg, KS chaser

The wave of the storm chase future? Internet piped directly into your car and broadcast as a local hotspot is made possible with AutoNet Mobile, released in 2008. We've come a long way from plugging the Compaq SLT into an acoustic coupler in a phone booth to get text data, which some chasers did during the late 1980s. *(AutoNet)*

Mobile radar data

I use radar data in the field like many other chasers. It helps me relate certain visually-observed storm features with the precipitation patterns in the storm. It is important to understand that the radar senses only the precipitation pattern in the storm. These are different than the cloud patterns; an updraft is invisible to radar.

Precipitation areas in storms can also be nearly optically-invisible, especially near the hook echo. The radar senses the reflected power of the precipitation, which is a function of the average cross-section diameter of the precipitation particles. That means a volume with many small rain drops may reflect the same amount of energy as a volume with very few but very large hail stones.

Visually, a very large hail core may seem to be precipitation free, but the radar may show very high reflectivities in the same areas. Radar data is also useful to identify nearby storm cells that might not be visually apparent. Radar helps me gain situational awareness when I might temporarily become "tunnel-visioned" on my closer storm.

Users new to radar interpretation should be aware of the limitations of operational radars, especially in the area of radar precision when approaching a storm at close range. Precipitation isn't impacting the ground at exactly the locations shown on radar, and radar data is rarely up-to-date in the field (a few minutes can make a world of difference given rapid storm evolution).

Observers should combine radar and visual observations of storm structure to remain safe. Visual observations are extremely limited at night, so chasers should typically increase their margin of safety rather than giving the radar their absolute trust.

GREG STUMPF
Norman, OK research meteorologist

it offers data speeds that are barely adequate. Starting in 2005, the newer, faster EV-DO ("BroadbandAccess", 3G) cellular phone service arrived. EV-DO is still largely limited to cities and major highways, while 1xRTT is widespread in rural areas. A 1xRTT phone cannot use EV-DO, but an EV-DO phone can fall back on 1xRTT if the EV-DO network is unavailable. However, roaming between EV-DO companies is not currently implemented, with the exception of the Sprint-Alltel agreement. As of 2008, the majority of chasers depended on these cellular broadband systems for their data access in the field.

So how do you connect your laptop to the 2G or 3G Internet? "Tethering" is the simplest scheme for mating a laptop computer to a cell phone connection. With this setup, the computer taps into the user's cellular phone using a USB cable or Bluetooth. Some cell phone companies, namely Verizon, have attempted to ban tethering in order to divert customers to their more lucrative data card solutions, while others such as Alltel welcome tethering. One downside of tethering is that it ties up the phone and prevents voice calls from being made. The upside? Tethering is cheap. Alltel dropped its tethered access rates to only $25/mo in 2007.

Nowadays, many chasers cut out the middleman and give the computer its own "cell phone" in the form of a PCMCIA card. Thus whenever the laptop is on and a tower is in range, the Internet is available. This is called a "data card" and is slightly more expensive to use since the card has its own distinct cell phone account. No external cell phone is needed. The cost for a data card is about $100 for the card itself and about $60/mo for service.

With a data card, the chaser has interesting options. Instead of plugging the PCMCIA card into the computer, a chaser can plug it into a router that accepts the cards. The router then creates a Wi-Fi hotspot in the vehicle, allowing all passengers in the vehicle to surf the net on their own computers. An example of a router that takes data cards is the NexAira NexConnect 3G ($150).

The BMW of mobile Internet is a portable hotspot. This setup provides a semi continuous Internet connection for all laptops in the vehicle. The only company offering a portable hotspot is AutoNet Mobile <*www.autonetmobile.com*>, costing $499 for equipment and

$29-$59/month for service. It grew out of an Avis project and began sales in August 2008. It's the closest thing to Wi-Fi at home; just plug the device into the cigarette lighter and an Internet hotspot appears in the car. It runs on redundant 3G connections to the Verizon, Sprint, and Nextel cellular phone networks. The main downside of AutoNet Mobile is the 5 GB per month bandwidth cap, but for chasers who can handle the initial sticker shock and don't plan to leave GRLevel2 on all the time, it may be a good deal.

Blackberry devices are still popular and can be used to gather data for chasing. These are consumer devices that are tied towards a broadband Internet network. Blackberry PDAs tap into AT&T, so accessibility may be limited in rural areas of the Great Plains.

Finally, dual-way satellite Internet has existed since about 2000 with WildBlue and HughesNet the main players. Their equipment cannot be used on chase vehicles due to the precise alignment required on the dishes and the use of hardcoded polarization parameters that are dependent on location. Mobile satellite Internet is available from TracStar <*www.tracstar.net*>, KVH <*www.kvh.com*> and Motosat <*www.motosat.com*>,. However they are geared towards yachts and RVs, and the financial outlay for the first season can quickly run over $10,000.

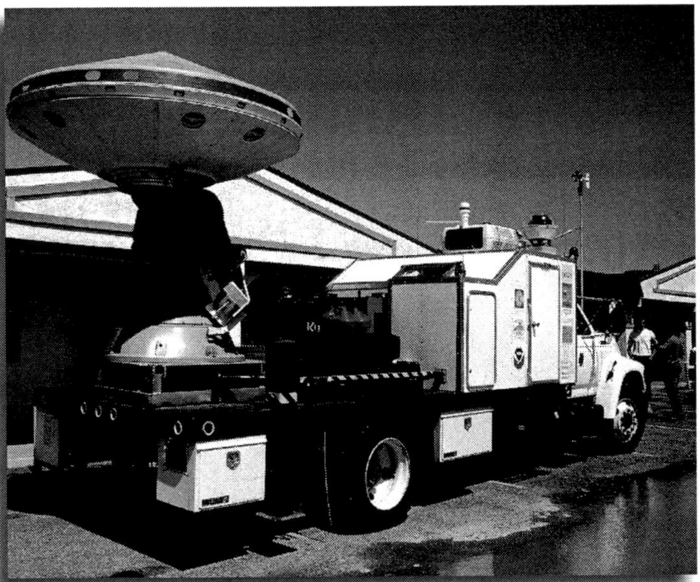

The ultimate data gathering platform, Doppler on Wheels (DOW), photographed at a motel in Plainview, Texas. *(Tim Vasquez)*

The technology boom

Technology has revolutionized the way we chase, not so much the way we forecast but allowing us to see what's going on beyond what our eyes allows us to see when out in the field. I remember the days of sitting out in the countryside looking along the horizon hoping to catch a towering cumulus going up, with technology such as TheatNet, StormHawk and mobile internet and the various radar software you can use with internet connection, you can now see what's going on beyond the horizon.

Having access to weather radar while on the road is very useful, but I think we do sometimes get caught up in the technology and often miss important clues that the sky tells us. It is important to have a balance between technology and the old school method of chasing. Too many time chasers have got caught in sticky situations because they rely on radar so much only to find out that their radar hasn't updated and thus they are looking at old data.

We are in an era where wireless technology is improving each year, we're getting to a point where no matter where you are you will always have a form of data connection so I think these devices will only continue to improve.

With the way technology is rapidly changing, it's hard to say what storm chasing will be like 5 years from now. 10 years ago I would have called one crazy if they would have told me I would have the ability to view radar right in my vehicle while chasing.

JOEY KETCHAM
Pittsburg, KS chaser

Using the data connection

Mobile Internet is most commonly used by chasers to receive weather data, especially radar and visible satellite imagery. Since this is a forecasting activity, it is covered in detail in the *Forecasting* chapter.

Data connections are rapidly becoming used for severe weather reporting purposes. Chasers are able to provide first-hand accounts to the local NWS office. Streaming video, only seconds old, from the front line can be viewed by the meteorologists and compared to radar returns which helps in the decision making process.

Through eSpotter <*espotter.weather.gov*> for certified spotters and SpotterNetwork <*www.spotternetwork.com*> for spotters and all interested individuals, NWS forecasters can identify a chaser who may be able to provide detailed storm structure information of a particular storm and even call them directly. The reports can be augmented with the GPS-enabled APRS (Automatic Position Reporting System). With VoIP (voice over IP) technologies like EchoLink and IRLP (Internet radio linking project), spotters and even chasers can create simulated "CB radio" networks to make contact even in the most distant reaches of their county watch area.

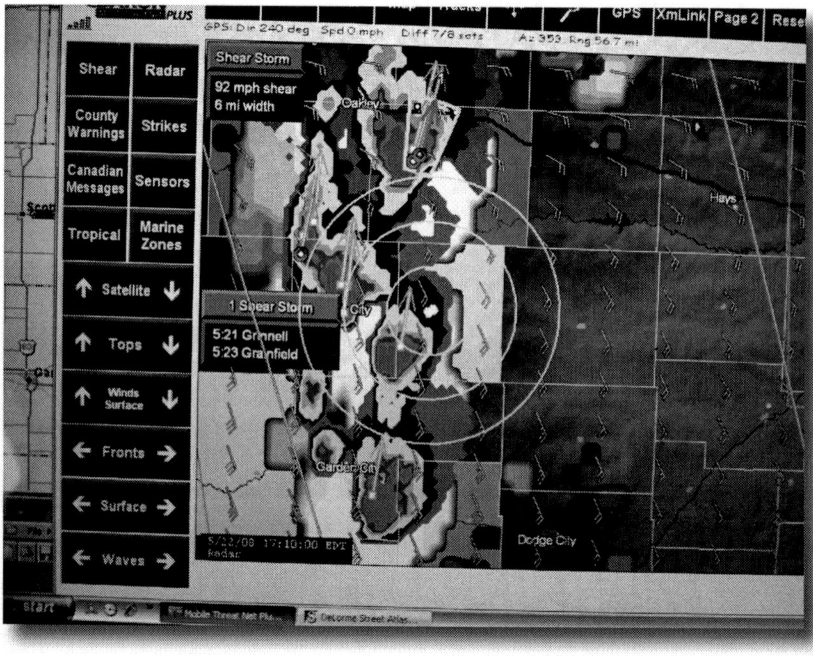

Bill Hark's Mobile ThreatNet screen while he was chasing on 22 May 2008. The package has served many chasers over the years as a portable "appliance" for receiving radar and other wether products in the field. (Bill Hark /

Data broadcast receivers

As of 2008, devices using weather data broadcasts are up against serious competition from mobile broadband Internet. Data broadcasting has actually been around in various forms, such as the television subcarrier data streams in certain markets and the EMWIN VHF broadcasts that saw some chaser use during the late 1990s.

In 2001, XM Radio and later Sirius Satellite Radio revolutionized entertainment, beaming satellite radio to pocket-sized consumer devices. Realizing that its satellite network had information potential that went far beyond music and talk radio, XM Radio engineered the idea of weather datacasting into consumer products without the use of bulky satellite dishes that require aiming. This allowed mobile devices to get weather products all the time, even in a moving car, as long as the unit is on and it can "see" the sky.

Each XM Weather device has access to a special subset of weather products, so spend time doing homework to make sure you select a plan that includes what you want. Radar is the most popular offering of XM Weather, but it must be noted that these products consist of composite re-

The Yaesu VX-170 has been a longtime favorite handheld radio for basic spotting use. When driving into rural areas of a county, a more powerful mobile station and external antenna is often a better solution.

Chasing to serve

Recreational chasers may be well intentioned but most often are just going out for the chase experience and aren't typically involved in a primary public safety and storm reporting mission. I think this group could benefit from more engagement with the local spotter effort and should make better effort to initiate contact with a local forecast office and/or spotter group while in the field.

In a given year our office will receive several reports from this type of group, often second hand and usually much after the fact. If we receive reports, they may be interesting but are often several miles off in location (time recollection can also be a problem), which renders the reports quite useless for either validation or verification use.

I would hope that all serious chasers attend SkyWarn classes of some type, on a regular basis, where they live, so they are retaining an active engagement in the public service aspect of this endeavor. I would further encourage serious chasers to attempt to link up with the local HAM nets where they travel, since the HAMs will likely have a much better working knowledge of the area and can help in identifying critical locations.

My personal feeling, having operated in some relatively sparely populated parts of the northern plains, is that reporting to 911 is usually most beneficial when it also involves a report to the forecast office. Then it does help in community alerting, and doesn't cause conflicting messages or adversely affect the public.

GREGORY GUST
warning coordination
meteorologist, Grand Forks

Caveat emptor

We don't always listen to spotters. The reports can be misleading. What does that wall cloud you heard reported *really* look like? You could be lured away from the storm of the day. Be careful!

DAPHNE LADUE
Norman, OK chaser

Advice from a ham

I'm just starting out in storm chasing but have been a spotter for about 10 years. I am an amateur radio operator and a volunteer examiner and instructor. The best way to get started in ham radio is to get the book "The ARRL Ham Radio License Manual" from the Amateur Radio Relay League. Their web site is http://www.arrl.org. If you would like to know what is Amateur Radio go to http://www.hello-radio.org.

On the ARRL web site you can find ARRL Amateur Licensing Classes in your state and ARRL Exam Sessions near you. After you do some studying, you can see how well you would do on the exam at the following web sites:

http://aa9pw.com
AA9PW FCC Exam Practice

http://www.qrz.com/ham
QRZ Ham Radio Practice Tests

http://www.eham.net/exams
Ham Radio Practice Exams

http://www.kb0mga.net/exams
KB0MGA.net Practice Ham Radio Exams Home

TOM LEVENDUSKY, JR, AC0CH
chaser

flectivity, rather than base reflectivity images. This makes it possible to see nearly all precipitation, including the start of new cells at higher levels, but does not lend itself to viewing hook echoes and low-level structure.

The first entry-level XM Weather system to be introduced was WxWorx Baron Mobile Threat Net <*www.mobilethreatnet.com*> ($930; $50 to $100/mo). It arrived during the 2004 chase season and remains the system of choice for many chasers due to its simplicity and dependability. The Master Mariner plan ($50/mo) is perfect for the budget chaser, allowing access to radar, surface observations, watches and warnings, as well as patented storm tracking and tornado/hail detection algorithms. A higher budget buys the Responder package ($100/mo), offering extras including graphical and textual display of SPC's convective outlook and its mesoscale discussions.

While WxWorx is a computer-based solution, there are now GPS-enabled personal handheld devices arriving on the market which tap into the XM Weather system. XM Weather GPS systems have actually been on the market for some time, but have remained in the realm of aviation with high price tags. Costs are coming down, though. The Garmin StreetPilot 7200 and 7500 devices ($800 and $1299, respectively; $100/mo) are GPS units that tap into the XM Weather feed and also receive the music channels. Pushing prices down even further is the Bushnell Onix 400 ($500; $79 per month). These budget systems have the same basic radar as WxWorx but lack the detailed weather data and storm algorithm overlays.

StormHawk <*www.stormhawk.com*> offers a cellular-based PDA that displays high-resolution composite radar, watches, warnings, and more. This is similar to the XM Weather genre, but without the slight delays that are reported to exist on the XM Weather datacast. The cost is about $1000 for the complete handheld unit, or about $500 for a software package that runs on your own PDA. In February 2008 the company is expected to release a version that works with data card enabled PCs with Bluetooth GPS units.

Although mobile Internet now offers a clear advantage when it comes to month-to-month pricing and flexibility with weather products, weather datacast devices offer proprietary value-added features such as warning alerts, and are not tied to the limitations of the cellular broadband network.

NWS Skywarn liaison Rick Sagers, the radio focal point at the Fort Worth forecast office, during a 2003 tornado outbreak. *(Tim Vasquez)*

Radio

A fraction of chasers, probably about 10 to 20 percent of the community, are amateur radio operators (known as "hams"). In the context of severe weather, amateur radio serves two purposes. The first purpose is to provide a backbone of emergency observations by qualified spotters in the field, which are funneled to the National Weather Service. This program is known as Skywarn <*www.skywarn.org*>. The second purpose is to allow chasers to directly communicate with one another, though cellular phone has rapidly replaced this role, leading to a diminished emphasis on amateur radio in chasing in recent years.

Listening equipment

A license is not required to listen to transmissions. A large number of chasers in fact do this. Monitoring amateur radio traffic requires nothing more than a $100 scanner. Such a radio can be bought at Radio Shacks, pawn shops, second hand stores and the Internet. Depending on what type of scanner is chosen, chasers can tune in not only to the amateur radio frequencies but also to NOAA Weather Radio (NWR). This is a nationwide network of radio stations broadcasting continuous weather information directly from

Amateur radio advantages

Amateur radio has given me an additional level of safety while chasing. I can coordinate with other chasers in a group or exchange information with chasers viewing a storm from different locations. I've used amateur radio to report tornadoes and damage in areas without cellphone service. It also adds to the enjoyment while chasing in a caravan as all the chasers can discuss forecasting, chase strategies or storm features, or just chat to pass the time during long drives.

BILL HARK
Richmond, VA chaser

the nearest National Weather Service office. NWR broadcasts official Weather Service warnings, watches, forecasts and other hazard information 24 hours a day, 7 days a week and can be received when the chaser is within 40 miles of the transmitter site. Broadcasts are found in the VHF public service band at these seven frequencies (MHz): 162.400, 162.425, 162.450, 162.475, 162.500, 162.525 and 162.550. It can provide a few more clues to the forecasting puzzle. More information about NOAA Weather Radio can be found at <*www.weather.gov/nwr*>.

It should be mentioned that a number of states and municipalities prohibit the use of scanners in vehicles. One prominent example on the Great Plains is Minnesota. However, all states with such a restriction, except New York, waive it if the driver is a licensed amateur radio operator. Chasers should check local and state laws for the areas they will be chasing in prior to venturing out if they anticipate utilizing a scanner.

Ham advantages

Ham radio has proven to a beneficial part of my chasing experiences. There is no way that's simpler to talk to someone in an often-high stress situation than to pick up a microphone and push a button. This beats digging for your cell phone and trying to scroll through your contacts.

This year, I found myself stuck on a muddy road, with no cell phone nor internet connection. Fear was rising as the weather radio continued to alert tornado warnings for where we were, yet we were helpless, as night was already falling!

After getting over the shock of being without such everyday equipment, I knew our HAM radio was an only option. We were able to raise a few individuals on a local repeater to come assist us with getting out, and after that occurence I have never chased without a HAM Radio, and have never chased without submitting a report to an emergency net or talking with another chaser or local spotter. HAM radio is a failsafe method of communication and it will continue to be a part of my chasing career.

BRANDON SULLIVAN
Macomb, IL

Transmitting

There are three classes of licenses: Technician, General, and Extra. The Technician class is sufficient for chase purposes. You can obtain a Technician license by passing a 35-question multiple-choice examination. No Morse code test is required, even for Extra. The exam covers basic regulations, operating practices, and electronics theory, with a focus on VHF and UHF applications. Each successive level of license comes with an expansion of privileges. Earning each license requires passing an examination.

Although regulated by the FCC, license exams are given by volunteer groups of amateur radio operators. Operating under organizations called Volunteer Examiner Coordinators, volunteers administer and grade tests and report results to the FCC, which then issues the license. U.S. licenses are good for 10 years before renewal. The Amateur Radio Relay League <*www.arrl.org*> offers an on-line licensing preparation course for the Technician license for those who are interested. For more information, get *The ARRL Ham Radio License Manual*, published by the ARRL. The web site <*www.qrz.com*> is a wealth of information and is a good resource for locating local testing locations. Finally, see Keith Brewster's exhaustive spotter frequency list at <*www.caps.ou.edu/~kbrews/spotfreq*>.

How does a prospective chaser get started? After you have obtained your "call sign", start slow and don't buy a lot of equipment at once. Determine how you will be using the radio, plan, and budget accordingly. For those who will be within the "line-of-sight" of the repeater, a handheld radio may suit your needs. A "gently used" handheld radio costs around $100 or so and has significantly better reception with an external antenna mounted on the roof. Another consideration is that handhelds use batteries as their power source, which limits their effective use due to power consumption and strength.

For chasing, a mounted mobile unit is much better. It provides better reception for distant stations, more transmitting power, and is one less loose object moving around inside the vehicle.

With today's technology, there are many options to consider. All radios are programmable, and some have weather radio frequencies pre-programmed. There are single, dual and tri-band radios that can operate on different bands simultaneously, but since this requires fiddling with the buttons to switch between them, it can be confusing as to which one you're about to transmit on. Some chasers choose to simply have two radios if they want to monitor

Starting out

I bought my first ham radio in the winter of 2005 after joining Southern Oklahoma Skywarn. The radio, an Icom I2200H, made my chases a lot easier with live radar updates from Murray County EOC, hearing spotter storm reports, and listening to cross talk. I would advise anyone who wants to start storm chasing: get your ham ticket. It will make your chase go easier, could get a tornado warning out faster, and could save a life .

JASON YOUNG, KE5PCA
Sulphur, Oklahoma

A radio stack in the vehicle of chaser Jesse Risley. The top radio is a police scanner which helps monitor public safety agencies. The small item in the middle is a Kenwood TM-D700A dual-band amateur transceiver. At the bottom is a high-power commercial VHF radio for longer distances where more power is necessary. *(Jesse Risley)*

two stations consistently. Whichever one you choose, always keep the manual handy as it can be technically challenging to program some of the newer radios manually.

Are you ready to transmit? The most important thing to do before making your first contact is to listen and determine how the other operators are making their contacts, as different modes and bands have slightly different approaches. It helps to have heard a few exchanges on the different bands.

The best way to get involved is to do so slowly and locally. Get involved with your local Skywarn net, local amateur radio club, or service organization. You'll get a feel for how much money to invest and what you can do with the equipment locally and on the road. Clubs tend to have a "shack" featuring a variety of radios operating in several different modes. This allows operators to experience the many diverse aspects of amateur radio. There is no age restriction for amateur radio, which might help channel the interests of a young person interested in storm chasing but who cannot yet drive to the storm.

The value of amateur radio

I've found amateur radio to be an invaluable tool for chasing. Amateur radio gets through when other forms of communication, such as cell phones, will fail. Amateur radio allows chasers to maintain communications with each other in times of need, and it allows for the facilitation of severe weather reports to be passed along to the National Weather Service in a timely manner. I would recommend that interested parties obtain a copy of Radio Shack's Now Your Talking introduction to amateur radio manual. The website qrz.com also has sample tests online to help prepare for the exams.

JESSE RISLEY
Colchester, IL chaser

Common simplex

While most VHF/UHF amateur radio uses a nearby repeater that broadcasts all traffic for better reception, simplex is the technique for simply talking to each another direct, as if using walkie-talkies or CB radios. This is usually done on the 145.520 MHz National Simplex Calling Frequency, and known in the storm chasing community as "chaser common". It is the universal frequency to monitor for other chasers, make contact and then move to another simplex frequency, assuming both parties are in range of one another. Alternate frequencies are 52.525, 146.460, 146.550, 223.500, 223.520, 446.000 and 1294.550. Government and university research programs may operate on other frequencies such as the 163 MHz band.

Chaser Brandon Sullivan talks on 2-meter in the field with a base station unit, visible under the glove compartment. *(Brandon Sullivan)*

Skywarn

In 1965, two unrelated severe weather events were the impetus for the NWS to convene a Weather Bureau Survey Team led by Paul H. Kutschenreuter. It found disturbing inadequacies in the areas of communication, public awareness, severe storm reporting networks, and radar coverage. At the same time, the amateur radio community was already recognized for a tradition of using their talent for community service. The solution was obvious.

The Natural Disaster Warning system (NADWARN) plan was formed, including a tornado-specific plan that we now know as Skywarn. This program was brought to life in 1968 largely through the efforts of Sherman Carr, W9NGT (d. 2000) and NWS Milwaukee employee Dave Theophilus, W9KWQ, who in Wisconsin created the nation's first severe weather network. Over the 1970s, 1980s, and 1990s, the Skywarn program built on Wisconsin's success, evolving and expanding to include nearly all NWS offices and over 280,000 trained severe weather spotters.

Anyone with an interest in public service and access to communication services may attend the training and contribute, regardless of whether they have a radio license. Classes are free and from two to six hours long. Contact your local NWS Warning Coordination Meteorologist <*www.stormready.noaa.gov/contact.htm*> to obtain a schedule of classes or check the web page of your local NWS office <*www.weather.gov*>. Most training is done during the first few months of the year.

Though the NWS sponsors Skywarn and conducts spotter training, it is the responsibility of county and city emergency managers to implement the network. Skywarn operations may be conducted under the government-sponsored Radio Amateur Civil Emergency Service (RACES) <*www.usraces.org or www.qsl.net/races*> or the ARRL Amateur Radio Emergency Services (ARES) <*www.ares.org*> program. Due to interpatations of the regulations, some emergency managers prohibit non-RACES members from transmitting during a net, but this is the exception as more groups are leaning towards either ARES or simply an informal "weather net".

Spotters are deployed within watch areas and they report to an emergency operations center (EOC) when they witness reportable severe weather events. The emergency manager (EM) makes whatever decisions are necessary to

Skywarn in the field

Having a scanner or radio tuned to the local Skywarn or chaser frequency can offer much information. While we take internet access in our vehicles for granted now, there is still some delay.

Spotters or chasers need to see features before they are reported to the NWS and then the NWS has to disseminate that info if necessary in the form of a warning or SPS before it shows up on your laptop. Having the radio on can allow you to hear that info as it happens. Someone could see something in a different part of the storm than where you are looking. If they report it and you hear it, your attention could be shifted in time to see that brief tornado or rotating wall cloud.

BRYAN HOWELL
Lockport, IL

initiate life and property-saving actions, such as turning on tornado sirens. Spotter reports are passed on to the NWS, providing feedback for warning operations and radar interpretation.

Over the years, many of the local NWS offices have incorporated amateur radios into their operations so that they can monitor all Skywarn traffic in real time. Some offices have dedicated teams of operators that can staff the radios and pass pertinent information to the meteorologists. As technology has changed, new methods of receiving storm and damage reports have been added to the array, providing more avenues for timely information to be used in the decision making process.

If chasers cannot or choose not to interact in Skywarn nets, they can use their cell phone to make reports. See the *Cellular Phone* section for more information.

Many NWS office websites have storm reporting pages; chasers with wireless internet may use these. Reports from online services such as the NWS program *espotter.weather.gov* and independent network *www.spotternetwork.org* are being integrated into NWS monitoring systems. Many NWS offices have dedicated storm reporting numbers which are monitored during storm events. If a call must be placed to a local law or fire agency, the regular administrative number for these agencies is a better option than using 911.

The original Meatwagon

The Meatwagon was, I think, the first multi-owner vehicle with the sole purpose of chasing. Me and four other meteorology students paid $25 each for it in late 1989 after I sold Roger Edwards the soon-to-be Roachmobile. He took the Roachmobile to Miami and we kept the original Meatwagon, a brown 1972 Vista Cruiser station wagon. We had fun with flat tires on the March 1990 Hesston day and another chase in early April of 1990, when we discovered that the spare tire was the wrong rim size!

It broke down on us during a chase, on 24 April 1990, when the fan clutch failed and it badly overheated while we crept through a hail core near Shamrock. Unable to drive more than 20 mph on the shoulder of I-40, after a successful revival of the engine in Shamrock, we simply gave up and called for backup from Erick. Its final resting place was a salvage yard in western Oklahoma.

RICH THOMPSON
Norman, OK chaser and
SPC forecaster

Television

By 2002, mobile television reception fell sharply out of favor as a method of getting weather information due to the appearance of mobile Internet and its vast potential for delivering data to the field. However since a TV set is essentially just an appliance, the technique will be briefly discussed here as a cheap alternative. It can work as a spotty source of radar data in highly competitive weather markets where local severe weather coverage is frequent.

Since the mid 1980s and the appearance of quality inverters and solid-state portable sets, chasers have dabbled with "chaser TV". However it requires the vehicle to be within 50 miles of a large city. Luck and timing determines whether the chaser gets a peek at the radar. Furthermore, a chaser need not bring an actual TV set along. Reliable USB tuner devices exist which allow on-air broadcasts to be displayed on a laptop screen. These devices generally have a marginal antenna and will work only within about 25 miles of a transmitter, though the models with more features can be connected to an external antenna.

A direct broadcast satellite (DBS) system opens up access to The Weather Channel, requiring about $70 for the equipment and $30/month for the subscription. Though the equipment will work anywhere as long as there is electricity and a line of sight, the dish has to be aimed, which requires a roadside stop and manual adjustment. Unfortunately, after 1996 the Weather Channel's niche meteorological products were largely dropped and the channel became heavily geared towards the lowest common denominators of its market, limiting its usability for chasers.

Electrical power

If you want to recharge a cell phone, you just plug it into the cigarette lighter. But what happens if you want to run electronics and radios? The answer is add more 12-volt plugs. You may even want to install an inverter to provide standard household outlets.

An inverter is a box that plugs into the vehicle's 12-volt DC current and offers 110-volt AC current with regular household sockets. The easy part of picking an inverter is matching up the inverter's power output to the wattage that you expect to draw. A 300-watt system will work well for the leisure chaser, while a 750-watt system will be good for

The author's TV experience

I gave portable TV a try on a chase southeast of Dallas in February 1987. I brought a yagi antenna which, unfolded, was almost as big as the car. I tuned in Troy Dungan at 5:15 pm on a Sears portable color TV and confirmed that storms did initiate. But even at 30 miles from the Cedar Hill antenna farm, I couldn't get a good signal. The wind kept nudging the antenna off the roof. After that trial, the TV gear stayed at home.

TIM VASQUEZ

One criteria for chasemobile selection is the space required for all the gear! An SUV compartment also allows access to all the equipment while on the road. During a lightning barrage, you won't find any volunteers wanting to get a spare battery out of the luggage in the trunk! This vehicle belongs to George Kourounis. *(George Kourounis/stormchaser.ca)*

Failures and their symptoms

Some common failure points for a chase vehicle, their symptoms, and treatment are as follows:

- **Broken water hose**. Causes a burst of water and a rapid engine temperature rise. Pull over and shut down immediately.
- **Oil starvation**. The only symptom is a low-oil light, until the engine seizes. Irreparable damage can occur if the vehicle is driven further. When the light comes on, pull over and shut down immediately, and replenish with oil.
- **Broken fuel pump**. Engine bucks and runs rough, and stalls, or won't start. The pump has to be replaced.
- **Water in distributor cap**. Driving into puddles, flood waters, or a rainstorm can cause the engine to run rough or stop. The ignition turns the car but it won't catch. Remove the distributor cap and blot dry or spray WD-40 inside, which alleviates the water problem.
- **Broken fan belt**. Alternator light comes on and steering is more difficult. Turn off all lights and electronics. The vehicle may run another 10 to 30 minutes, so you may be able to make it to a service station.

Car care. Knowing how to do a few minor repairs is one way to ease the strain on the chase budget. *(David Hoadley)*

high-tech users. As of 2008 the vast majority of inverters on the market were of good worksmanship and it's possible to pay as low as $25 for a good inverter. The basic modified sine wave inverters work fine for almost all chase electronics, and the more expensive pure sine wave inverters are generally considered by most chasers to not be necessary.

One important feature to look for is an automatic shutdown mechanism that kicks in when when the input voltage is low. Drawing 110 volts on low DC voltage causes a high current load, resulting in a damaging overheat. An inverter with overload protection will keep the system running safely. It should also be noted that inverters with fans can produce RF noise and be picked up on radios and video camera footage. It's just one more reason to test your setup before committing to a big chase day.

A good chase vehicle needs to have a robust electrical system. Most onboard electrical troubles are caused by poor connections. If you use the cigarette lighter regularly, that's a good indication that its time to use it only for cigarettes. Wire your own dedicated 12-volt bus directly to the battery using 12-gauge wire and use high-quality 12-volt outlets. Likewise, wire the inverter directly to the battery using a similar gauge of electrical wire. Then protect this circuit with a fuse. All these steps will make an enormous difference in mitigating power troubles and will protect your equipment.

Vehicles

What kind of vehicle is best to chase in? The criteria is simple: comfort and reliability. In spite of the image presented in the film *Twister*, a storm chasing vehicle does not require rugged handling and 4-wheel drive. The Great Plains has an excellent road network and no chaser has ever taken an off-road excursion through a crop field. A high-clearance vehicle, however, can be of some help in passing over downed limbs and for crossing shallow flood waters.

More important than the type and brand of vehicle is *maintenance*. A chase vehicle is not suited for the job if it's not dependable enough to handle being quite far from repair shops and tow truck services most of the time. Fortunately, a surge of quality in automotive worksmanship from the 1990s onward has made breakdowns in remote rural towns a rarity. But to insure this good fortune, chase vehicles must be kept in prime shape all the time, with belts and oil changed on schedule or when required. At the beginning of each spring the vehicle should be taken to a competent dealership service department, not just an oil and lube shop, to have a complete inspection done.

Flat tires still continue to be an occasional annoyance. A can of "fix-a-flat" can be a lifesaver for minor punctures, but it's often necessary to use the spare tire. Unfortunately many "donut" spare tires are laughably inadequate for Great Plains chasing and are not rated to last more than 50 miles. With a lot of chase action unfolding in the evenings and on weekends, this can easily leave chasers stranded. It's highly recommended that all chasers pack a full-size spare tire. This costs money and involves having to purchase a wheel from a junkyard and have a new tire mounted, but the peace of mind is immeasurable Not only does it help chasers cover long distances to a repair shop, but it also gives flexibility to defer the repair or drive straight home, a boon on Sunday when everything within 150 miles is closed.

If you're driving an older vehicle or are frightened about breaking down in the Plains, get an AAA (Automobile Association of America) membership. This gives you a hotline to towing and vehicle repair services anywhere in the U.S. The dependability of AAA services have left a large number

Maintenance guide

First and foremost, make sure maintenance is done according to the owner manual maintenance schedule. Even so, follow these tips to make sure your vehicle is the least of your worries.

Before the chase season

- Have the vehicle wheels aligned to reduce hydroplaning and prolong tire life.
- Check to make sure you're carrying an adequate jack and tire iron.
- If you don't know how to change your tire, practice at least once to give yourself skill and insure you have the tools needed.
- Get the oil filter and oil changed. Change them again according to the manual recommendation for additional mileage -- usually after several thousand miles.
- Check the condition of the spare tire for air level and damage.

As often as practical

- Check radiator fluid reservoir.
- Check tire air levels.
- Check oil level.
- Clean corrosion off battery terminals using a stiff brush and water with baking soda; use eye protection.
- Check belts for fraying and hoses for damage and replace if needed.

Tire problems tend to be an occasional chase headache. Never drive with a tire in this condition. Note the abraded, smooth tread and serious wear. This tire had been bought 4 months earlier and succumbed to bad alignment. *(Tim Vasquez)* of chasers satisfied, even well off the Interstates. Be aware that websites like Consumerist have reported problems with complimentary roadside services provided by some credit cards.

One problem area for storm chasers is the optical characteristics of the dashboard-windshield area. Some vehicle models have reflective dashboards tops that cause visibility and photography problems. Such problems have been cited on Saturns and Chryslers. A workaround for the problem is a dash cover (about $40), available from big-catalog retailers such as J.C. Whitney, or made at home from black velvet or felt. The low-gloss formulation of Armor All protectant can help lessen glare from the dashboard top.

Some chasers have installed flashing safety lights or lightbars, similar to those seen on utility service vehicles. While "cool factor" is a driving force behind many of these purchases, there is a lukewarm consensus that these lights can improve safety — *providing they are not used to park illegally and drive recklessly.* Amber lights are the color to use. Red and blue flashing lights are only for use by emergency services, and many states impose a third-degree felony for unauthorized use.

Odds and ends

Here we present some other items that are useful to the chaser:

■ **Water** is a must-have. Not only does it give hydration to thirsty travellers but it can also be used to fill a blown radiator, give emergency refreshment during a breakdown, cleanse dust from the eyes, and wash cuts. A case of 12 liters of water can be purchased for about $5.

■ **Portable seating** is a great accessory. A folding chair, a portable director's chair, a lawnchair, or even a tall bucket (inverted in the vehicle to carry supplies) can come in handy for enjoying the scenery.

■ **A tow strap** can help others pull you out if you get stuck in the mud. If you drive an SUV or truck, tow straps are likely to break. Pack a chain instead.

■ **Jumper cables** are handy when you accidentally leave an interior light or device on all night or the car battery decides to give up the ghost. Always follow the vehicle instruction manual for connecting cables, as one of the hookups is often on the engine block or a special terminal post.

Equipment inventory

The following is a suggested list of items from the 1986 edition of Tim Marshall's Storm Chase Manual. Even 22 years later, it remains useful as a starting point for a chaser's own checklist.

"Must" items: Cameras, film, batteries, filters and lenses, tripod, highway maps, tape recorder for documentation, cassette tapes, money, jacket, food, first aid kit, sunglasses, radio, credit cards, telephone credit card.

Car operation: Extra fan belts, fire extinguisher, jumper cables, tire inflator can, extra coolant, small board to mount jack on muddy surfaces, tire pressure gauge, extra oil, air pump, road flares, flashlight.

Optional instrumentation: Thermometer, water and wet bulb thermometer, wind meter, binoculars, compass, barometer, weight scale, graduated cylinder, ruler, signs or stakes, camera cable release.

Odds and ends

It may not seem odd to some, but no matter if you are going on a one-day chase or a whole week, always bring extra clothes. You never know when you'll get soaked or muddy from a Kansas road that will require that one extra set of clothes. I also always have bug spray, those warm and muggy evenings when you're watching the lightning or still chasing away, the bugs will always be there to bother. Lastly, a few hand tools and a flashlight are always good to have with you, whether it's mechanical or for comfort you can never have too many tools.

JAYSON PRENTICE
Ames, IA chaser

■ **Sunscreen** is a must-have when spending time out of the vehicle under a hot sun that's already heating things up. It protects against carcinogenic UV rays.

■ **Sunglasses.** Storm chasing involves a lot of daylight driving under a fair sky. Polarized lenses will not only cut down on glare but will actually improve the contrast of the sky and allow distant storm towers to be seen more clearly.

■ **Rain repellent.** A good rain repellent applied to the windshield will cause rain to roll right off, minimizing the need for wipers and producing much not only better chase video but an extra margin of road safety. Unfortunately most stores carry only Rain-X, which tends to wear off after a week. Aquapel is a newer product and is considered by car aficionados to be vastly better than Rain-X. One application can last an entire chase season. To get it you'll probably have to visit online vendors such as TireRack and Amazon.

■ **First-aid kit.** Buy a kit for your vehicle and make sure it's not just packed with cheap bandages and aspirin. It's also recommended to check labels for cheap kits made in China, due to the country's widespread problems with industrial melamine contamination. As many chaser ailments involve road food, viruses, and allergies, it's wise to beef up the kit by tossing in some antacids, anti-diarrheals, analgesics, and decongestants. After all, there's no 24-hour pharmacy in Trego, Kansas.

■ **Emergency keys and money** will keep you from getting stuck. A spare key in a special case, available from automotive stores, can be hidden under the vehicle frame to get you on your way if you get locked out. A few twenties hidden in the vehicle will keep you from being delayed at out-of-the-way stations that can't take a credit card or are having equipment problems.

■ **Safety glasses or goggles** are worth considering for downburst or "hail blast" situations where glass might become a problem. Even while videoing the storm, they can protect your eyes from irritating windblown dust.

■ **Lens cleaning wipes** should be kept handy for cleaning optical equipment. A few of them tucked away around the chase vehicle helps make sure one is easy to reach.

■ **Insect repellent** will keep the inevitable swarm of mosquitoes away. *Important: DEET degrades plastic and will harm not only contact lenses but also chase equipment such as radios, cameras, and computers with plastic parts.*

Choosing a partner

If you must have a chase partner, the first thing to look for is someone of equal enthusiasm. There's nothing worse than getting worked up over a potential chase day only to have your partner scoff at you, saying, "You're overreacting again!" Not because they believe you really are — but because they just don't feel like chasing. Sometimes I think the best chase partner is none at all!

SHANE ADAMS
Norman, OK chaser

The ideal chase partner. You did read the chase partner tips, right? *(David Hoadley)*

Chase partners

The proliferation of E-mail lists, chase parties, and vacation planning has made partner selection something like buying an item off the shelf. Chase partners are not only social companions. They help drive, serve as relief for a weary driver, assist in scanning the sky for clues, nagivate, and help make tactical decisions. This can be a very important consideration.

It might be tempting to choose a chase partner by imagining what happens in the heat of action. Can they deal with the equipment? Can they quickly find road options? Can they take over the driving? It must be remembered that 90% of chasing is enduring the boring hours of a chase day.

A much more important set of criteria emerges: How well do I know this person? Do we share non-weather interests and views? Does this person have similar chase objectives? Is this person mature, dependable, and responsible? Does this person's system of personal values and personal standards agree with me? Is this person known to have a temper problem? Does this person have annoying habits? Might this person conflict with my own schedule and obligations?

The answers to these questions will define how well you get along with each other during those all-day drives across Kansas. It's a good idea to start simple and go on a few "gentleman's chases". It will then be obvious what's in the cards for the inevitable long-distance trips.

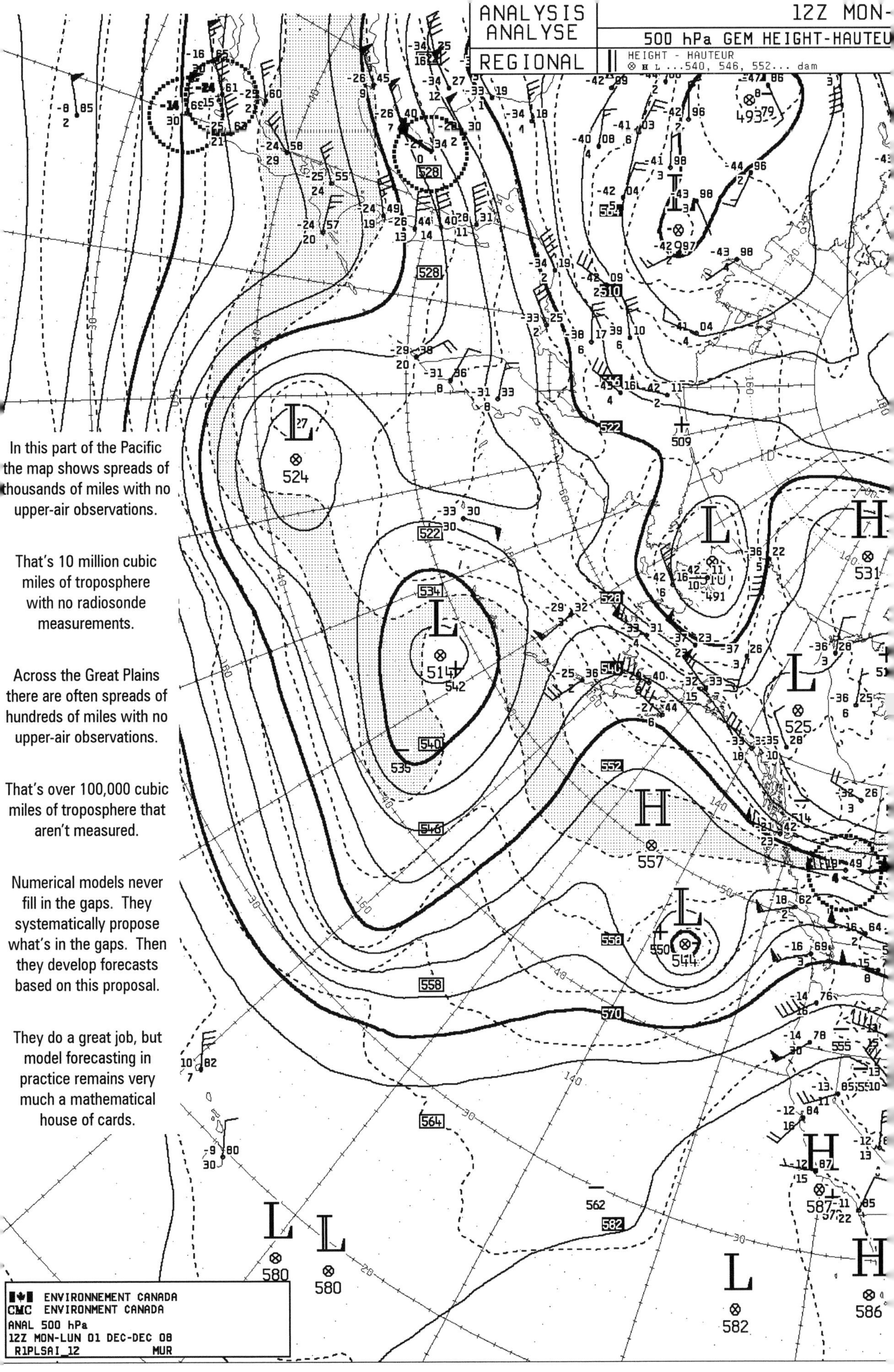

In this part of the Pacific the map shows spreads of thousands of miles with no upper-air observations.

That's 10 million cubic miles of troposphere with no radiosonde measurements.

Across the Great Plains there are often spreads of hundreds of miles with no upper-air observations.

That's over 100,000 cubic miles of troposphere that aren't measured.

Numerical models never fill in the gaps. They systematically propose what's in the gaps. Then they develop forecasts based on this proposal.

They do a great job, but model forecasting in practice remains very much a mathematical house of cards.

CHAPTER THREE
THE THUNDERSTORM

The bulk of what we know about thunderstorms originated in 1946 with the Thunderstorm Project, a Weather Bureau program headed by scientists Horace Byers and Roscoe Braham Jr. It was an incredibly ambitious field project for its time, sampling individual Florida thunderstorms with a variety of small-scale surface observation networks, radar observations, and airplane traversals. The project findings were published in 1949, and they identified all of the building blocks of thunderstorms: downdrafts, updrafts, outflow, inflow, and boundaries. It also established the fact that a thunderstorm is not an object, but a complex process.

The thunderstorm is the direct result of moist air rising rapidly through deep layers of the troposphere. This rising motion is produced when an imaginary parcel of air is warmer than its surroundings: it is buoyant, just like a hot air balloon. If there is no moisture, the buoyant air rises invisibly in the form of thermals. If sufficient moisture is present, however, the buoyant air is manifested visually by the appearance of a cumulus or cumulonimbus cloud, and other important processes come into play.

Buoyancy of an air parcel is *convection*, which in a meteorological context refers to the vertical transport of heat. The weather that occurs due to convection is called *convective weather*. Thunderstorms, however, are not the only type of convective weather that occurs. Rainstorms, wind squalls, hurricanes, and dust devils can have deep roots in atmospheric convection. These are all fascinating phenomena which are often pursued by chasers, but this book will focus squarely on the thunderstorm.

The mystery of tornadoes

The land tornadoes of the United States form, by their dimensions and their dreadful mechanical effects, a transition from the spouts to the cyclones, exhibiting the phenomena of the former on a gigantic scale, and emulating the latter by their widespread fury.

The width of their path along the surface of the earth amounts in some cases to as much as an English mile; its length varies from two to eight hundred miles. The rapidity of their progressive movement is very great, as they advance on an average at the rate of thirty-seven miles per hour, but it is far surpassed by their whirlwind velocity which takes place within their vortex, and imparts to it its irresistable power.

DR. G. HARTWIG
The Aerial World, 1886

Thunderstorm basics

The rising, buoyant air that creates a thunderstorm is known as the *updraft*. As it leaves the ground, it rises like an invisible bubble. However, as it rises, it cools. In many cases the updraft will cool to its dewpoint temperature, which causes the air to saturate and condense. On a typical thunderstorm day, this occurs at just under a mile above the ground. The saturation and condensation process continues for the remainder of the updraft's ascent, forming a visible cloud.

The thunderstorm updraft. This developing cumulonimbus cloud represents an upward surge of buoyant air. *(Tim Vasquez)*

In most cases, the updraft will lose strength and the cloud will cease growing. This results in fair-weather cumulus clouds. However when the updraft has more strength, the it will rise all the way to the stratosphere. Here it reaches warmer air, which suppresses its upward motion, and it is then forced to spread horizontally and form an anvil-shaped cloud. Meanwhile this updraft may continue being fed from underneath by inflow air that convergences into the thunderstorm.

Within the middle levels of the storm, many processes occur, such as collision, accretion, and aggregation, which cause the rapid growth of liquid and ice crystals. Therefore, not only does cloud material form, but large rain droplets and ice particles begin appearing *en masse.* Many of these droplets and crystals evaporate in the middle and upper portions of the cumulonimbus cloud, producing a blob of chilled, dense air which quickly begins sinking, called the *downdraft.* This downdraft air is usually filled with precipitation, and brings cooler temperatures and higher barometric pressure to the Earth's surface. When it reaches the ground, it spreads radially along the ground, producing a divergence of cool air known as outflow.

Thunderstorm ingredients

Now that we know all the building blocks of the thunderstorm and have some idea of its workings, how do we know what actually causes the thunderstorm to occur? What are the prerequisites that make the difference between a fair-weather cumulus cloud and a monstrous cumulonimbus tower?

In 1943, pioneer storm forecasters Albert Showalter and Joe Fulks published the first list of ingredients required for a strong thunderstorm. These ingredients included horizontal shear, such as that found along a front or boundary, convergence, unstable air, latitudinal wind shear, and local wave development. The list was further refined by Ernest Fawbush and L.G. Starrett in 1953, then boiled down to their simplest elements in 1987 by Charles Doswell. These are *instability*, *moisture*, and *lift*. The ingredients are the elements which will be used in this book to understand and forecast thunderstorms. A fourth ingredient, shear, will be examined also.

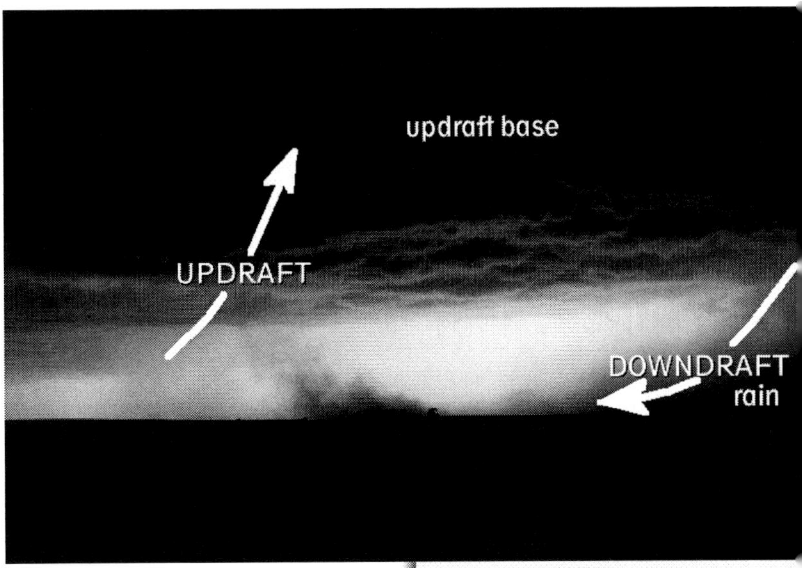

Photo of simultaneous updraft and downdraft areas in a thunderstorm. *(Gene Rhoden / Weatherpix)*

1 — Instability

The pure definition of instability describes the reaction of a parcel, an imaginary box of air, when it is displaced from its original position. If it is *unstable*, it accelerates in the direction of displacement. For example, a parcel is nudged upward by lift over a mountain, so it continues upward, gathering speed. If a parcel is *stable*, it accelerates in opposite of the direction of displacement. In this case, a parcel is nudged upward by frontal lift, but it resists the motion as it rises, and when the force is relaxed, it sinks back to its original position.

What does this mean in meteorology? What determines whether a parcel can be stable or unstable? This is given by the lapse rate in the atmosphere: the existing difference in temperature over a given vertical distance. A random parcel of air superimposed on this atmospheric profile starts with the same temperature as the air around it, but if it is forced upward or downward, its temperature changes according to the dry adiabatic lapse rate (about 10°C/km) or the wet adiabatic lapse rate (about 6°C/km). It is easy to see that this can introduce radical differences between the temperature of the parcel and that of its environment.

For example, assume that the temperature at the ground is 24°C, and at the height of 3 km it happens to be -15°C. We're about to launch a radiosonde weather balloon, and just before we do, we tie a red balloon filled with air to it. The temperature of air in the red balloon is 24°C, same as the air around it, and it rolls around on the ground, sometimes lofted up with a passing breeze, neither wanting to rise nor sink. We release the radiosonde balloon, and our red balloon goes with it. The air inside the red balloon

From peak to peak,
the rattling crags among
Leaps the live thunder!
Not from one lone cloud,
But every mountain now
hath found a tongue,
And Jura answers,
through her misty shroud,
Back to the joyous Alps,
who call to her aloud!
And this is in the night:
Most glorious night!
Thou wert not sent for slumber!
let me be
A sharer in thy fierce
and far delight,
A portion of the tempest
and of thee!
How the lit lake shines,
a phosphoric sea,
And the big rain comes dancing
to the earth!
And now again 'tis black,
and now, the glee
Of the loud hills shakes
with its mountain mirth,
As if they did rejoice
o'er a young earthquake's birth.

LORD BYRON
Childe Harold's Pilgrimage,
1816

Working with soundings

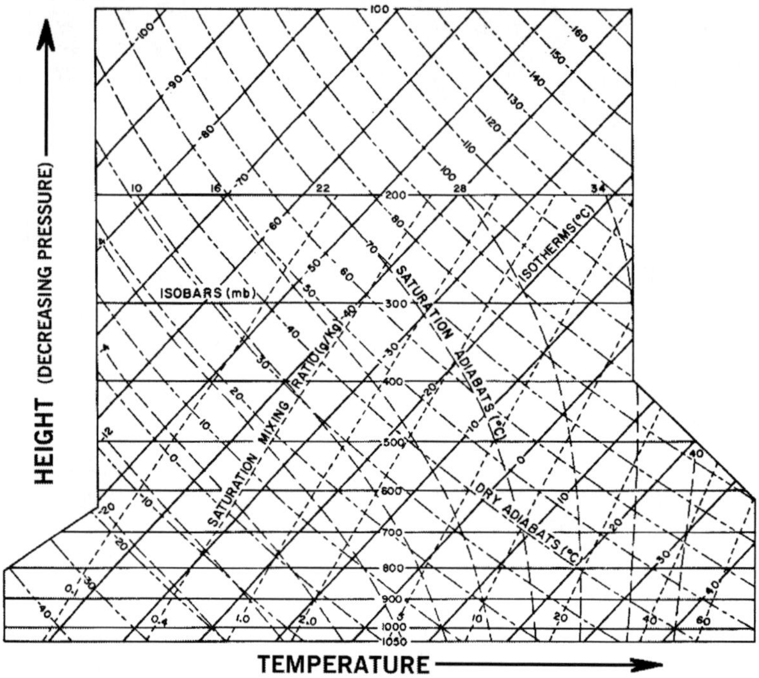

The SKEW-T diagram is widely used in the meteorological community to calculate and visualize atmospheric instability. First, the existing profile at a given station is plotted on the chart with respect to temperature and height. This forms a line that indicates the existing temperature at any given level. Next, hypothetical parcels are evaluated with respect to this line. As the hypothetical parcel changes height, it will change temperature according to one of two lines: the dry adiabat if it is unsaturated, or the wet adiabat (saturation adiabat) if it is saturated (100 percent relative humidity).

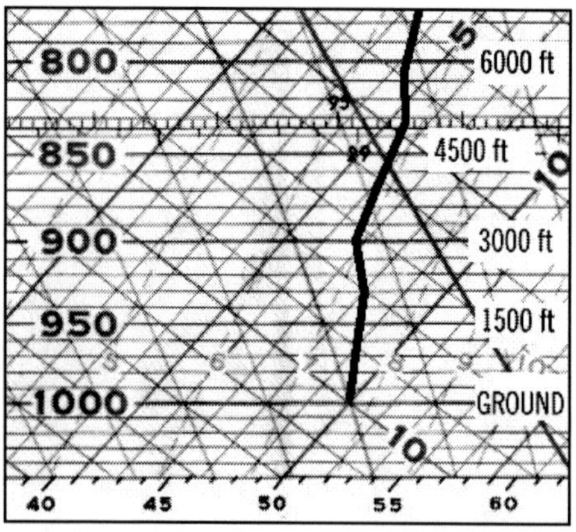

STABLE LAYER. In this example, the temperature at the ground, where the pressure is 1000 mb, is 10°C. At the 850 mb level, roughly equating to 4500 ft MSL, the temperature is 6°C. This shows a weak temperature fall with height, or mildly cool air atop warm air. This is also known as weak lapse rate (4°C over the given layer).

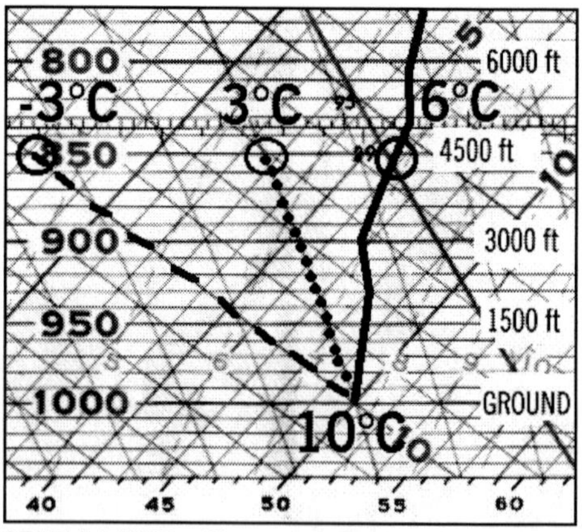

STABLE LAYER. Closer examination shows that if we lift a parcel from the bottom to 850 mb, it cools from 10°C to -3°C. A parcel lifted with latent release cools from 10°C to 3°C. Both of these are much cooler than the environmental 6°C observed at 850 mb, so in either case, the parcel is colder than the air around it and sinks back to its original level.

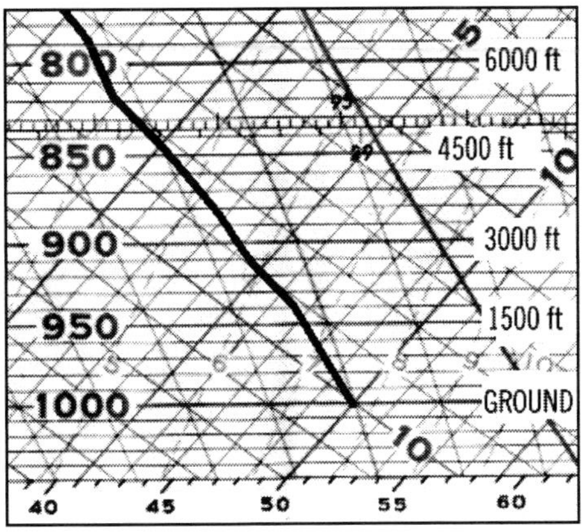

CONDITIONALLY UNSTABLE LAYER. In this example, the temperature at the ground, where the pressure is 1000 mb, is 10°C. At the 850 mb level, roughly equating to 4500 ft MSL, the temperature is 0°C. This shows a moderate temperature fall with height, in other words, cold air atop warm air. This yields a moderate lapse rate of 10°C over the given distance.

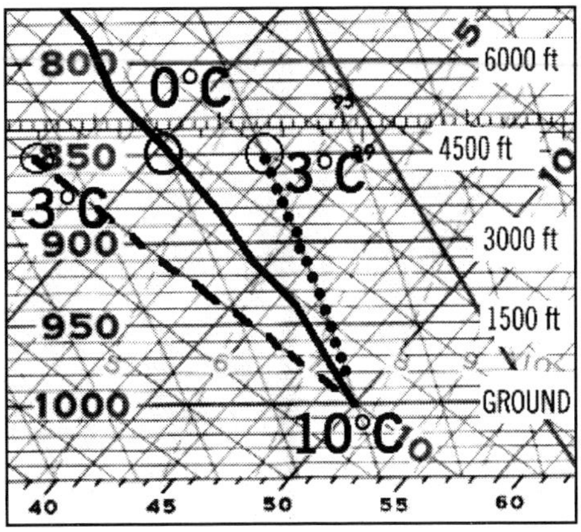

CONDITIONALLY UNSTABLE LAYER. Closer examination shows that if we lift a dry parcel from the bottom to 850 mb, it cools from 10°C to -3°C. This is colder than the environmental 0°C at the same level, so the parcel will assume a stable configuration and sink back to its original level. However if a saturated parcel is lifted over the same distance, it cools from 10°C to 3°C and is warmer than the environmental 0°C. This gives it an unstable configuration, so it continues rising.

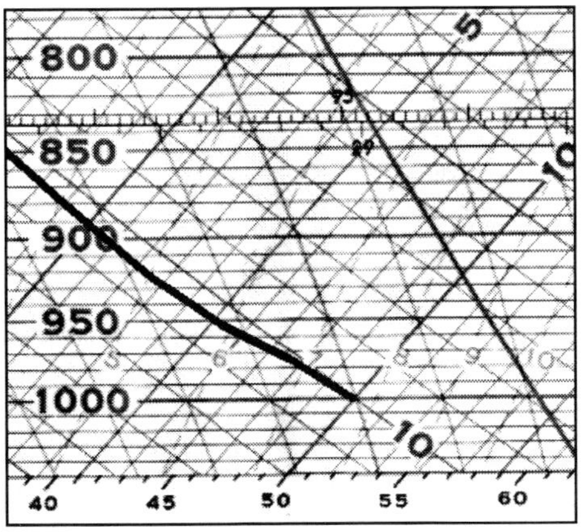

ABSOLUTELY UNSTABLE LAYER. In this example, the temperature at the ground, where the pressure is 1000 mb, is 10°C. At the 850 mb level, roughly equating to 4500 ft MSL, the temperature is -4°C. This shows a strong temperature fall with height, in other words, very cold air atop warm air. This also yields a very steep lapse rate of 14°C over the given distance. An absolutely unstable profile is almost never seen on real soundings, and if it occurs, the atmosphere tends to overturn itself spontaneously, reducing the lapse rate.

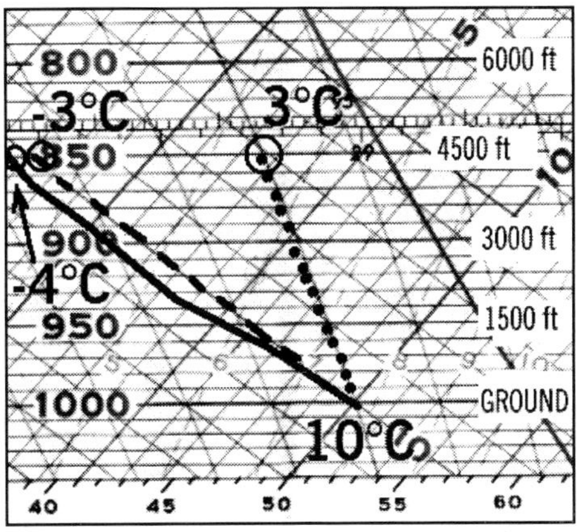

ABSOLUTELY UNSTABLE LAYER. Closer examination shows that if we lift a dry parcel from the bottom to 850 mb, it cools from 10°C to -3°C. A saturated parcel cools from 10°C to 3°C. Both of these are much warmer than the environmental -4°C observed at 850 mb, so in either case, the parcel is in an unstable configuration and continues accelerating upward.

Notice how regardless of the instability, the parcel reaches the same temperatures when it rises to a given level, since the dry adiabat and wet adiabat represent a constant, predictable rate of change.

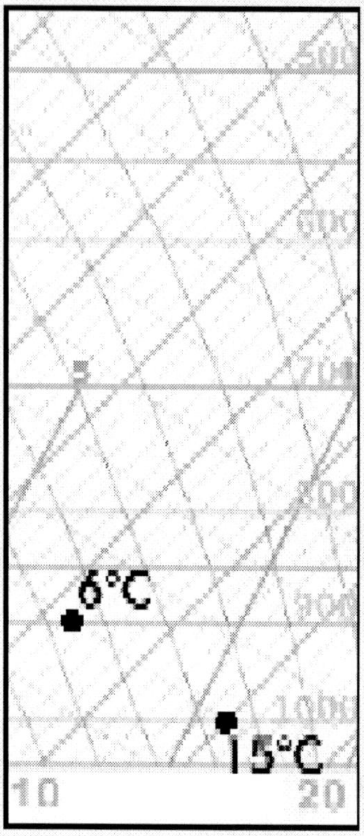

Lifting a parcel. If we lift a 15°C parcel from the 1000 mb level to 900 mb, it will cool to a temperature of 6°C. The dry adiabat lines on the sounding chart help determine this. They slope from the upper left to the lower right.

Approximate height relationships used in analysis & forecasting.

1000 mb	Surface	0 km
850 mb	5000 ft	1.5 km
700 mb	10,000 ft	3 km
500 mb	18,000 ft	5 km
300 mb	30,000 ft	9 km
200 mb	39,000 ft	12 km

begins cooling at the dry adiabatic lapse rate, about 10°C per km. This means that by the time it reaches 3 km, its has cooled by 30 C° to a reading of -6°C. If we compare this to the surrounding air, the red balloon is 9 C° **warmer** than the air around it! The red balloon is thus very buoyant, and strains in an upward direction to accelerate the balloons in their direction of displacement (upward). This is a model of an unstable system. It should be easy to see that the higher the rate of environmental cooling with height, the better the chance that a rising parcel can become buoyant and the more likely the system is to be unstable. Upper-level systems bringing cold temperatures aloft are excellent candidates for producing thunderstorm activity!

To examine this further, check out the short story "Studies of Instability", presented at the end of this chapter.

2 — Moisture

The heat of an atmospheric parcel is not composed entirely of its sensible heat: that which is immediately measurable with a thermometer. A parcel may also contain latent heat, which can be released under special circumstances. This release of latent heat will make the parcel even warmer, and will increase its buoyancy. The presence of this type of heat is extremely important in producing thunderstorm activity, as well as larger storms such as hurricanes and deep frontal lows.

The amount of latent heat available to a parcel is determined by the amount of water vapor that it contains. This can be measured by evaluating its dewpoint temperature. It's why high dewpoints are so important when we are examining surface conditions across a threat area. Furthermore, the release of this latent heat cannot begin until the parcel cools to its dewpoint temperature and saturates.

A rising parcel's humidity increases gradually as it rises due to adiabatic cooling, but if it starts with a very low relative humidity (for example, in deserts and on the hottest of summer days), the parcel may have to rise to a great height for latent heat release to begin. High cloud bases are the result. The delayed latent heat release actually diminishes the total latent heat that can be released, and reduces the buoyant energy available to the parcel. Thus, many high-based storms tend to be relatively stable compared to low-based storms.

3 — Lift

A source of localized mechanical lift is needed to initiate thunderstorm development. Virtually all unstable atmospheres are of the conditionally unstable type, which means that some sort of lift is required to set a rising parcel into motion. In some cases, especially on the Great Plains, the parcel must surmount an mid-tropospheric inversion of considerable depth before its instability can be released. Such an inversion is called a cap or a lid.

To obtain this source of lift, we turn to processes such as low-level convergence, upper-level divergence, upslope flow, and lift along mountain slopes. Even on benign weather days, these processes are occurring, albeit at smaller scales. More complex sources of upward motion, such as isentropic lift across vertically-sloped potential temperature gradients, are also reviewed by forecasters. Most sources of lift encountered in storm forecasting tend to be highly localized or linear. This explains why on an unstable day, we usually don't get 100% coverage of thunderstorms across a region all at once.

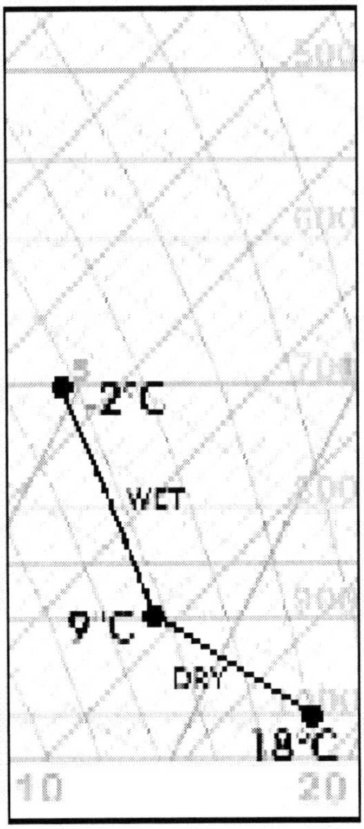

The release of latent heat. The assumptions here are that the parcel starts at 18°C near the surface, at 1000 mb, and saturates when it cools to the 900 mb level. Note that while the parcel is dry, its cooling rate is parallel to the dry adiabats. After it saturates, it is said to be "wet", and it rises parallel to the wet adiabat lines (the tall, curved lines). The wet adiabats suggest a much slower cooling rate over a given height compared to the dry adiabats. This, in its essence, is the release of latent heat.

4 — Shear

If there is a strong band of upper-level winds traversing the area, the precipitation particles are lofted downstream from the cumulonimbus tower, and they fall many miles away from the updraft. This allows for separation between the updraft and downdraft. It allows the updraft to persist, and the life cycle of the storm can continue unchecked. There is a direct relationship between the strength of the upper-level winds (especially relative to the storm's motion) and the greater the persistence of the storm cell. The most persistent of storm cells are described as *long-lived.*

Perhaps the simplest way to assess shear is simply to look at the upper-level charts and see if winds are strong. Upper-level winds of 40 to 50 kt at 500 mb are considered excellent for severe weather. However shear requires both an upper and lower bounding surface, and by just looking at upper-level winds we are making the gross error of assuming that surface winds are calm. After all, a 500 mb wind of southwest at 40 kt with a surface wind of southwest at 40 kt equals zero shear!

There is a very basic and crude forecasting index that is helpful: it's called the *bulk shear*, also known as *0-6 km shear*. This is simply the vector difference in the winds between the

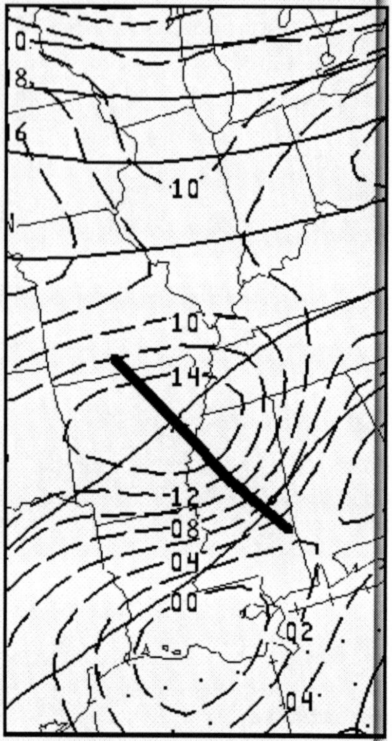

Short waves. One of the most widely-known features associated with lift are short waves, which may be revealed indirectly on 500 mb charts by looking for high concentrations of vorticity. The lift usually occurs ahead of (downstream) of a short wave trough.

Earth's surface and the wind at 6 km. This is usually 500 mb (or 400 mb on the high plains). The value must be calculated using vector math, a hodograph chart, or a computer program. Values of 30 kt are considered adequate for severe weather, and values of over 40 kt are considered excellent.

Storm type

Storms tend to organize into one of several different configurations, depending on the wind profiles and available boundaries. These types serve as conceptual models, because no particular storm will fit perfectly into any given category.

The most basic configuration is called a **single-cell**, or unicell. It is composed of a single primary updraft and a single primary downdraft, and occurs at the meso-gamma scale (2-20 km). A strong unicell storm is sometimes called a *pulse storm*, as its severe weather seems to occur in one main pulse at the peak of maximum updraft and downdraft intensity. Single-cell storms with significant updraft rotation are called *supercells*. These will be discussed separately.

Single-cells frequently aggregate and interact with each other, forming a more complicated storm called a **multicell.** They have a shared cold pools or a shared precipitation area, and can range from small multicells, encompassing storms at the meso-gamma scale (2-20 km), to squall lines, large MCS complexes, and tropical storms with structures on the order of the meso-beta and meso-alpha scales (20-2000 km). The multicell thunderstorm is very common, and probably comprises well over half the thunderstorms that occur on the planet.

With small linear multicells, the newest development is at one end of an axis while the oldest development is at the opposite end. The rainy or virga-strewn downdraft consititutes the decaying phase, while the towers and updraft represent the growing phase, so the storm activity actually *propagates* down the storm axis toward the updraft activity. This type of small multicell is most common when there is poor cold pool production. If the multicell produces a significant cold pool, cell development can become more complicated and chaotic.

Large multicells, often referred to as *mesoscale convective systems* or an *MCS*, have structures of well over 20 km in size, and often closer to 200 or more km. The mode of organization is largely a function of the mean tropospheric

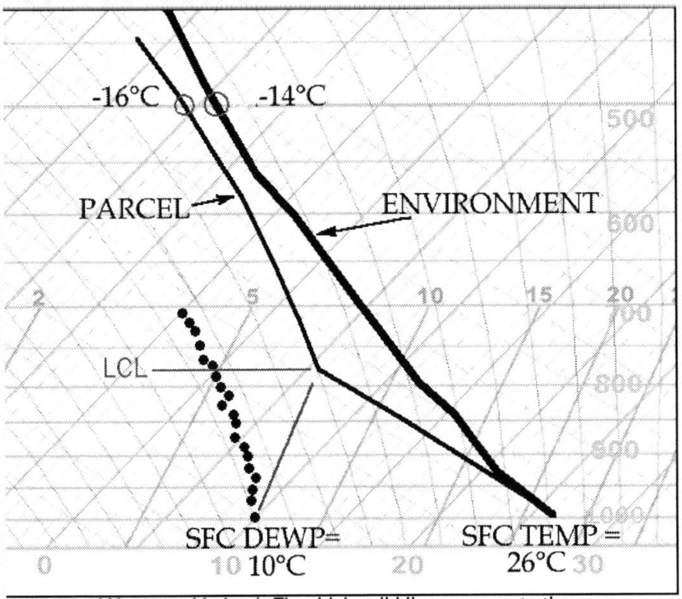

(Above and below) The thick solid line represents the environmental temperature, while the dotted line represents the environmental dewpoint. In these examples we use only the lowest dot on the dewpoint line. Experienced forecasters will use a representative mean of the lowest part of the dewpoint line to represent a thoroughly mixed parcel. Note how we use the mixing ratio lines (sloped lines marked 2, 5, 10, 15, 20) and the surface dewpoint to establish the LCL.

When moisture is scarce, the rising parcel will have to ascend to a very large height to reach its LCL (lifted condensation level). It cools along the dry adiabat until it reaches the mixing ratio line corresponding to its original dewpoint. In the process, it often cools at such a rapid rate that it remains colder than the surrounding air. From then on it rises along the wet adiabat, but this may not even be enough to provide it with sufficient latent heat. In this case, we see that after rising to 500 mb, the lifted parcel is still 2 degrees colder than the surrounding environment. The parcel has no buoyancy and will resist all attempts to lift it. This type of sounding is associated with fine weather and fair skies. *(Karen Leszke)*

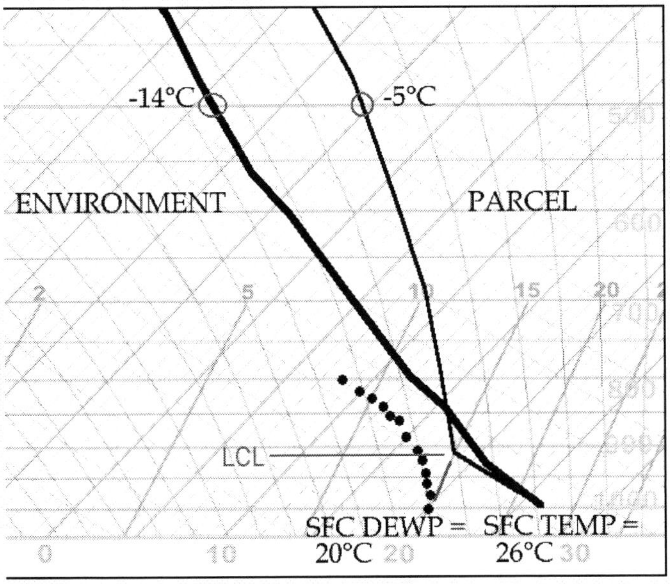

When a parcel contains rich moisture, it only has to rise along the dry adiabat for a relatively short distance to the LCL, then it can contribute latent heat. This gives it an excellent chance to be warmer than the surrounding air, giving it large amounts of buoyancy. Here, the parcel is 9 degrees warmer than the surrounding air at 500 mb. *(Tim Vasquez)*

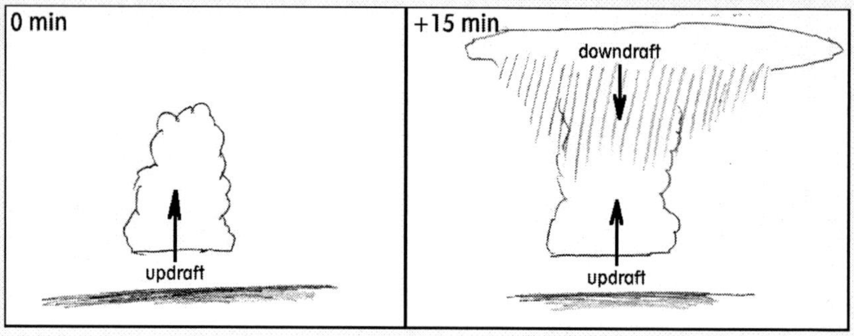

Nonsheared environment. The developing downdraft forms on top of the updraft. This ends the life of the cell.

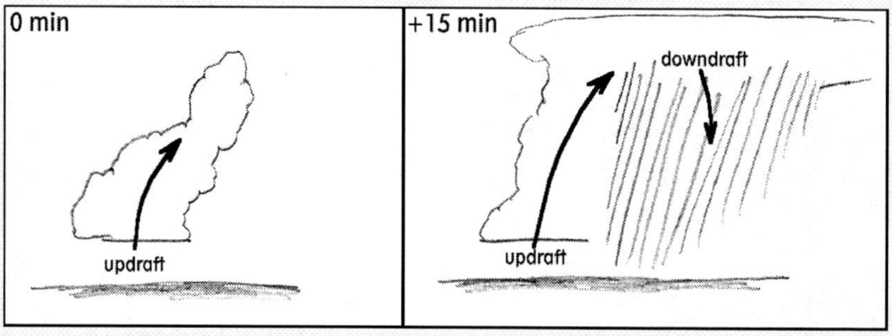

Sheared environment. If winds in the upper levels are different from that in the lower levels, the developing downdraft forms at a distance from the updraft. Both can coexist, prolonging the storm's life.

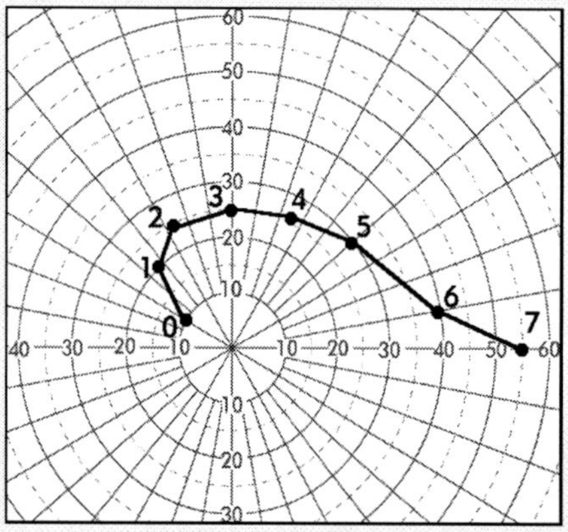

The hodograph is an important severe weather forecasting tool. It allows us to plot the wind readings above a given station at different heights. By reading the line from one end to the other, we can pick out the wind speed and direction at any given height. The line, by convention, is labelled at each whole kilometer height as shown here. For example, the wind at 3 km is blowing FROM the south TOWARD the north at 25 kt. Some charts, particularly journals, may be calibrated in meters per second; read the legend or the chart markings carefully. Multiply meters per second by 1.94 to get knots.

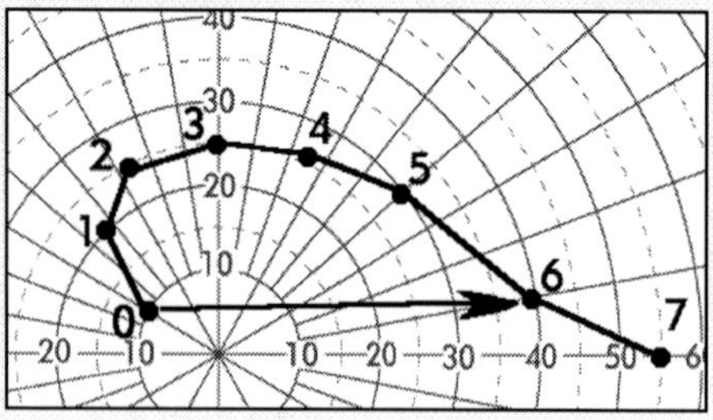

This example demonstrates how bulk shear (0-6 km shear) is measured. A vector drawn from the 0 to 6 km level is drawn. The length of this vector is directly proportional to the bulk shear — the longer it is, the greater likelihood of long-lived cells. By measuring the length of the line relative to the radial pattern formed by the graph, we can obtain the value in knots. In this case, the line represents a bulk shear of about 50 knots.

flow in relation to the low-level forcing axis. Flow parallel to the boundary deposits precipitation cores along the boundary, producing a linear precipitation core or *squall line*, while flow perpendicular to the boundary carries precipitation cores away from the initiating boundary and produces more of a broken structure. The direction and speed of the mid- and upper-level winds relative to the storm system has an effect on how development progresses.

MCS systems readily develop unique circulations, such as the rear-inflow jet which descends from the cold pool to the back edge of the precipitation core and has been found to be associated with damaging *derecho* wind events. The MCS is also subject to deformation from the Coriolis force, which eventually gives the line a subsynoptic-scale "bow" or "comma" shape.

Supercell types

During the first decade of the research chase programs, it became quite clear that supercell storms had highly varied structure. It was discovered that some had a dry, highly visible appearance, while others contained vast amounts of rain. Yet others seemed to fit a rather "classic" model seen in most tornado events. This eventually led to the designations LP (low-precipitation), CL (classic), and HP (high-precipitation). It is important to remember that these categories do not serve as distinct storm types. Rather, these categories serve as waypoints in a broad spectrum of supercell characteristics, which can help serve as a frame for understanding other storms we see. Aberrations, hybrids, and exceptions occur all the time, and it can greatly complicate chase strategy. A successful chaser will recognize what area of the spectrum a given storm occupies, or if it doesn't even fit on the spectrum, and will adjust field tactics accordingly.

The "standard" downdraft which occurs in the supercell is called the forward flank downdraft (FFD). This designates that it occurs on the forward flank of the storm (i.e. if the mean tropospheric wind is from the southwest, the forward flank is on the northeast side). A second type of downdraft is very common, called the rear flank downdraft (RFD). In its weakest form, the RFD is invisible except perhaps for the appearance of a "clear slot" on the rear flank of the updraft base and perhaps some virga. In its strongest form, it contains a massive shaft of rain and hail, and appears completely merged with the FFD. The behavior of

The early days of forecasting

There are three principal types of thunderstorms, each of which may be readily recognized from the synoptic situation:

(a) air mass thunderstorms,

(b) cold front thunderstorms,

(c) warm front thunerstorms.

GEORGE F. TAYLOR
Aeronautical Meteorology,
1938

Bizarre lightning

During a thunderstorm in the Washington, DC area in the summer of 2008, there were many warnings being issued by the local NWS office (Sterling, VA WFO). At about 3:45pm, after the main storm had passed, I received a phone call from the NWS office, asking me if I had seen any severe weather.

I explained that from my home, the highest winds were about 35mph. There was no hail, or damage to report. Then I said, "But the lightning today has been...." and at that exact moment, a big CG lightning struck nearby temporarily knocking out the phone lines. The NWS called right back...and the phones were fine. I explained that there was a very close CG....we laughed since that is exactly what I was saying... that the lightning was very frequent with this storm.

JASON FOSTER
Gaithersburg, MD chaser

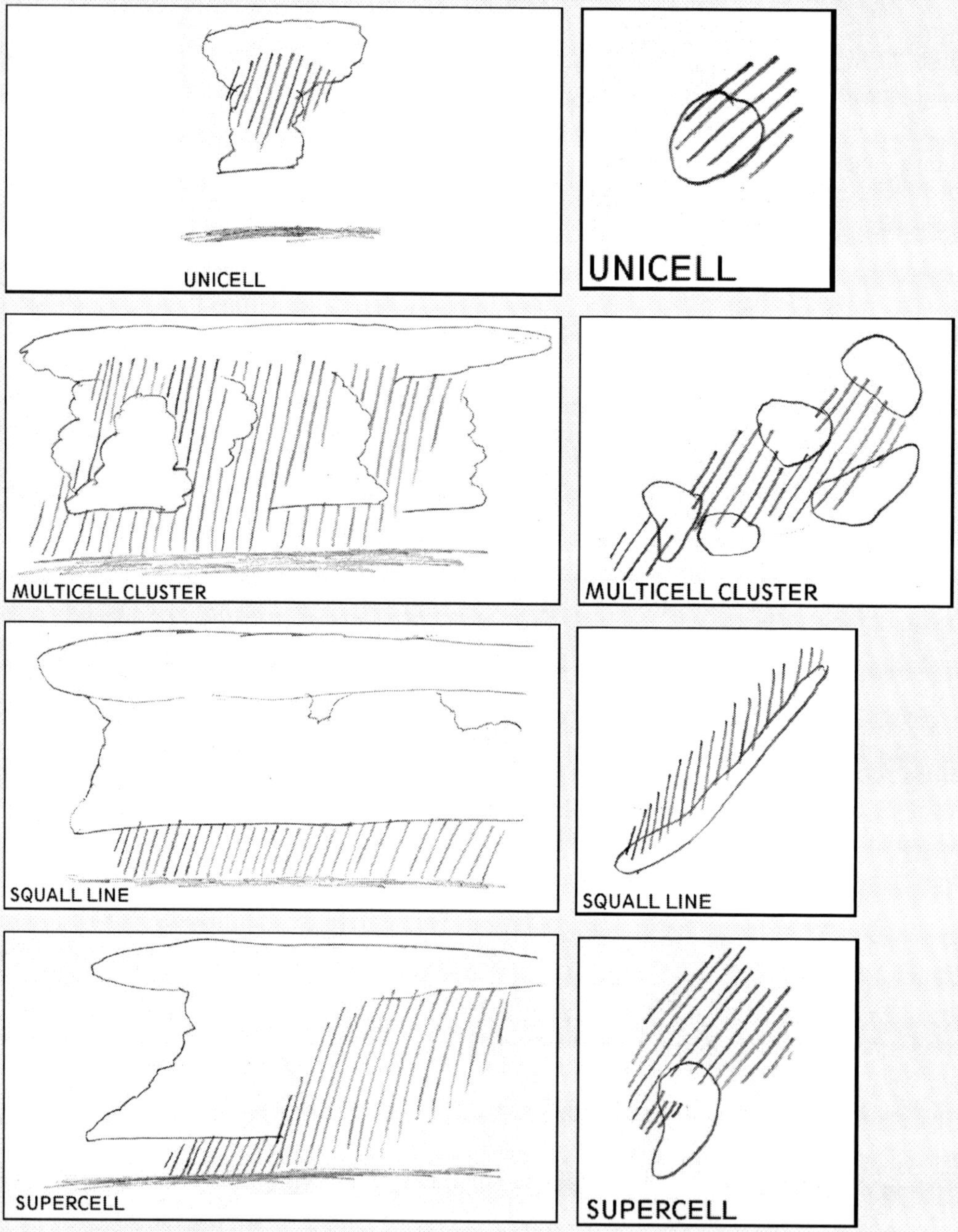

Highly simplified profile and overhead views of different types of thunderstorms. Updrafts are shown as hollow shapes, while downdrafts are shown as hatch-filled shapes. The profile view looks westward, assuming a typical storm envirnoment and appearance. Since weather radar units detect rain drops, the hatched shading is what appears on radar displays.

these downdrafts is thought to have some bearing on what causes the tornado. Most research chase work focuses on these features.

It should also be noted that while supercells are often composed of a single persistent updraft-downdraft pair, as is typical with the LP supercell, many CL and HP storms exhibit multicellular behavior and produce cyclic mesocyclones.

Classic (CL) supercell

The familiar supercell seem on diagrams, on television documentaries, and in magazines is the classic supercell — a storm which gives us an excellent model with which to compare all other supercells. Its inflow and outflow are well-balanced, and it has a well-organized mesocyclone. Because of this, the classic supercell tends to be a very efficient tornado producer. Most of the tornado incidents that have occurred throughout history were spawned by classic supercells.

Visually, the classic supercell contains a broad area of heavy rain in the forward flank downdraft. This generates a healthy outflow area. Some rain may be found underneath the updraft base. The outflow and inflow are rather well-matched, leading to a balanced storm and good tornado potential. Good temperature contrasts along the small-scale outflow boundaries only improves the tornadic environment. The classic supercell produces a moderate sized area of large hail. The rear-flank downdraft becomes a player and may produce damaging straight-line winds. As the updraft collapses and the mesocyclone wraps with rain, the classic supercell can take on temporary characteristics of the HP supercell (to be discussed next), however this phase often passes and the storm cycles back to its original classic mode. A careful chaser can usually distinguish what is happening.

Low-precipitation (LP) supercell

When the downdraft region is almost invisible and contain virga or very little rain, we have an LP supercell. Visually the storm reminds chasers of a massive hole in the sky, manifested by a tall cumulonimbus tower and anvil, and little else. The updraft base may be quite small, covering only a few square miles. Nevertheless, the updraft may contain amazing plate structure and helical striations, and may resemble a hovering flying saucer, such as those from *War of*

Birth of the supercell concept

The striking echo similarity in the echo features of the Geary (Oklahoma) storm to these observed in the severe Wokingham (England) hailstorm . . . may be representative of an important class of local storms; namely those developing within strongly sheared environments which remain persistently intense and tend toward a steady state circulation.

K. BROWNING and R. DONALDSON
Airflow and Structure of a Tornadic Storm, 1963

From a new chaser

Probably my most impressionable experience as a new chaser was the nearly overwhelming experience of being close to a supercell. I chase solo, so the urge to simply watch the storm competes with other tasks like driving, navigating, and looking for a safe parking place.

The workload was higher than I expected. One of the biggest lessons I learned is that storm structure doesn't always match the pictures in the textbooks, and it can be very disorienting trying to figure out what is going on around you while managing all the other distractions. It was much more work than I expected it to be.

CRIS SCHROEDER
Clearwater, Kansas chaser

The beauty of LPs

Without a doubt, they are my favorite type of storm to chase, mainly for photography purposes. Some notable examples for me over the years have included May 18, 1990 in Wheeler, Texas; May 15, 1991 in Reydon, Okla.; April 3, 2003 in west central Okla. (at least early in its life); May 24, 2003 in Altus, Okla.; May 4th 2007 in Arnett, Okla.; and May 1, 2008 in the Oklahoma City area.

In most of the more significant LP's I have seen, such as those above, they seem to be prolific hail producers. With the May 24, 2003 storm we saw 4-inch hail and several small tornadoes and a spectacular tornado with the May 4, 2007 storm.

I've seen a lot of LP's that weren't very impressive visually, but still produced severe weather. On May 12, 2004 we were on an LP in northwest Okla. looked puny and unimpressive, but dropped 1-inch hail. Not amazing stuff I know, but the storm looked horrible! And not too far away, Harper County Kansas was going nuts.

I'll say it again, I loves me some LP's and I ain't talking records!

ROB SATKUS
Norman, Oklahoma chaser

the Worlds. Names such as the "mothership" or a "stack of plates" come to mind. During the 1970s, this type of storm was often called the "dryline supercell", and sometimes it still is, as the relatively shallow moisture often found immediately along the dryline results in weaker precipitation features.

The storm is relatively unbalanced, with its inflow much greater than its outflow. The lack of important downdraft interactions vastly reduces the potential for tornadogenesis. The storm is capable of dumping large hailstones, and since it may change its position on the supercell spectrum at any time, chasers on the forward flank of the updraft are in a potentially dangerous location.

High-precipitation (HP) supercell

When prolific amounts of rain and strong outflow are produced by a storm, they can completely dominate the storm's structure and lifecycle. These precipitation areas tend to wrap aggressively into the developing mesocyclone. If tornado production occurs, rain wrapping is often well underway and the tornado can only be seen along a dry "notch" ahead of the mesocyclone where rain-free inflow and the updraft base itself are wrapped into the circulation. This notch is called the "*bear's cage*". Chasers have a brief window in which to observe the tornado before it becomes completely wrapped. Such chasing is extremely difficult and hazardous, and many windshields are busted by large hail when chasers venture into the bear's cage to get that brief glimpse and fail to get out before the rain wraps full circle and the mesocyclone fully occludes. Other chasers lose visibility in the wrapping rain and lose sight of the tornado, something that can be a truly frightening and dangerous experience. As both downdrafts wrap into the circulation, the tornado tends to disappear into the core, and the entire occluding mesocyclone shifts to the forward flank (usually the northeast side) of the storm. New circulations may develop well to the east or to the south outside the storm's core.

During the 1970s the HP supercell was often referred to as the "Southeast U.S." or "Gulf coast" supercell, since tornadic weather in those regions is certainly associated with these types of rain-shrouded structures. Because the storm is an efficient hail producer and has a relatively large size (typically more than 30 miles from end to end), it is associated with the most damaging hailstorm events. The

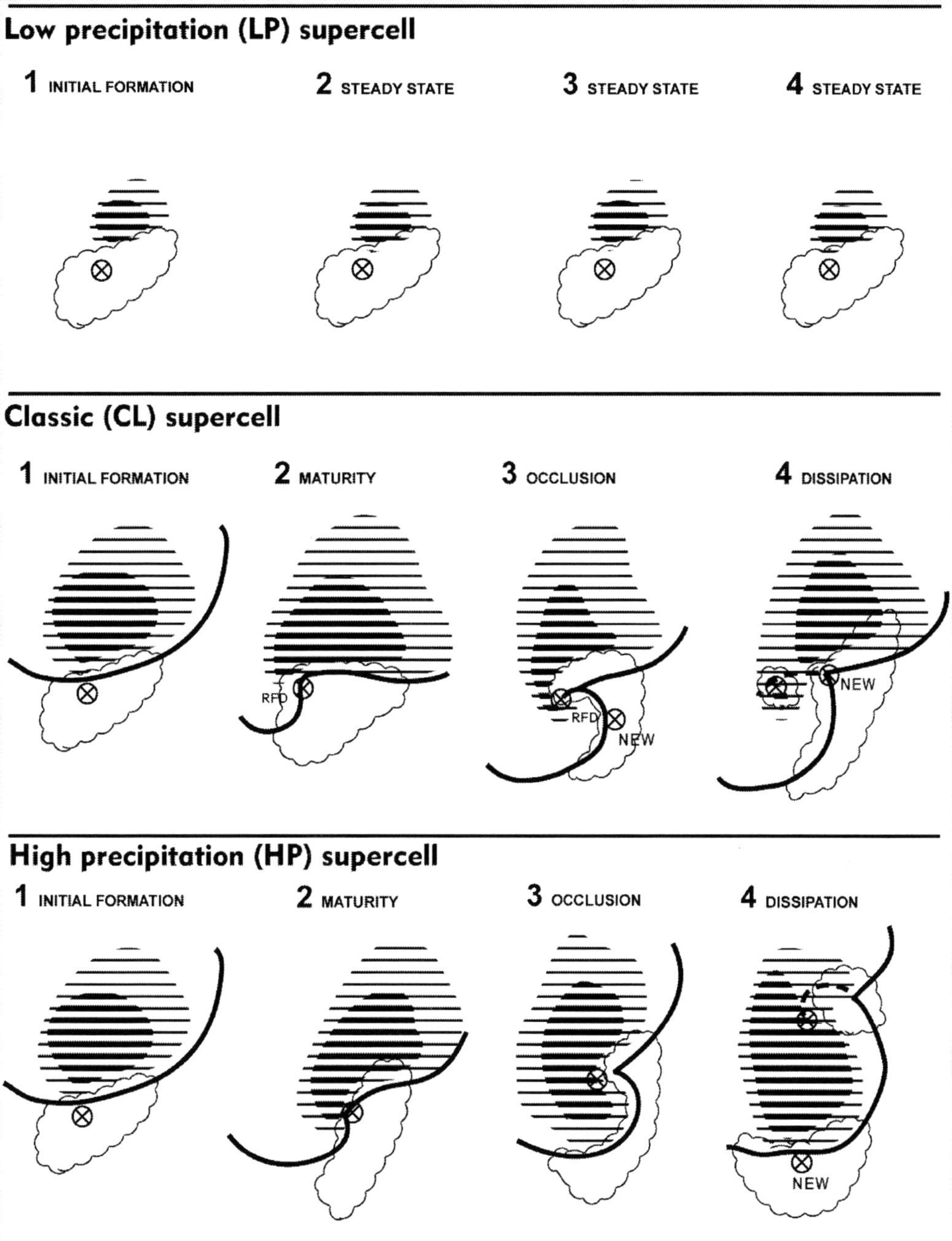

Life cycle of the three main types of supercells. The thick line indicates the boundary of outflow air at the surface. Light shading is precipitation while heavy shading is hail. The circle with the X in it is the mesocyclone (and possible tornado). The HP life cycle is adapted from *High-precipitation supercells: a conceptual model and documentation* (1990) by Moller, Doswell, and Przyblinski.

Low-precipitation (LP) supercell

Visually, the precipitation cascade of an LP supercell is quite weak. The storm is inflow/updraft dominant, and in most cases is smaller than what is shown here. The lack of updraft-downdraft interaction tends to suppress tornado potential. *(Roger Hill)*

Classic (CL) supercell

The classic supercell shows both a beefy, well-organized updraft base and a pronounced updraft area. These storms are most prone to producing a long-lived tornado. *(Tim Vasquez)*

High-precipitation (HP) supercell

A very extensive downdraft cascade and outflow area is associated with the HP supercell. Upraft bases tend to be relatively small or linear. Classic supercells may briefly take on this appearence while going through an occlusion stage. *(Roger Hill)* storm does contain the downdraft interactions necessary for tornadogenesis, however the downdrafts tend to dominate the storm's lifecycle and reduce tornado potential. The initial wrapping of rain can bring prolific straight line winds south of the mesocyclone, as storm motion and outflow motion combine to produce high ground-relative velocities.

Note that in some cases, what looks like a HP supercell may actually be a classic supercell undergoing a collapse and occlusion cycle. Though the distinction between the two types can be rather fuzzy, a basic rule of thumb is that the classic supercell's mesocyclone remains unoccluded and unobscured throughout much of its life cycle, while in the HP supercell rainwrap is very aggressive.

Some HP supercells are poor tornado producers but are efficient at producing incredible amounts of wind. These storms are called Pakwash-type storms. The term is derived from a spectacular convective wind burst that was videotaped in the Pakwash Forest near Red Lake, Ontario in 1991, and was repeated in Oklahoma in 1994. It is thought that unusually rich boundary-layer moisture combined with high instability and weak mid-level winds produces such storms. Pakwash-type storms are still being investigated to understand what causes their affinity for producing extreme winds.

Thunderstorm phenomena

Tornadoes, hail, lightning, high winds, and mammatus transcends all thunderstorm types, and they are the primary target of many storm chasers. Surprisingly we don't know nearly as much about these phenomena as we do about the storm itself. Part of the reason for this vacuum in scientific knowledge is that these phenomena occur at extremely small scales and are difficult to sample. Therefore their behavior can be quite unpredictable. It is easy to see why chasing can be dangerous, at the very least adding a small dose of thrill to the experience. On the other hand, the unpredictability also adds to the hobby's beauty. We never quite know what we will see underneath any given storm, and it is never duplicated quite the same way again!

Tornado

During the early years of meteorology, it was thought that the tornado was a concentration of the Earth's angular momentum (its rotation) within the thunderstorm updraft.

Choosing from the spectrum

Being a tornado guy, I naturally prefer the Classic supercell, because of its combination of tornado efficiency and decent viewing. However, LP supercell tornadoes, while not as frequent as classic supercell tornadoes, can be some of the most picturesque.

HPs are okay if you get them early, but by far they're the most dangerous to sample. Because of their multiple precipitation areas, they don't always follow the classic supercell pattern of rain/hail/large hail/tornado. You can be driving in only heavy rain and suddenly encounter a wedge. Despite all these negatives, I still like HPs because of the usually-visible foward flank tornadoes they sometimes produce.

SHANE ADAMS
Norman, OK chaser

Chasing in Europe

Chasing in Italy is so difficult: you pay an incredible price for gas, you pay tolls on all the freeways you take, you don't have free hot spots, and radars are not public as NEXRAD ones. We have few radars but not so defined; my project with the Thunderstorm Team of the Italian meteorological association MeteoNetwork is to make something to create a good public radar network as the American one. Chasing in Tornado Alley is another world.

ANDREA GRIFFA
Cantu, Italy chaser

Classic supercells can briefly take on the appearance of an HP supercell as they go through an occlusion stage. This view looks north at the rain-filled RFD region wrapping into the mesocyclone. A dissipating tornado is present just beyond the bright area, but is largely obscured by rain. *(Tim Vasquez)*

Tornado performance

I love the rope-out stage of a tornado. Watching it dance its waning life away, shrinking, withering, and suddenly evaporating, leaving the mysterious dust swirl near the ground.

RON RIEMERSMA
Fond du Lac, WI chaser

A few Pakwash storms

Some memorable "Pakwash"-type storms over the years include:

5/3/79: Lancaster TX

7/18/91: SE of Red Lake, ON (the original Pakwash storm)

8/17/94: Lahoma OK

5/5/95: Mayfest at Fort Worth TX

Very little was known about the tornado's structure and its relation to the parent thunderstorm until Theodore Fujita did a detailed photogrammetric study on the 1957 Fargo tornado. This essentially broke ground on tornadogenesis knowledge. The actual bedrock was laid down in the 1970s thanks to Oklahoma research chasing efforts, culminating in a series of papers including the landmark paper by Lemon and Doswell (1979).

The first sign of a tornado is increasing spin underneath the updraft base, which may lower towards the ground or "fill in" with debris. The spin is quite rapid and is unmistakable. Meanwhile, a *clear slot* containing downdraft air, higher bases, rain, and possibly even hail wraps into the circulation from the west. The clear slot gets its name from the absence of cumulonimbus cloud material. Rain usually falls within parcels which are free of cloud, but since it appears cloudlike, the clear slot may be called a *rain slot* or *visual hook* (thus named since it looks like a hook on radar). Eventually the clear slot is wrapped completely around the mesocyclone and tornado, cutting it off (occluding it). If significant rain is wrapped into the circulation, the tornado may become rain wrapped and may even disappear completely behind shrouds of rain. The tornado eventually dissipates into a ropelike structure, and if rain wrap is not too extensive, the contorted remains of the tornado are visible, an impressive sight!

The mechanism of the tornado is not understood. Considerable research has focused on the importance of downdrafts, most notably the RFD, in helping to spin up a tornado. For over a decade a favored theory was that baroclinicity (temperature contrasts) were an important mechanism for generating vorticity, however recent VORTEX field research has showed poor temperature contrasts across RFD boundaries in tornadic storms. There is some evidence, however, that the required baroclinicity occurs above the ground in the downdraft, setting up vortex lines that are then tilted into the vertical by the downdraft's descent. It remains a complex puzzle and science is still not close to understanding the key processes responsible for tornadogenesis.

The term "landspout" has been loosely used to describe a long-lived, thin tornado that originates from a relatively benign, non-supercellular thunderstorm or even a cumulus cloud. It is thought to be more of the result of pure stretching of a vorticity tube rather than from complex downdraft interactions. Such tornadoes are responsible for the vast majority of oceanic waterspout sightings, as well as the slender, high-based tornadoes occasionally found on the High Plains. There is endless debate on whether a landspout is a true tornado or in a category of its own, no doubt in part due to our fundamental lack of available field research and understanding of the tornado itself. Therefore chasers should be aware of the enigmatic nature of the term "landspout", and never use it to imply the occurence of a weak tornado. Landspouts have been known to produce F3 damage and can be extremely dangerous! In this book we will consider spouts to be a type of tornado.

On a good day when all the ingredients are in place and shear profiles look excellent, why is it that some storms produce tornadoes and some don't? This has been a subject of university and government research for quite some time. It's thought that some sort of balance between mid-level storm-relative wind, storm-relative helicity, and low-level dewpoint is required. A lot of this is tied to the evolution of the rear-flank downdraft in supercell thunderstorms, which in turn is instrumental to tornado development.

Currently there is no definition for tornado intensity. There are only two reliable indicators of a tornado's ferocity: Doppler frequency shift measurements with mobile research radars, and Fujita scale damage estimates which require a post-mortem survey by a structural engineer. While mile-wide "wedge" tornadoes are typically very intense and small tornadoes are usually weak, this relationship does not always hold true. For example, the Jarrell tornado in 1997 was producing extreme damage while the funnel cloud was

19th century tornado theories

The polar current and the equatorial current thus balanced are now of course in a state of extreme tension, and the compression of the air at their region of meeting is the cause of the sultriness so universally observed just before a tornado. If in this critical condition of the storm no disturbance takes place in the plane of meeting of the two balancing currents, the return oscillation toward the north sets in. If, however, a disturbance from any cause takes place, a tornado or rotary storm is generated, which travels in the diagonal of the forces of the two currents through the region of calm between them . . .

When the tornado-cloud has approached the ground, the surrounding air on the surface will rush into the space of rarified air of the vortex with a velocity proportionate to the difference in pressure outside and inside of the vortex. This current will be made visible by a mass of detached objects, such as sand, dust or water, which it whirls up off of the ground. Thus a second cone, looking like a cloud, with its base on the earth, will be attached to the inverted cone of the tornado-cloud, which has its base in the cumulo-stratus of the southeast storm. When the cloud of loose objects has all been whirled up, the lower part of the rotating current becomes again invisible, and the cloud seems to rise.

WILLIAM BLASIUS
Storms: Their Nature, Classification, and Laws, 1875

quite small. Therefore it is considered presumptuous to call a large tornado "violent", much less assign it a damage-scale rating when damage hasn't even been assessed.

In 1983, *Stormtrack* published a letter by Tim Marshall which described a technique of measuring intensity by estimating the tornado's width and then estimating the time it takes a piece of debris to make half a revolution around the tornado. Such a technique is about the only conceivable way of getting an intensity estimate in real time, and even then it is subject to significant errors. Fortunately the rule of thumb is very easy to remember, and may be of some use out in the field.

Gustnado

A gustnado (sometimes written "gustinado" in the 1980s) is a term given to any vortex at the surface that does not appear to have a connection with the thunderstorm cloud. It does not matter what type of thunderstorm is present, or whether a mesocyclone exists. In terms of meteorological scale, the gustnado exists a notch below that of the tornado, encompassing a size of tens of meters and a life cycle of tens of seconds. Its presence is marked by a swirling plume of dust that rises above a treeline, which lasts just long enough for the camcorder to capture the footage before it dissipates. Very often, others may be occurring at the same time.

Gustnadoes barely register on the Fujita damage scale, so it is thought that their danger to chasers is very low. However if you see one organizing nearby, never allow yourself to be 100 percent confident that it is nontornadic. There may be processes going on beneath the storm that aren't readily apparent. The swirling plume may actually have an invisible but very solid connection to the cloud base, and what looks like a gustnado may be the formation of a violent tornado. You simply can't be sure. Enjoy the spectacle, but be prepared to use your escape route or take cover!

Lightning

Much to the delight of photographers, thunderstorms produce a separation of different types of particles within the cumulonimbus cloud. This produces enough of a differing voltage between the different particle areas, the air, and the ground, to where the insulative property of air breaks down and a spectacular spark flashes between the particle

The best lightning display

One case that comes to mind was the monster "Beloit" supercell from 15 June 1992. The most continuous lightning display I've witnessed in 23 years of chasing allowed for a visual chase until 1 am across northern Kansas. The awe-inspiring scene overshadowed many tornadoes I've witnessed. A recent example of vicious cloud-to-ground lightning occurred near Perry, OK, with the tornadic supercell from 24 May 2008. The strikes were so frequent and focused that I feared for my wife's safety during the few seconds it took her to move a few feet from my truck to her van!

RICH THOMPSON
Norman, Oklahoma meteorologist and chaser

A close one

One memorable experience was the lightning bolt I was hit by on May 2, 2008 in Earle Arkansas. We had pulled off the highway after observing an EF3 tornado. There was a snap, thunder, a flash and shock at the same time. The main bolt hit 100 yards behind us in a field. Even though there isn't any lightning in your immediate vicinity, you aren't safe. Bolts hit experienced chasers too. Always be aware of your surroundings and follow the safety rules no matter how long you've been chasing!

LAURA HEDIEN
Grayslake, IL chaser

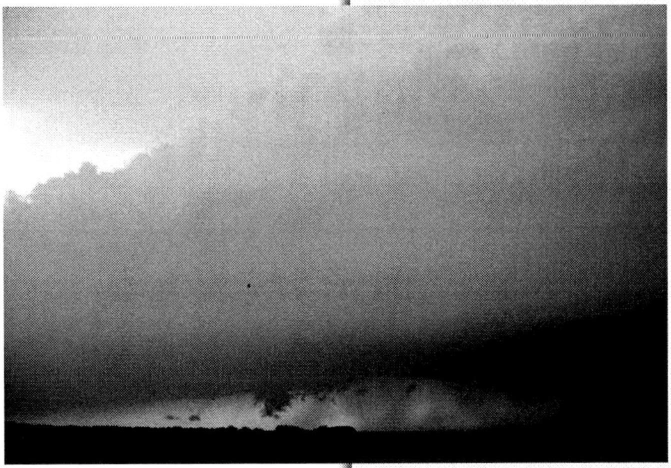

Many photographs often narrow in on the tornado and the wall cloud. However, here we pull away to see what's above the wall cloud and updraft base of a storm approaching its tornadic stage. Note the bulky updraft (right side) and the flanking line merging into the updraft tower (left side). This frame was photographed in 1991 near Clearwater, Kansas. *(Gene Rhoden/Weatherpix)*

regions to equalize the voltage gradient. This spark is, of course, lightning. The entire life cycle of a lightning spark is known as a *flash*. This, in turn, may be made up of many *strokes*. The average cloud-to-ground lightning flash carries a current of 25,000 amperes (amps). A current of only 0.07 amps is considered sufficient to cause death.

There are four main classes of lightning: cloud-to-ground (CG), in-cloud (IC), cloud-to-cloud (CC), and cloud-to-air (CA), these categories and abbreviations being an extension of the scheme that's been used in surface observation reporting since the 1950s. The CG abbreviation has gained universal fame in chasing circles. In-cloud lightning is actually the most common type, almost entirely hidden within the cumulonimbus cloud and responsible for most of the ambiguous flickering that lights up a storm cloud. The more rare cloud-to-cloud lightning sparks long distances between discrete storm towers, often up and down a squall line, and may form into bolts 20 or 30 miles long. Finally cloud-to-air lightning reaches towards clear air or toward thin, fibrous parts of the anvil and often has a divergent, forked appearance. These discharges are often called "anvil crawlers", though in some cases they may spark directly into clear air.

Cloud-to-ground lightning will usually strike the tallest conducting object in the area. Therefore there can be a cone of protection which radiates outward from the object. If a chaser takes refuge near a tall antenna tower, the lightning will preferentially hit the tower instead of the chaser. Telephone poles, high tension poles, their wires, and buildings

A close call with lightning

Lightning is one of my favorite phenomena and I have a healthy respect for it, because I think it tries to find me as hard as I try to find it. One of my favorite close encounters occurred on June 4, 2005. Shane Adams, Mickey Ptak, Chad Lawson, Jo Radel, and I were chasing southeast Kansas, repositioning after viewing two small tornadoes. The guys were in the lead car and Jo and I were in my car.

I was driving us down some little back road repositioning, and the CGs were hitting quite frequently. Suddenly there was a loud explosion just outside my window. I could feel the heat coming in through the window and my hands and arms were tingling. My reaction?? "YES!!!!!!! THAT WAS AWESOME!!!!!!"

We didn't even see the bolt that almost got us until we got home and reviewed the video.

ANGIE NORRIS
Norman, OK chaser

Estimating tornado intensity

The only possible way for a typical chaser to measure tornado intensity is to follow the motion of debris tags. This is often impractical but in theory can be done. Tim Marshall's 1984 letter in Stormtrack specified photogrammetric tornado intensity as being given by:

V = 3.28 * D / 2 * T * 0.682

where

D = diameter of orbit in feet

T = time for half-revolution in sec

V = tangential speed in mph

Taking this a step further, this can be approximated to:

V = D / T * 1.07, or more simply

V = D / T

This is extremely easy to do in your head. So if the tornado is 1300 ft wide (a quarter mile) and a chunk of lofted dirt along the funnel's edge takes 10 seconds to go from one side to the other, the wind speed is about 130 mph. You can also get a very crude conversion to Fujita damage scale by remembering that F0/F1 are below 100, F2/F3 are in the 100s, and F4/F5 are in the 200s (of miles per hour).

This entire technique is hardly scientific, of course, and is subject to a lot of assumptions. Remember that you are trying to measure the diameter of the debris or cloud tag's orbit, not necessarily that of the tornado width, so adjust your estimate accordingly. Also it is usually impossible to see debris from the highest wind speeds since it occurs near the ground out of sight.

themselves will all create cones of protection. Though the chaser is protected from being struck directly by lightning, a nearby flash will produce extreme voltage gradients in the ground that may electrocute the chaser through his feet. Herds of sheep and groups of athletes have been injured or killed in this manner. It's also possible to be hit by a smaller "side flash".

Cloud-to-ground lightning also has polarity: it either lowers negative charge to the ground (a *negative flash*) or lowers positive charge to the ground (a *positive flash*). It is generally recognized that anvil strikes, which carry a much greater current and have a longer path length, are generally positive flashes, and may be responsible for the majority of fatal strikes and "bolts from the blue".

See the safety chapter for more lightning information.

Hail

Hail is often one of the key signatures of a severe storm. Current theory holds that it is formed by the recycling of precipitation in the updraft. The ice particles grow, accumulating alternating layers of clear ice and rime ice. However, it is said that at least one respected hail researcher now believes that ice particles receive their coatings as they cross the updraft, without ever going through a recycling process.

Traditional elements that are favorable for large hail setups include high instability, which favors storm development, and low wet-bulb temperature throughout the atmospheric column, which retards melting of the hailstone. Newer techniques coming into use prescribe the identification of steep mid-level lapse rates, strong vertical shear, and large buoyancy in the -10 to -30 deg C layer to judge large hail potential. Some recent research by Richard Thompson and Roger Edwards, suggests that vertical wind shear is a better predictor than other methods. Older techniques have referred to hail potential being inversely proportional to freezing level height, but bear in mind that the three largest hailstones on record: the 2003 Aurora, 1970 Coffeyville, and 1928 Potter stones, all fell with very high freezing levels in a summerlike troposphere.

Hail should be avoided at all costs. The sheer force created by a hailstone impact increases exponentially with its size, and three-inch hailstones can have the same effect on life, limb, and automobile as baseballs raining out of the sky.

Mammatus

One of the most spectacular sights a chaser can savor is the rounded bumps that may form underneath an anvil. They look like hundreds of udders. The bumps have a spacing of about half a mile, and are usually about 20,000 to 30,000 ft above the ground. The best displays usually last about 20 minutes, but can persist for hours. It must be pointed out that *mammatus has no relation to tornado formation* and is not thought to have any meaning in terms of storm forecasting.

Oddly enough, mammatus has been largely ignored by the academic community, presumably because of its lack of economic importance. Much of what we know is still based heavily on the 1960s work of British meteorologists David Ludlam and Richard Scorer, who thought that the clouds were pockets of subsidence and evaporation underneath the anvil. It is not fully understood what causes the cellular structure, or why some anvils produce mammatus and others don't. Fortunately research in this area is beginning to accelerarate. It is thought that gravity waves and shear overturning are important factors in the development of mammatus, but the mechanics are not thoroughly understood.

Most of the time, mammatus takes on a dull, featureless gray because of a lack of direct sunlight. Scattering of sunlight by nearby storm towers can help the mammatus glow, and is generally responsible for the best grayish, greenish, or bluish mammatus displays. Illumination by the setting sun yields, by far, the most spectacular mammatus, tinged with fierce orange and red colors. Generally this type of display is rare because the bulk of the storm obscures the western horizon, or

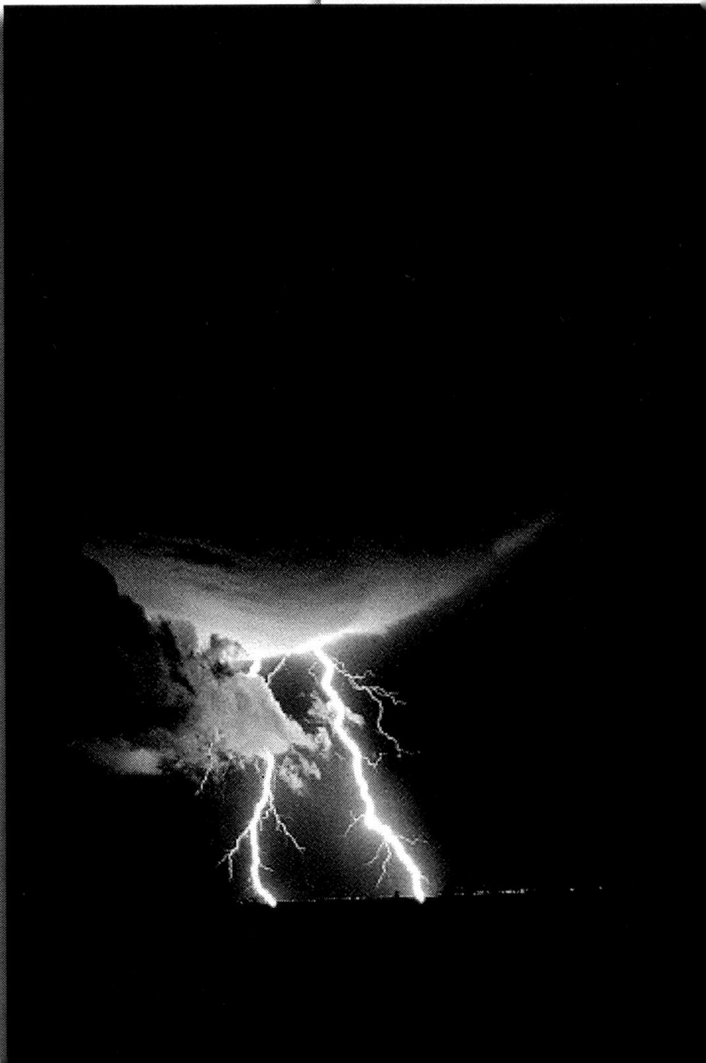

Nighttime cloud-to-ground strike near Lubbock, Texas. Most lightning strikes from the updraft base lower negative electrical charge to Earth. *(Tim Vasquez)*

because the slant of the solar rays cannot reach the underside of the anvil. This is overcome by early-season storms in northwesterly flow and by late-season storms in southwesterly flow, which creates the largest angle between the mammatus, the storm body, and the sun. Such displays are also limited to a window of about 45 minutes before to 10 minutes after sunset.

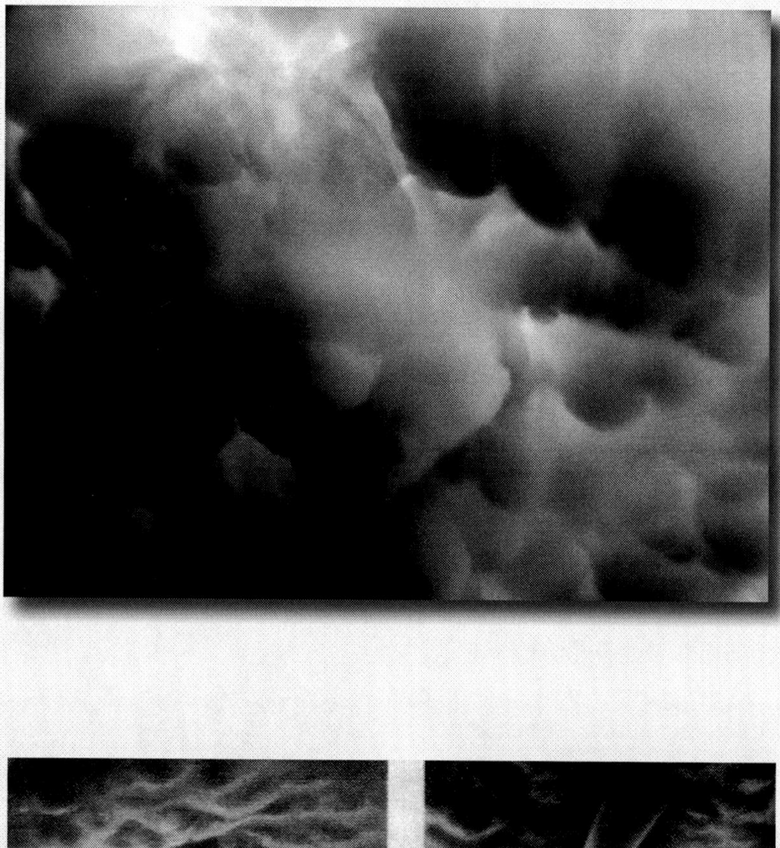

Mammatus clouds photographed 21 June 2007 south of Thedford, Nebraska. *(Dean Cosgrove / chasetours.com)*

Mammatocumulus clouds form.

Funnel forms as tornado develops.

Though the *Golden Book of Weather* is has been one of the best children's books since the 1950s, it contains a notorious misconception about tornadoes: that they originate from mammatus. It is true that thunderstorm rain-free bases can at times develop turbulent undulations resembling mammatus, but true mammatus is highly distinctive and is strictly an anvil-level feature. Chaser Robert Willis remarks, "As a child, I spent countless hours waiting for a tornado to drop 40,000 feet from a mammatus field!" *(Illustration from Golden Book of Weather, Western Publishing)*

Studies of instability

or

The controle of crowes through potential energy conversion

A tale of physics
spun on the foundation of
Jules Verne's From the Earth to the Moon

Barbicane and Michel worked feverishly to prepare the massive hot air balloon for its launch. The eccentric farmer, Mr. Jonesboro, was positively insistent that it must be returned within the hour so that he could inflate it to serve as a giant scarecrow.

"And not a moment too late," he said, watching the two work. "The crows will soon be making their daily rounds from the lake to devour my corn crop, and that positively won't do!"

Impey Barbicane, president of the Gun Club, called out to his friend Michel. "Let us get a temperature reading!"

Michel Ardan, the eccentric Frenchman, looked at the thermometer. "It is 30 degrees Celsius."

"Very good," said Barbicane. "Now we'll get this thing off the ground. Please hand me the dark cylinder in that box, Michel."

With that, Michel reached into the box and pulled out a bottle of red wine. He peered at the label. "Merlot? Oh, fine, if you insist.!"

Barbicane was livid. "What's this? Wine? I asked you for a propane cylinder! And how shall we inflate the balloon with this sort of thing?"

"But Barbicane, there is no propane in the box! Look for yourself!"

The two were nearly in fisticuffs when Farmer Jonesboro stepped in. "Gentlemen! Enough! Save this for your experiment. I can't spare propane for your balloon, but perhaps you can use this device." The farmer reached for a shiny red cubical device on his tractor and handed it to Barbicane.

"What is this?" asked the intrepid Yankee, peering at it with suspicion.

"It is the most fantastic of devices: an anti-gravity pack. I discovered it among the remains of a cigar-shaped spaceship that had crashed into my field. I went to investigate, and a pilot named Elvis pulled himself up from the wreckage, kicked it out of the debris, and beat on it with a piece of metal. He said I could have this 'worthless junk', and then he stormed off, to town I presume. But I assure you this device works wonders. Every September I lash it to my bales of alfalfa and cart them off to market!"

"Zounds!" said Barbicane. "How wonderful. Let me see this invention!"

The farmer explained the device and the working of its fanciful buttons.

Studies of instability / 2

Then Barbicane and Michel Ardan turned their attention to the matters of the balloon. There it rested, a man-sized sphere rolling slowly on the ground with the breeze. Without the benefit of the propane, it was completely impotent.

"Shall we deflate the balloon and cut it off?" asked Michel.

"No! Leave it be! I have a great idea, and we shall start by measuring the temperature inside the balloon."

Michel walked to the balloon, opened a flap, and inserted the thermometer. He waited a short while, then withdrew it and looked at the mercury. "The temperature inside this balloon is also 30 degrees Celsius, same as the surrounding air."

Barbicane noted this, then shouted, "Come, Michel! Let us take to the air!"

Michel leapt into the gondola, and Barbicane, having lashed the antigravity machine to a webwork of ropes, turned a dial on the red device. The balloon and its occupants began rising into the sky. As they ascended, Barbicane let out sections of a long coil of rope, which remained tied to a fence post below.

"What is that rope for?" asked the Frenchman.

"Excellent question, my friend," replied Barbicane. "I will let this rope out as we rise. It measures exactly three kilometers in length. When it stretches taut, we will stop and take our measurements."

"I already notice a pleasant draft," said Michel. "It is cooler already."

"Certainly," said Barbicane. "The temperature falls as we rise, as our pressure is decreasing. Surely you feel a discomfort in your ears now?"

"I do," said Michel. "The pressure is certainly falling."

In a matter of a few minutes, the full length of the rope had played out, and Barbicane halted the balloon at the height of three kilometers.

"Now we begin our measurements," said Barbicane. "First, what is the temperature outdoors?"

Michel glanced at the thermometer. "It is 10 degrees Celsius. And it feels every bit as cold."

"Now what is the temperature in the balloon?"

"Why, I am sure it is 30 degrees, same as when we started." He shivered. "How I wish I could be inside it right now!"

"It is foolish to make assumptions!" said Barbicane. "I predict we will be quite surprised."

Michel looked over the railing at the balloon. "Zounds! Look at how it grew! Is it twice as large? What happened here?"

"It is a demonstration of Boyle's Law," said Barbicane. "The pressure has fallen, so the air has expanded to occupy more volume."

The giant balloon hung oddly beneath the gondola, and Michel had to scurry carefully down some netting. He inserted the thermometer into the limp fabric, withdrew it, and noticed frost on it. "It is minus 1 degree Celsius! This is confusing! How did the heat escape?"

"That proves my theory," said Barbicane. "The only measurable thing that has changed, as we have risen, is the pressure. The pressure falling inside the balloon has produced a fall in temperature, according to the Ideal Gas formula worked out centuries ago by Robert Boyle. I have calculated this rate of change as 10 Celsius degrees per kilometer."

"Yes, this makes sense," said Michel, "but if that is so, the air temperature all around us, at this height, should also be minus 1 degree!"

"Ah," replied Barbicane. "That is another foolish assumption. That would indeed be true if the air had been lifted directly off the ground to this height, but the air we breathe at this moment could have come from distant sources, from mechanisms we don't understand. From the storms of Africa, from the shores of Indonesia. Who knows? Who are we to assume that it simply rose off the corn fields below?"

"I see," said Michel. "We can accurately predict the temperature of the air inside the rising balloon, as it rises and sinks, but there is no formula that can predict the temperature of the surrounding air!"

"Exactly," said Barbicane. "Now imagine what would have happened if the air at this height was minus 20 degrees Celsius!"

"Well, with the air inside the balloon being at minus 1 degree, it would be hotter than the air around it. By nineteen degrees! In that case I would be quite sure the gas bag would be straining skyward above our heads, rather than dangling as it is now."

"Very good!" Barbicane exclaimed. "You have learned the principle of the thunderstorm!"

"I see," said Michel. "The thunderstorm air is like our balloon, no? And the more the surrounding air cools with height, the more buoyant is our balloon."

"Exactly," said Barbicane. "And now you see that cold temperatures aloft above this height, and warm air at the surface, allows for the greatest buoyancy."

"Yes," said Michel. "But if we observe a rate of cooling of the atmosphere which equals that within the balloon, 10 Celsius degrees per kilometer, there is a neutral effect, and we cannot be sure whether the air will rise or sink."

"Exactly, my friend! Let us drink a toast!"

With that, Michel pulled the cork off the Merlot and the two saluted the fruits of their labor. The remainder of the bottle was thrown down onto the cornfield. The tremendous impact caused an explosion of glass and wine, sparking panic among the crows and scattering them to all points of the horizon. For many months the crows never returned, and Farmer Jonesboro felt compelled to appropriate the antigravity pack to Barbicane in a gesture of gratitude.

CHAPTER FOUR
FORECASTING

To those unfamiliar with the black art of stock trading, it might seem that the Dow Jones and NASDAQ numbers and the pundits on CNBC are what make or break an investor's portfolio. Likewise, a beginning chaser reads a storm chase forum and gets the impression that the proper method for forecasting a chase is to look at the Storm Prediction Center (SPC) convective outlook and review what the latest models have pinned down as a target.

Just as a savvy investor knows that a market rally does not necessarily mean that shares of AT&T are rising, an experienced storm chaser knows that the SPC outlook or a RUC 00Z chart is not the holy grail for pinning down a chase target. A deeper immersion into the fundamentals are required. The investor carefully scrutinizes the company, trying to understand its character and composition, and looks for hints of what lies beneath the surface to figure out what he's dealing with. The weather forecaster looks at the atmosphere and does the very same thing. This immersion into the current state of a system is what we call *analysis*.

Naturally, a firm grounding in meteorology and forecasting knowledge is required to make the most of the analysis process. For chasers, this knowledge must be coupled with a synergistic ability to read the sky while on the road and make inferences about larger-scale trends.

The ingredient-based approach

Newcomers often get the impression that in order to forecast severe weather, they have to find as many objects as they can: fronts, lows, arrows, shaded areas, and concentrations of lines. The spot where all these things pile up on the chart is supposedly the best target area to chase. While such an approach seems ridiculous, it has at times been embraced as a correct "starter" method for forecasting. A few decades ago, storm forecaster Robert Miller published a set of indicators useful to highlight on weather charts. During the 1970s

The reality of chasing

Chasing boils down to going out on synoptic possibilities and succeeding or failing based on unresolved mesoscale events.

CHUCK DOSWELL
Norman, OK chaser and researcher

A forecasting lesson

I've been forecasting severe storms for more than 20 years, and the atmosphere still finds ways to humble me each season. Forecasting tornadic storms is the ultimate "put your money where your mouth is" exercise. Sure, you can adjust your chase on the fly and see tornadoes when your forecast is flawed.

A more honest and interesting test is to stick with your forecast area and timing through the chase and see how things turn out. You'll soon realize how little you actually know when you check your ego at the door and look at tornado forecasting from the meteorological perspective.

RICH THOMPSON
Norman, OK meteorologist and chaser

A SPC mesoscale forecaster analyzes a threat area for dewpoint temperatures in order to locate parcels that have maximum instability. Hand-drawn analysis is preferred over computer analysis. It connects the analyst intimately with the state of the current weather and it's more sensitive to small-scale detail than computer analysis. Photographed in October 2008. *(Tim Vasquez)*

and 1980s it was common for chasers and forecasters to draw these indicators on charts, stopping short of taking time to understand what the patterns represented. In a similar vein, a substantial number of chasers and forecasters now use numerical model data (computer forecasts) exclusively without taking time to understand the meteorology behind the forecast.

These examples describe a failure to achieve proper *diagnosis* of the atmosphere. In other words, the forecaster fails to understand details of how the atmosphere is configured. Furthermore, when things don't go as planned or there is a sudden, unexpected development, a failed diagnosis collapses the entire strategy and forecast for the day, and can leave a chaser marooned in the wrong part of the state, unable to understand what the sudden appearance of overcast stratocumulus means.

The proper technique to forecast severe weather is to start with a proper analysis of the atmosphere. Using this, the forecaster then uses an *ingredient-based* approach to review the charts and maps within this framework. It helps to remember the key three ingredients elemental to convective weather: moisture, instability and lift, plus the severe weather ingredient of shear.

Analysis

A successful chaser starts their forecast by looking at the current state of the atmosphere, slowly and methodically. This process is called *analysis*. The objective of analysis is to build up a three-dimensional picture of the atmosphere, and ideally, to visualize a four-dimensional picture of what is happening (i.e. looking at trends with time). The analysis session can start simply by looking at the radar composite or at surface charts, noting where the fronts and precipitation are, and thinking about what kind of regime the region is under. Is a front sweeping through the target areas? Or is broad southerly flow bringing up moisture? Is a big convective storm raging across part of the area? What does all this

Webster's dictionary defines

- **Analysis** as the examination of a complex, its elements, and their relations.
- **Diagnosis** as the investigation of the cause or nature of a condition, situation, or problem.
- **Prediction** as the act of foretelling on the basis of observation, experience, or scientific reason.

stratus and fog mean? These are precursors to diagnosis, which is explained in the next section.

Once the chaser gets a feel for the patterns and regimes affecting an area, it's time for that closer, more detailed look. The best way to accomplish this is to print a surface weather map, sharpen a pencil, sketch in obvious fronts, wind shifts, and drylines, and pencil in isobars that connect points of equal pressure.

A common sentiment heard is: "Why do all this grunt work? I can see the front and the low pressure quite plainly!" If such tough analysis work was unnecessary, the majority of veteran chasers would just look at a surface map, review the model output, and hit the road. They wouldn't waste dozens of minutes drawing on weather maps and studying radar and satellite loops intently. By their example, we see one aspect of the black art of storm forecasting: *to know the atmosphere in detail, we must examine it in detail.* Absentmindedly filling the chart with lines while listening to news stories on CNN accomplishes isoplething, but not analysis.

But by visualizing the conditions in the threat area as we draw, *the process forces us to think about things we are seeing on the map that we wouldn't otherwise notice:* things smoothed out by numerical models and anomalies that barely show up in the data. Furthermore *it hardens in the brain's understanding of what's taking place at different locations in and around the threat area*, creating total awareness of the ingredients at hand. Once you hit the road for Dodge City and hear on NWS Radio about thunderstorms popping up near Clayton, the analysis you completed gives you a mental starting point that helps determine what those developments mean and if it's worth chasing. Proper analysis defeats "tunnel vision" centered on the initial target area.

As you trace an isobar past Amarillo, you suddenly notice that the dewpoints are lower than you thought. Aha — that dryline is on the move. Your hand brings an isobar past Liberal. You happen to see the wind barb there and realize you're wondering what's causing the strong easterly wind. Are the dynamics aloft indeed stronger than you had thought? What's going on? You'll have to watch for pressure falls around the Raton Mesa in case something is emerging from the Rockies. You have trouble drawing a precise location for a front near Wichita, and decide to use a satellite image to pin it down. In the process you notice it's moving slower than you thought. What does this mean? Is the

The importance of analysis

In my opinion, a proper analysis is crucial in visualizing not only the present but also the future state of the atmosphere. It's not enough to merely draw pretty contours on a map. A proper analysis requires the forecaster to synthesize various data into a mental picture of the "base state" of the atmosphere. And it's not enough just to look at plan views of the atmosphere. The learned forecaster will evaluate how things evolve in time as critically as how they evolve in space.

Proper analysis is a skill that cannot be taught at the university level. Only practice and experience will train both sides of the brain into seeing patterns in station model plots. I share the need for putting pencil to paper, but if a forecaster can perform a diagnosis without breaking out the Prismacolors, that's cool, too. Whatever works, as long as it works well!

This is not an either/or, folks. Model data are extremely valuable, but only if the forecaster can synthesize these data with what's going on outside the window. This business can be mightly humbling, so why make it worse by not using the best model we have...the one behind your eyes?

BRIAN CURRAN
Midland, TX chaser

Hand analysis in motion. A thorough analysis leads to a thorough diagnosis, the cornerstone for a successful forecast. *(Tim Vasquez)*

cold air mass going to be deep enough to keep it from moving north as far as the RUC model suggests? You make a note to look at the Topeka sounding and the current VAD wind profile, circling Topeka on your analysis.

The value in analyzing a surface map by hand is simply immense, and there is absolutely no shortcut to gaining the insight that it offers on the current weather situation. Experienced chasers have been known to analyze over six hours worth of surface charts on a chase day to get the atmosphere to reveal her most closely-held secrets and the subtlest trends. Many chasers will also sketch over upper air charts to bring out small features that might bring surprises later in the afternoon, such as subtle short waves and strong jet maxes.

When drawing on the surface map, it is important to consult other data sources. As you do this, look at visible satellite imagery, radar data, soundings, and more. By doing this you are maximizing the use of all sources of data to construct the best three-dimensional picture that you can. In fact, it is quite useful to examine radar loops at numerous sites to pin down outflow boundaries, then transpose these onto the surface chart. Very small-scale visible satellite imagery (often called "1 km visible imagery") can reveal a wealth of features lurking at the surface. These should be drawn on the chart even if they aren't understood. Their meaning may be obvious later. Write notes to yourself directly on the surface map highlighting unusual things you are seeing, and which might be worthy of checking up on during the next hour or during your post-mortem learning sessions.

When the map is completed, it's strongly recommended that you examine a sounding for each station in the region. Use any knowledge you have of sounding interpretation to assess the possibility of convection at each of these stations, and what the nature of the convection will be. This process will clue you in on where the cap is weak or strong, and

---

Data stops without a laptop

For getting weather data, Oklahoma public libraries all have Internet access available to the public. A complete list of locations and hours can be obtained from the State Dept of Libraries. Hours vary wildly, but this can be a wonderful resource. I put a partial list on our web site: *http://home.swbell.net/daphjim/oklibrary.html*

DAPHNE LADUE
Norman, OK chaser

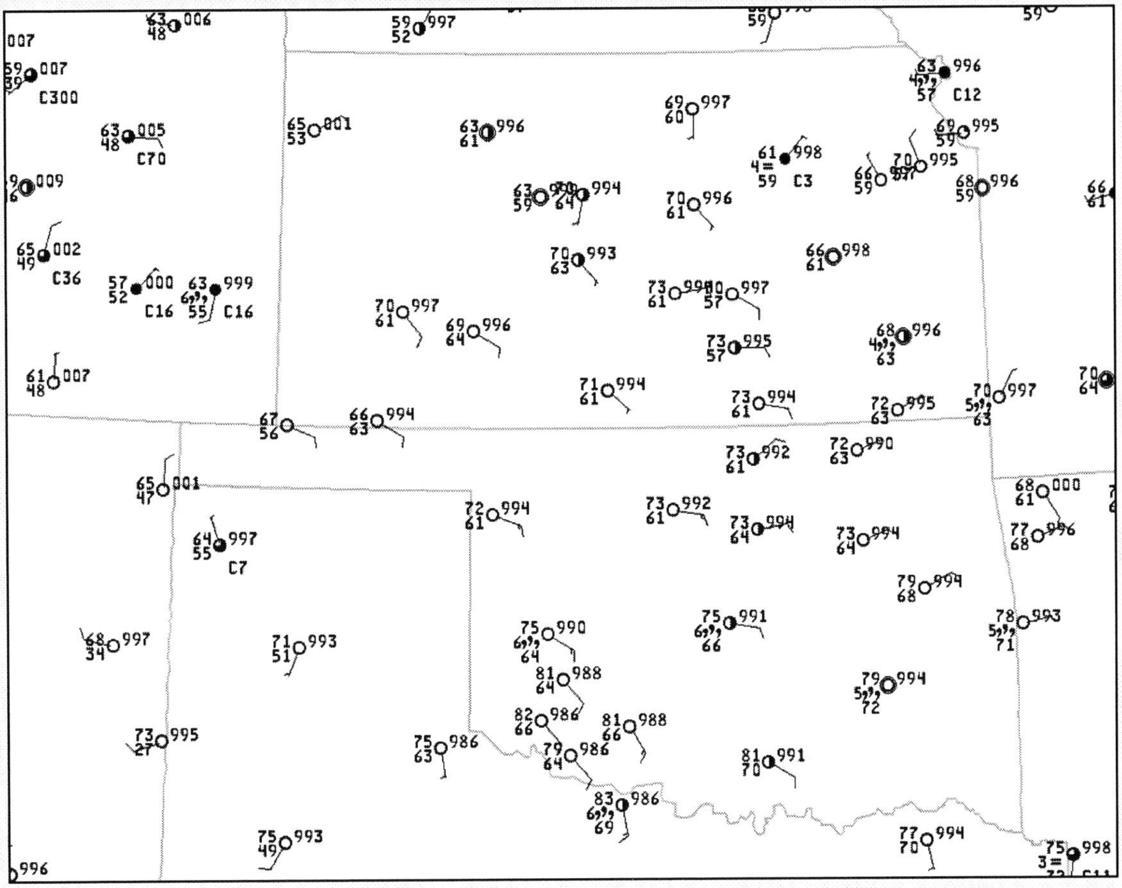

What goes through a chaser's mind when beginning an analysis. Here is a map for the morning of May 24, 1998. The stream of consciousness as the author examines the map are as follows:

1. Most of the entire area is under easterly flow.
2. Interesting -- northerly winds and some clouds in southeast Colorado.
3. These north winds extend to the northwest Texas Panhandle and paint out some sort of cyclonic circulation along the Texas-Oklahoma Panhandle border.
4. Temperatures are quite warm in the Wichita Falls region and much cooler in eastern Kansas. Is this a differing air mass?
5. There does appear to be confluence of the wind in this zone, sort of along an axis from southeast Oklahoma to western Oklahoma. This could be some sort of front.
6. There's a small area of difluent flow and north winds in far northeast Kansas. Drizzle is reported in the northeast part of this zone. This could be a dying MCS.
7. Northerly winds are also in the Goodland, Kansas area northward.
8. A preliminary frontal boundary or wind shift line should be sketched from around Fort Smith, Arkansas to Oklahoma City, Oklahoma and from there somewhere to somewhere in the eastern Texas Panhandle, where thermal contrast dies off.
9. There is a definite difference between the near-80 degree temperatures in southwest Oklahoma and the low 70s in northwest Oklahoma, so this confirms the front being roughly around I-40. It would be good to look at visible satellite imagery, radar, or mesonet to pin this down further.
10. Dewpoints in the 70s are in southeast Oklahoma into Arkansas, with 60s dewpoints to the Panhandles region.
11. It looks like the moisture is mixing out in the Amarillo to Lubbock area, preempting any storms there.
12. Northwest Oklahoma, northeast of the low, makes a good starting target until more data is available.

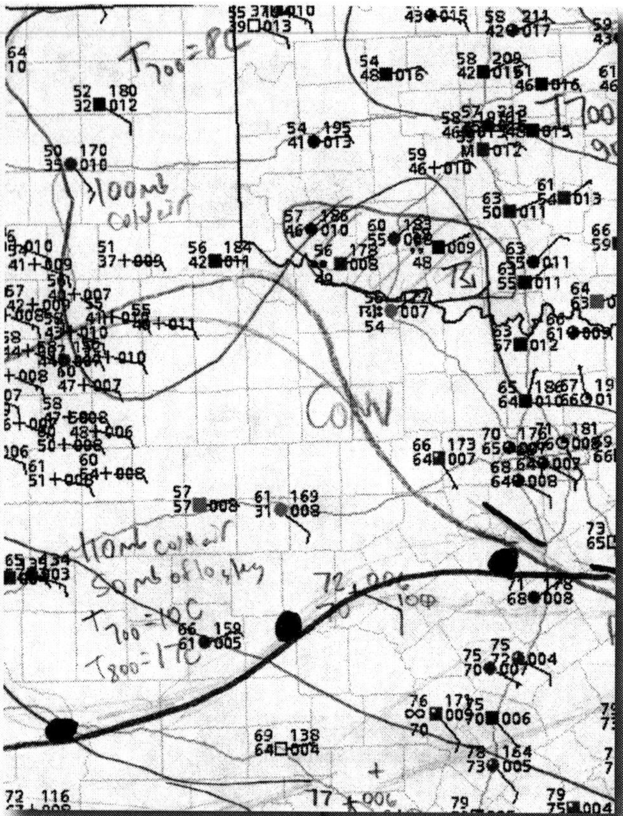

A thorough, completed analysis will often be a mess, as shown here. Note the annotations about upper-level temperature, precipitation areas from radar imagery, the extra observation drawn in based on an ASOS phone call, and refinements in frontal placement. What is important is not neatness but how much understanding was extracted and how efficiently it aids the diagnosis. *(Tim Vasquez)*

where moisture is deep enough to support thunderstorms. It will tend to give each region of the Great Plains its own "personality" for the day. This, in turn, spells out locations that are good and others that are bad, and when combined with the surface map, you have a plan for action. Make brief notes on your surface chart indicating your impressions from each sounding, such as "shallow moisture", "dryline passed", "strong LLJ", and so forth. Then, if upper level charts are available, we briefly analyze them and note important features, comparing them to what we've found on the surface chart and soundings.

While we are continuing this analysis work, we consider those three prerequisites for thunderstorms: moisture, instability, and lift; and the prerequisite for severe storms: shear. The surface chart and soundings bear out the location of the best moisture. These products also paint the best instability. Major sources of lift on the upper-air charts, such as deep troughs and short waves, indicate the locations where instability will increase further. The boundaries that were drawn on the surface chart paint out the key areas for a convective trigger. Finally, the surface and upper air charts will reveal the locations of the best shear.

Diagnosis

The step that follows analysis is *diagnosis*, referring to the procedure of using the elements found in the analysis to connect the pieces and understand the "big picture". The simplest example of diagnosis is a forecaster comparing surface and upper-level charts to "put the atmosphere together" mentally. Relating an upper-level short wave trough to thermal patterns in the lower troposphere is another form of diagnosis. So is figuring out what's causing the stratus in Kansas. In practice, most diagnosis occurs in the forecaster's head while the analysis is performed, often arising as the result of a mental conversation. But sometimes more time is needed to sort out what's on the charts and graphics.

A four-dimensional picture can help round out the diagnosis. This involves having some idea of how the three-dimensional picture is evolving with time. If you analyzed charts for the previous hour, you will already understand how things are changing and will be able to pick out trends that are occurring. Incredibly, you may not even need to consult numerical forecast models at this point. Trends can certainly be of considerable help, especially during the cool season when the timing of a front or a major upper level disturbance will have a huge impact on the forecast. During the summer season, however, numerical models will likely not have very much of an influence on your forecast, once you've completed your important analysis work.

A diagnosis requires the forecaster to explore the storm situation at the smallest scale possible, especially when data availability in the field allows. Even with this kind of detail, important process may not be uncovered. Observational data from the VORTEX field program revealed that there can be surprising, unexplained variations in the lower tropospheric wind field over a small region, which can put storm-relative helicity and shear all over the spectrum. In an operational setting, this means that forecasting thinking, and in particular, derived numbers such as SRH and CAPE, are ballpark figures at best and may not even be representative of a storm 50 miles away! This is where the subjectivity and art of forecasting excels. Look for the *underlying mechanisms* which are associated with important ingredients, rather than waiting on evidence in the actual data or scrutinizing automated products. For example a stationary boundary may be important whether or not SPC's automated analyses reveal the kind of SRH values you want to see.

Forecasting

The final step is to anticipate how these ingredients might change during

Master forecaster

A student was reviewing a forecast situation. He turned to the master and said, "I cannot figure out the initiation area. Let's just go by the SPC outlook."

Master forecaster sighed, and said, "Fine. I have a different task for you."

They went to the kitchen area, where pasta sauce was simmering. "This week Bureaucrat is visiting. He loves linguine. You alone shall cook linguine for him every night. He sets our budget, so I demand perfection. Now, add some salt."

"No, wait."

"You question me?"

"I do trust you, master, but if the meals are to come out right I need to do this myself and try to improve on each meal."

Suddenly the student was enlightened.

DAVID HOADLEY

the upcoming hours, and then find the best possible location for isolated, strong convection. This defines the target area, and is something that should emerge during the analysis and diagnosis process rather than appearing at the very end.

A thunderstorm, reduced to its simplest cause, is a rapid ascent of a moist unstable parcel of air into the free troposphere. For this to happen, there need to be the three basic ingredients of instability, moisture, and a source of lift, a triad of ingredients identified by Charles Doswell and others.

Instability

The most important ingredient for thunderstorms is instability. This is diagnosed by looking at sounding charts for each station across the target area and lifting a parcel of air. Remember that to lift a parcel, we look at the mixing ratio of its dewpoint temperature (its saturation mixing ratio) and its starting temperature. The parcel is then lifted at the dry adiabatic lapse rate until it cools to this mixing ratio value. This establishes the lifted condensation level (LCL). From

The chase decision. Charles Allison contemplates whether to pursue the tornado-warned cell in Texas or wait for it to cross the Red River and enter Oklahoma. Accurate short-term decisions require a rich understanding of the meteorological environment. *(Steve Miller, hamwx.com)*

there, the parcel rises along the wet adiabatic lapse rate, and we usually continue this lift to the top of the chart.

By marking the lifted parcel on a chart like this, we are simulating what would happen if it were forced to rise through the entire troposphere, given the initial starting conditions. This type of lift is hypothetical, and can occur only if the parcel can maintain enough buoyancy and momentum to rise the entire distance. The vast majority of the time, the parcel is suppressed because the parcel line rises to the left side (cold side) of the environment. The geometric area swept out between this parcel temperature trace and the environmental temperature trace (visualized by shading the space between them horizontally as we draw upward) corresponds to energy.

If the parcel line rises to the left side (cold side) as so often happens, the energy is negative, and the parcel resists upward motion because it is colder than the surrounding air. Looking at the amount of negative energy swept out (called CIN, or convective inhibition), the parcel will sink unless we can apply that much energy from an external source to resist the parcel's tendency to sink. This can often come from dynamic lift (short waves, upper disturbances, and surface convergence). In most cases, the amount of energy such external sources contribute is small, only enough to counter a small area swept out on the sounding.

If the parcel line rises to the right side (warm side), the energy is positive, and the the parcel will rise because it is warmer than the surrounding air. The more positive energy which is swept out, the faster the parcel will rise. This measure of energy is known as CAPE (convective availability of potential energy). This energy can only be realized if the rising parcel is not suppressed by negative energy in lower parts of the atmosphere. If such a negative area exists, the parcel will be suppressed unless some source of lift forces the parcel upward to where it can reach the positive energy area. This level is called the LFC, or level of free convection.

For reasons of simplicity, we have cobbled together the rising parcel using strictly the surface temperature and surface dewpoint. This is what we call a *surface parcel.* In practice, we lift entire layers of air from the lower levels. To do this, we take an average dewpoint and temperature in the lowest 100 to 150 mb of the atmosphere. The averaging is done by selecting an "average" dry adiabat that equally divides the environmental temperature trace over the given layer depth. We then select an "average" saturation mixing

A valuable tool

I tend to do a lot more spot chasing in late spring and early summer when I may drive 10 hours each way. After a few long distance blue-sky busts, I began spending more time analyzing skew-T's to gain a more reasonable idea as to whether or not the cap would break on any given day. So far, analyzing skew-t's has saved me a lot of money, but it isn't perfect!

SCOTT WEBERPAL
Janesville, WI chaser

ratio line that equally divides the dewpoint trace over the given layer depth. By sketching out this dry adiabat and saturation mixing ratio line until they intersect and form an LCL, we have created a *mixed layer parcel*. CIN and CAPE, we have a much more realistic representation of what type of parcel might develop. CAPE derived from a mixed layer parcel is called *mixed layer CAPE*, or *MLCAPE*, a term often seen on SPC weather discussions. In contrast, the earlier method of lifting a surface parcel to estimate CAPE yields *surface-based CAPE*, or *SBCAPE*. When a front is south of a forecast location and low-level air is too cold to produce a buoyant parcel, there is often warm, moist air just above the frontal inversion; in such a case, the entire mixed layer is positioned just above the frontal inversion to assess the likelihood of elevated convection.

Moisture

Moisture is considered an important parameter because thunderstorms require the warmest possible parcel. The higher the dewpoint, the greater the saturation mixing ratio, and the faster the rising parcel can saturate and begin releasing latent heat. This yields the best buoyancy and greatest acceleration against the cooler environmental air in the middle and upper troposphere. Therefore, the logical way to get a storm going is to maximize the low-level dewpoint, preferably through a layer that extends upward through a depth of 100 mb (3000 ft) or more to yield the best mixed layer parcel.

Rich moisture, however, does not materialize out of thin air. It depends on two principal sources: evaporation from water bodies (the larger and warmer, the better), and from evapotranspiration, a factor that comes into play later in the summer. The Gulf of Mexico is the original supplier for the vast majority of moisture involved in Great Plains weather events. Its influence is felt far and wide, from the summertime storms on the Canadian Prairies to the Arizona monsoon storms of July and August.

During the summer, moisture is plentiful enough to stagnate and move with impunity around the United States, reinforced daily with evapotranspiration and producing storms wherever the wind trajectories take the air mass. South or east winds are not necessarily needed for thunderstorms. However, spring weather outbreaks require a healthy fetch of fresh moisture from the Gulf of Mexico. This type of fetch requires south winds coming from the Gulf of Mexico, which establishes a conveyor belt of warm, moist air known as *moisture return*, or *return flow*. When return flow is underway, it is said that the Gulf is "open". Healthy return flow is accompanied by dewpoints exceeding 60 deg F dewpoints on surface and 850 mb charts. An open Gulf, however, does not always assure ample moisture. Cold water temperatures, especially on the heels of plunging polar outbreaks in February and March, can limit the ability of the water surface to evaporate, yielding 40 to 50 degree dewpoints at best.

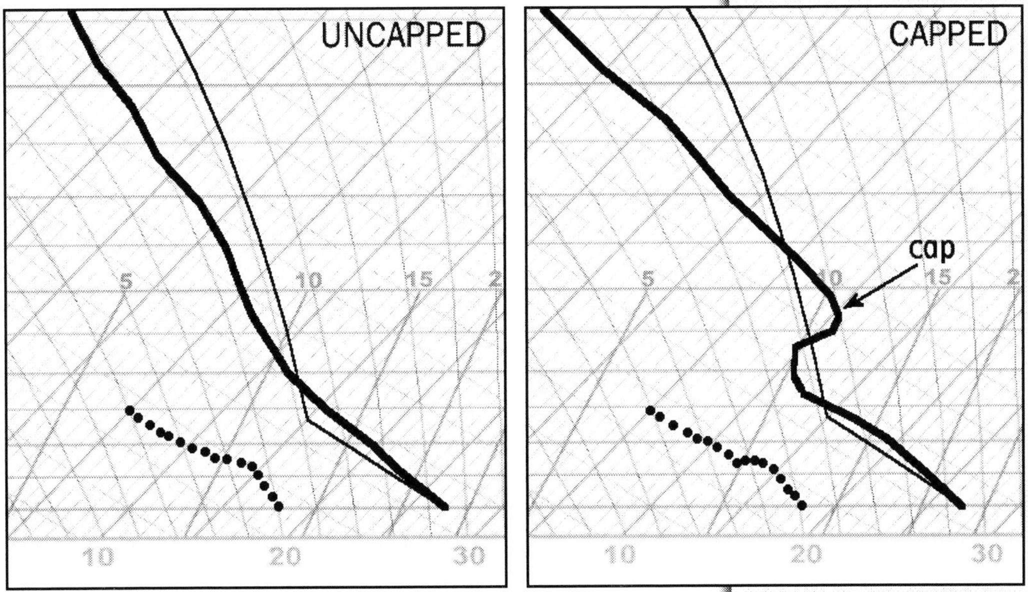

Uncapped (left) and capped (right) soundings, showing otherwise nearly identical conditions with similar stability profiles. Both soundings show a weak layer of warm air near the surface that must be surmounted, since the parcel is cooler through these levels than the environment. This can be overcome with more heating, more moisture, or weak lift. Above that, the capped sounding shows a layer of warm air that also must be overcome.

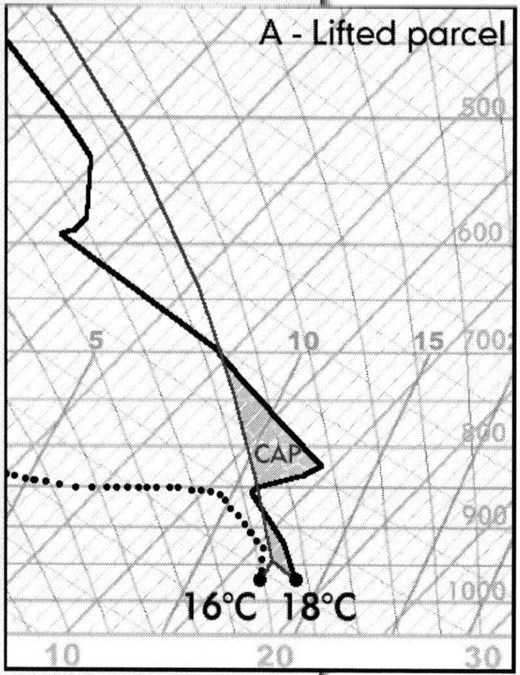

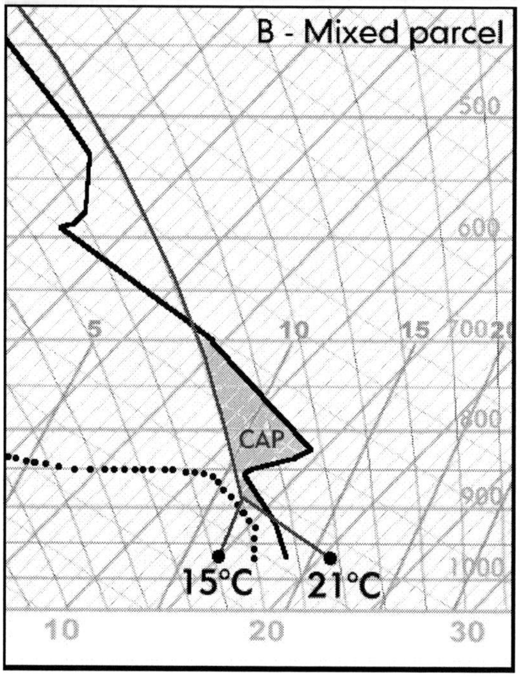

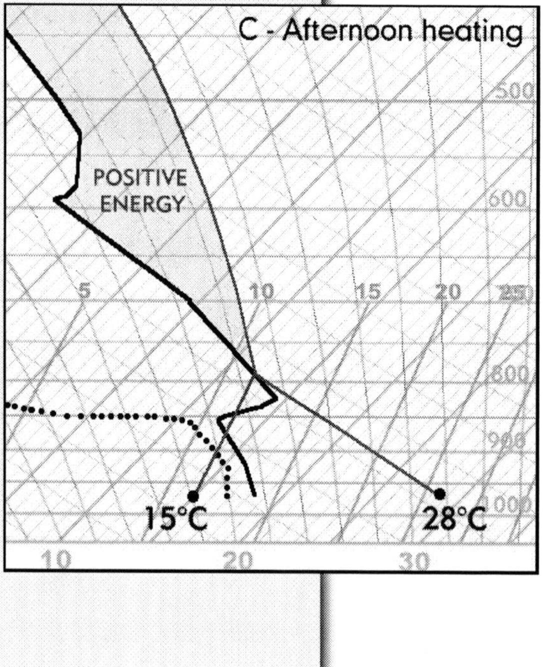

Diagram showing several ways of lifting a parcel. This data is for Oklahoma City on the morning of May 3, 1999, a few hours before the biggest Oklahoma tornado outbreak in recent times.

A — **A lifted parcel** is simply lifted from the surface. No changes in temperature are implied, and no layer mixing is done. The cap (shaded area) is quite strong as suggested by its large area.

B — **A mixed parcel** mixes a layer of air near the surface (in this case the lowest 150 mb).

C — **A modified parcel** factors in surface heating and mixing of a layer of low-level moisture. Here, the mixed parcel dewpoint has been extended upward along the mixing ratio lines to intersect the temperature profile. This intersection is the level of free convection (LFC). By bringing a line from the LFC down to the surface, we obtain the convective temperature (Tc). This implies that by the time it is 28°C (82°F), the air mass will be uncapped, assuming no other changes.

The magic does not lie completely in dewpoint values. Moisture *depth* is a prime consideration. Even if Abilene reports a dewpoint of 75 degrees, a very shallow layer of moisture (less than 50 mb, or 2000 ft deep) mixes this moisture with drier air above, reducing the mixed parcel's dewpoint. This homogenizes into a diluted layer of moisture. For example, if a 3000 ft deep layer of 70 deg F dewpoints lies underneath a 3000 ft deep layer of 30 deg F dewpoints, mixing of both layers results in a single 6000 ft deep layer of 50 deg F dewpoints. It should be clear that you must think vertically! The top of a moist layer can also be eroded and replaced with dry air when strong westerly winds exist at the top of the moist layer. In terms of moisture depth, this causes it to decrease. Profiler and WSR-88D VAD data can be used to keep tabs on such erosion processes.

So far, we have talked completely about low-level moisture. Is mid- and upper-tropospheric moisture important? The answer is that yes, it's important, but no, it's not desirable. Significant amounts of upper-level moisture are associated with dense cirrus and cirrostratus clouds, which dampens surface heating and causes low-level parcels to be cooler. CAPE values are reduced and CIN values increase. An extreme example is the "subtropical cirrus" situation, common in the cool season, in which a deep upper-level trough taps into tropical weather systems and draws the debris northward into the United States. Not only is solar heating reduced, but in the presence of steep lapse rates and strong lift, this mid-level moisture will become buoyant, causing high-based showers to form rather early in the day. On one hand, these can create boundaries which are quite useful for deep convection later in the afternoon, but most of the time the elevated showers cause problems by producing massive evaporational cooling, making low-level parcels across a target area even colder.

The best way to find beneficial low-level moisture is, of course, to analyze surface charts and look at the 850 mb (5000 ft) upper air chart. Satellite imagery bears out excellent indicators of cloud forms, which hint at the type of return flow that is underway and where it is located. This can be used to see what type of moisture field is feeding a target area. The type of imagery to use is visible imagery, preferably that with a resolution of 1 kilometer. Water vapor imagery should not be used for this purpose, as it is only sensitive to upper tropospheric moisture.

Dave Hoadley on the big one

How should one feel missing out on the tornado? Several thoughts temper my disappointment. I know there will be many more opportunities to chase, and persistence and patience will be rewarded. Also is the realization that, sometimes, a missed tornado is just a down-payment on past successes. A lucky chaser the second day out shouldn't expect the same result every other day.

Finally, is often just thankfulness that I ended the day safely: after holding traction on a surprise, rain-slick curve; passing that semi- after a fountain buried the windshield for a few breathless seconds; and just missing getting broadsided at an intersection by "the other driver".

The wise storm chaser will go back and review his or her forecast decisions and try to understand what could have been different. Each failed chase is a learning opportunity. Which parameters were more important, depending on other circumstances that day? How did visual clues confirm or mislead what the data said would happen? It is only really disappointing, if we learn nothing from our mistakes.

DAVID HOADLEY
Falls Church, Virginia chaser

Mixing of sounding layers

TEMPERATURE

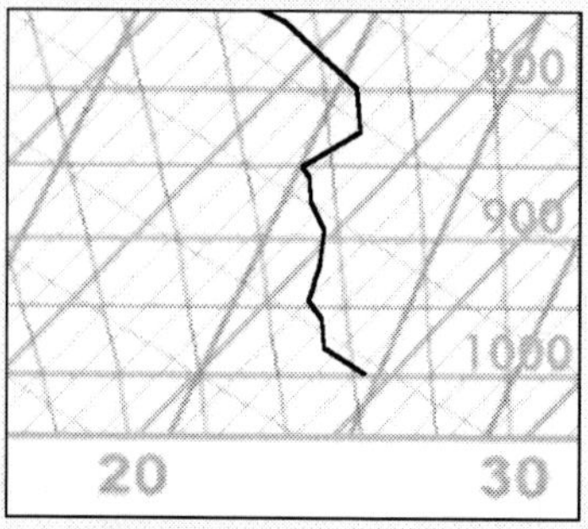

This is the initial depiction of the temperature plot on the sounding.

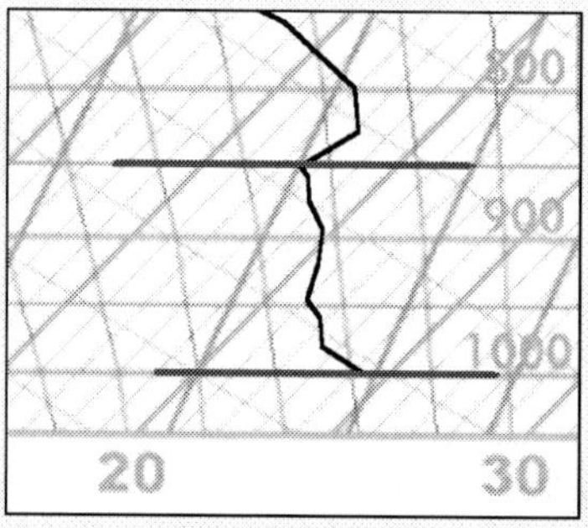

First, we decide the depth of the layer to be mixed. This is usually 100 or 150 mb in convective situations, or the depth of the layer below the capping inversion. The top and bottom layers are drawn. Here, a depth of 150 mb has been chosen.

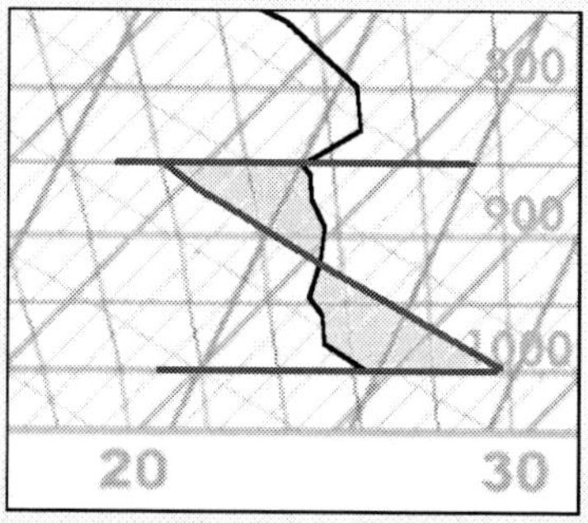

A line parallel to the dry adiabats is drawn. It must bisect the temperature trace to form equal geometric areas (when shaded as shown above). This line represents the new mixed temperature profile within this layer.

DEWPOINT

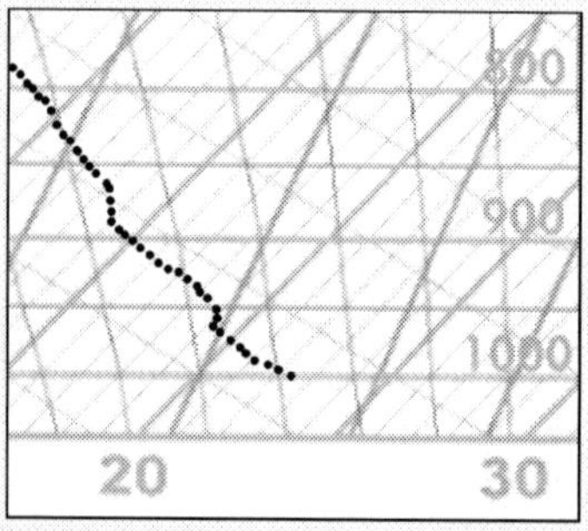

This is the initial depiction of the dewpoint plot on the sounding.

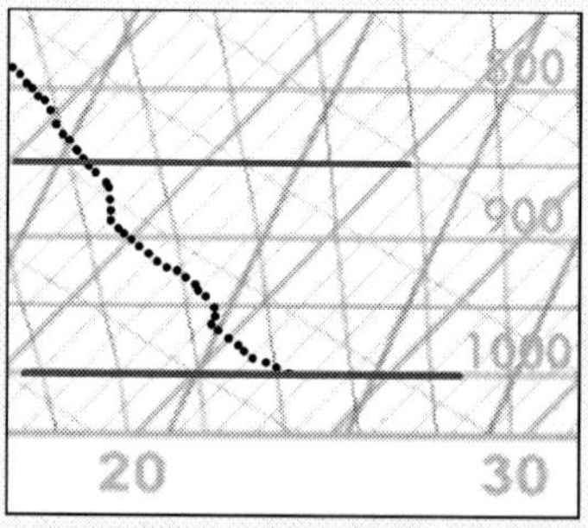

First, we decide the depth of the layer to be mixed. This is usually 100 or 150 mb in convective situations, or the depth of the layer below the capping inversion. The top and bottom layers are drawn. Here, a depth of 150 mb has been chosen.

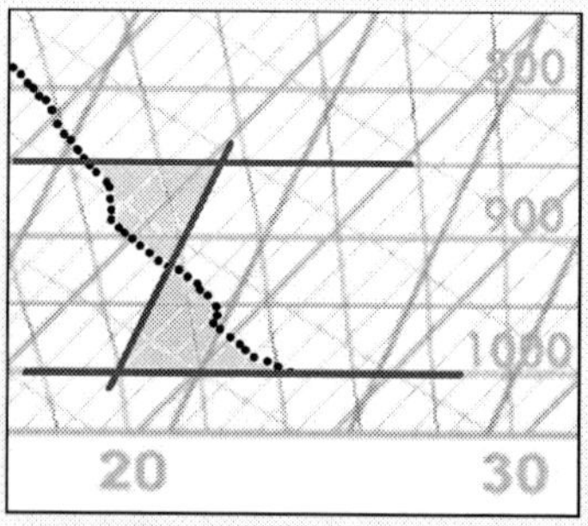

A line parallel to the mixing ratio lines is drawn. It must bisect the dewpoint trace to form equal geometric areas (when shaded as shown above). This line represents the new mixed dewpoint profile within this layer. Extend it upward to the temperature trace; the intersection is the convective condensation level (CCL).

During the morning, look at the target area and the neighboring source areas of moisture. Clear skies indicate a nonexistent or weak moisture return. Stratus, which appears patchy and featureless on satellite photos, indicates a moderate moisture return. Stratocumulus, which takes on complicated appearances on satellite photos and often is accompanied by higher layers, is associated with a strong moisture return. The north-south axis of the low cloud regions coincides with the thickest, most persistent low-level clouds and the strongest return flow.

Later in the day, heating causes the cloud forms to evolve into more vertically-oriented structures and this causes a gradual change in appearance. During these later hours, weak return flow is indicated by a continued lack of cloud material, or by small cumulus areas which form by midday and diminish into spotty elements during the afternoon. Moderate return flow is indicated by broad, dense regions of cumuliform clouds that persist throughout the afternoon. Strong return flow is painted out by wide regions of overcast stratocumulus, usually surrounded by congested areas of cumuliform clouds. Elevated convection may occur during the morning in strong return flow, producing upper-level cirriform debris, and this can make low-level features difficult to see.

Satellite clues

A wealth of information is available on satellite, such as from the image on 5 November 2008 at 1601 UTC. Cirrus (A) signals the arrival of lift and moisture from an upper-level disturbance over the Rockies. Tropical moisture feeds north in the form of multi layer stratocumulus fields (B) based at about 2000 to 3000 ft AGL. In some areas the clouds have formed into transverse waves (C). In other areas, the stratocumulus forms into streets (D) parallel with the surface wind. Both areas are indicative of strong capping. Some high-based cumulus towers exist (E) and (F) noted by numerous large elements and distinct shadowing. In other areas the cumulus is more surface-based (G) with small, bright elements and little shadowing.

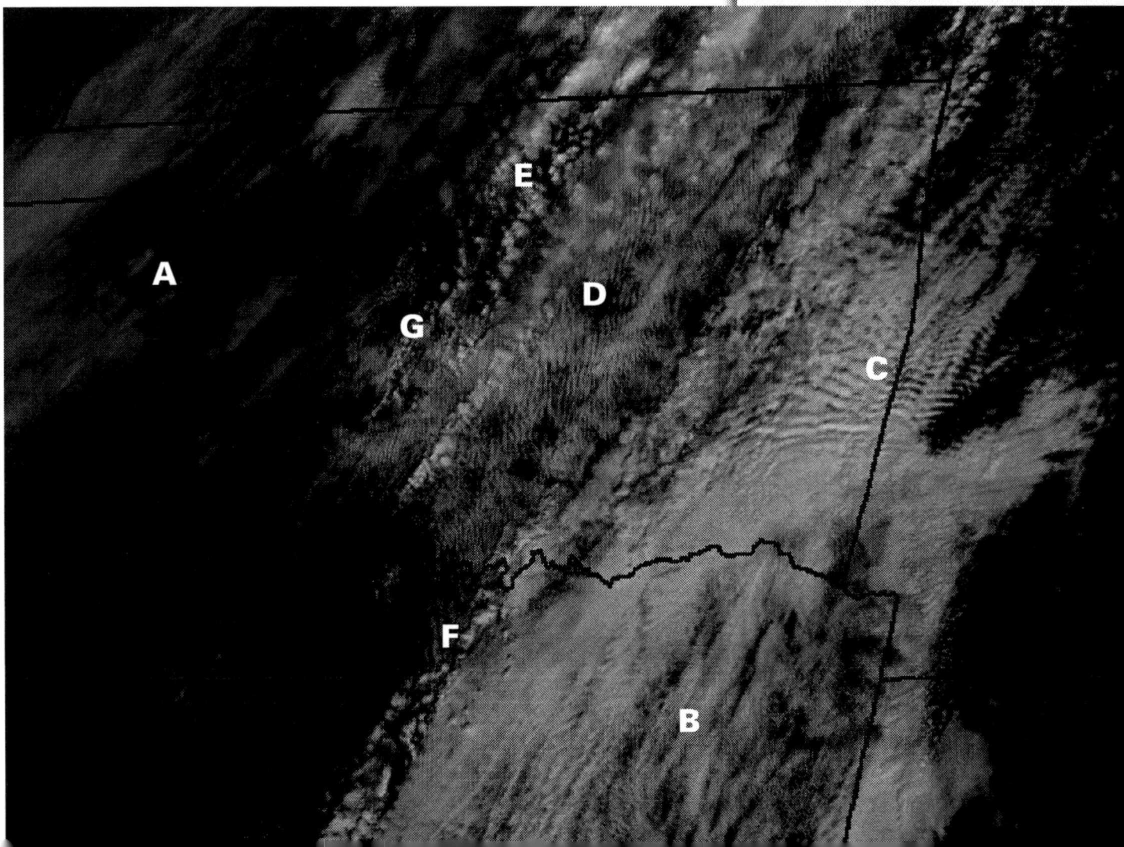

High LCL values are a special moisture situation that occurs because of low relative humidity, which also corresponds to large temperature-dewpoint spreads (dewpoint depressions). This type of situation results in high-based storms. Low dewpoints and poor moisture return are often thought of as the most common causes, but another cause occurs in summertime when moisture is abundant but temperatures are very hot. This also results in low relative humidity and large dewpoint depressions, even though dewpoints might be well up into the 70s. (The dewpoint depression is also known as the temperature-dewpoint spread, which is simply the difference between the two values in degrees) A general rule of thumb is that when the dewpoint depression exceeds 25 Fahrenheit degrees, a high-LCL storm situation is likely. There is evidence that high LCL's favor heavy outflow from thunderstorms due to enhanced evaporation of rainfall, while any rotation develops at a much higher level in the cloud, reducing tornadic potential. Rather than chase to an area with high LCL's, it is often wiser for chasers to seek different target areas, preferably those that offer better convergence and lower dewpoint depressions.

Lift

A special forecasting skill that takes time to develop is the the ability to estimate the magnitude of large-scale (synoptic-scale) lift over a region as indicated by different weather products. This is where numerical models come in handy. Although numerical models do produce sets of numbers that indicate the strength of upper lift, their

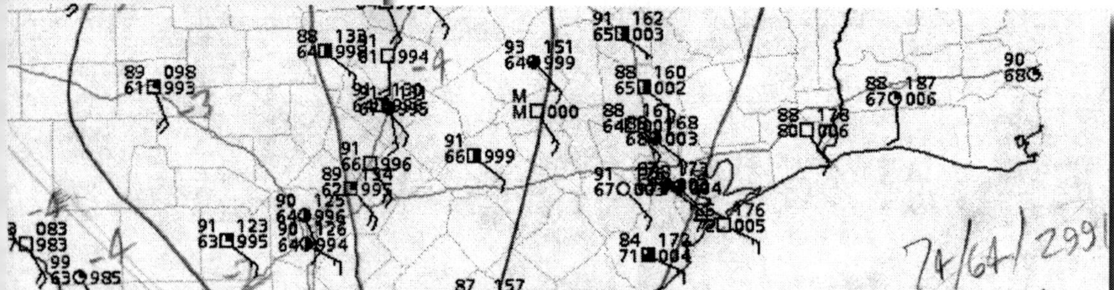

The Gulf is "open for business". Southeasterly return flow shown here brings near-70 degree dewpoints and stratocumulus layers to the Texas Gulf Coast. (May 10, 2002 21Z)

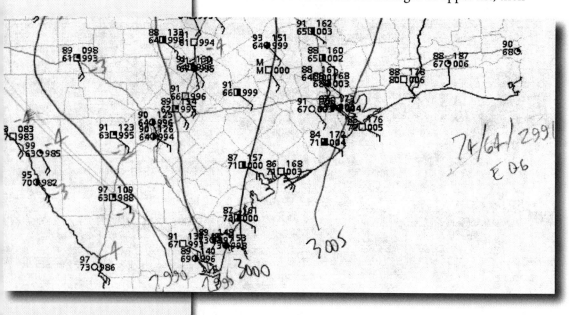

magnitudes are estimated indirectly and are not very accurate (though the horizontal positioning is often reliable). Not only do the models miss small-scale processes that can distort the amount of lift that actually occurs, but for a forecaster to interpret model-derived lift values and apply this to a sounding is impractical.

There are three ways a severe weather forecaster handles this: (1) look at vorticity advection, vertical velocity diagnostics, and/or omega patterns to get a subjective feel for how much lift will be affecting a target area, then estimate roughly how much this will affect the sounding; (2) look at upper-level temperature forecasts to see how much cooling will occur at a given location; in some cases this can be used to adjust the environmental sounding; and (3) see whether the model "breaks out" precipitation or not (bearing in mind that the model may be doing this for many other reasons instead).

With severe weather forecasting, the way that lift works is not as it seems. Synoptic-scale lift, such as from a short wave trough, does not "create" a storm or push parcels upward. Rather it prepares the environment by *steepening lapse rates*, *increasing instability*, and *eroding the cap* over a broad area. Conversely, synoptic-scale sinking motion, also known as subsidence, stabilizes the atmosphere and strengthens the cap.

Some good indicators of synoptic-scale upper-level lift and destabilization include upper-level divergence and upper- and mid-level cooling. The coincidence of the area with a divergent quadrant of a jet, or having a location just ahead of a short wave, can be a good pattern-based indicator. One technique involves watching satellite water vapor imagery for dark slots south of an upper-level cyclone, which tend to be associated with strong upper-level winds. The amount of response to a source of upper-level lift tends to be proportional to the existing lapse rate of the layer. Therefore, the steeper the lapse rates, the more pronounced the forcing will be from a short wave, divergent quadrant, or other upper-level feature.

One feature that has been consistently pointed out is the character of elevated cumulus and altocumulus fields in the dry sector (such as in New Mexico when the Texas dryline is active). Sometimes these fields have a distinct southern boundary, which seems to demarcate the location downstream in the moist sector where storms will not develop any further south. It is thought that the dry sector cumulus

From a chaser in Switzerland

I decided to try my luck at seeing a tornado in America. Actually it is not only the tornado which I found fascinating, but even more so the amazing photos I saw of some isolated LP supercells, hanging low over flat land like a spaceship, unreal, magical. I wanted to see those Great Plains skies, those amazing clouds, those natural fireworks of lightning!

In May 2000 I flew from Switzerland to Dallas, rented a car and started chasing. I spent 2 weeks and saw some great lightning storms. I remember a nighttime storm near Tulsa where the lightning illuminated the far horizon while in front of me there were thousands of lightning bugs in the fields.

But I saw no tornadoes. In fact, there are lots of days without tornadoes in the Great Plains, even in May. I learned that even in Oklahoma there are many folks who have never seen a tornado, except on TV. So I spent the next year learning more, reading more, searching more info on the web.

May 6, 2001: I drive to Ardmore. NOAA Weather Radio warns of storms developing west of Ardmore. I hit the road, heading west, towards the clouds. I clearly see rotation at the base! So I start the car, to catch up with the cloud which now just finished crossing the road. I momentarily stop filming, and that is precisely the moment when the tornado decided to come down! Touchdown!

OLIVIER STAIGER
Geneva, Switzerland chaser

Assessing low level moisture using midday (1700 UTC) visible imagery

Weak moisture axis. Benign fields of cumulus don't form until the afternoon hours. Upstream skies are clear. Cumulus may form into unusually even, parallel rows, indicating very strong capping.

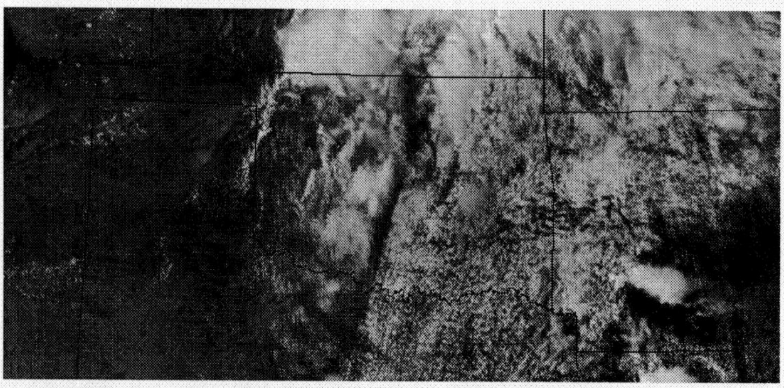

Moderate moisture axis. Cumulus fields show vigorous growth and persistence from the I-35 corridor eastward, with weaker moisture extending west to the 100 degree meridian. Areas of cirrus debris are found where elevated convection had occurred earlier in the morning.

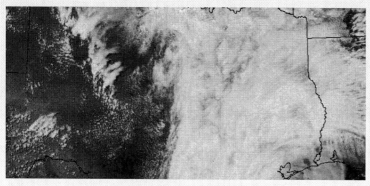

Strong moisture axis. Multiple levels of stratus and stratocumulus are found along the moisture axis. This suppresses heating, however storms form further west and northwest, and with backed low level winds can tap this excellent moisture. If large anvils form in the moisture axis, this is a bad sign — it indicates the low level moisture may become depleted by deep convection upstream.

corresponds to areas of upward lift that are weakening the cap downstream, with an opposite subsident effect further south and at points downstream.

Now we shall cover lift at the smaller, subsynoptic scales. A key factor in many tornadic storm and isolated supercell events is the appearance of *concentrated, mesoscale sources of lift* (less than a couple of hundred miles in size, often even smaller). These can manifest themselves in the upper troposphere, escaping detection on upper level charts and model output, but appearing plainly on satellite and profiler data by early afternoon. The most common culprit is mesoscale jet streaks embedded in the upper-level flow. Satellite imagery, profilers, VAD winds, and 1-hour altimeter setting pressure falls are instrumental in detecting these features. In the lower levels, small-scale lift can also develop from low-level point convergence. This can be the result of mesolows, barely detected by the surface observation network and often caused by mesoscale upper-level forcing or by unresolvable baroclinic interactions along surface boundaries. Low-level lift can also result from forcing by terrain (orographic lift).

The key to finding these mesoscale sources of lift is careful analysis and careful diagnosis, especially as convective initiation draws closer! Numerical models simply do not have the capability to handle subsynoptic lift very well. Out in the field, unexpected backing of the wind field or rapid changes in the pressure or weather conditions can indicate the presence of mesoscale lift.

It must be pointed out that there can easily be *too much lift*, whether from the synoptic or subsynoptic scale. This is common during the cool season when deep troughs emerge from the Rocky Mountains, accompanied by strong upper-level dynamics. Such systems produce very large, intense areas of synoptic-scale lift. Extreme lift, especially over a wide area, tends to produce multiple cells that rapidly combine into a squall line. Therefore "marginal" upper level lift is what chasers prefer on many chase days! The cap must be broken, but not overwhelmed, and in as small an area as possible. It's a delicate balance.

Shear

The role of shear in supporting thunderstorm development is a relatively new aspect of storm forecasting science. During the 1970s it was quite clear that increasing winds

Predicting the cap

Determining cap strength certainly has been the difference between BOOM or BUST for me. There are some key ingredients that I think are important.

First, low-level moisture convergence is a plus. I look for that especially northeast of dry-line bulges or mesolows. Next, its the all important temperatures at low-levels. I shy away from regions where the 850mb temps are greater than 25C. As for the other extreme, I don't like raging squall-lines.

So I try to keep south of the area of unidirectional flow. This is difficult with deep, dynamic systems so I always like to wait until late May or June for the storm systems to slow down. That remains the best time of the year for chasing to me.

I'll take a nice, slow-moving supercell at the tail end of a storm system any day.

TIM MARSHALL
Flower Mound, TX chaser

with height, as well as backed surface winds, were instrumental in producing severe weather. However, research findings during the 1980s provided dynamic insight and more findings. In 1984 Robert Davies-Jones from NSSL compared storm movement to the vertical wind profile and found several distinct types of storm behavior. In 1986 Douglas Lilly from OU devised the storm-relative helicity idea.

The simplest type of shear is bulk shear. This is the vector difference in winds between the surface and 6 km above ground level. For example, if surface winds are out of the northeast at 10 kt, and the 6 km winds are out of the southwest at 50 kt, the bulk shear is 60 kt. Bulk shear is expressed in a quantity known as *BRN shear*: a value of 25-35 knots is generally associated with weak supercells, while values beyond 35 kt are associated with long-lived supercells. Note that BRN shear is a *vector difference*; a 0 km south wind at 10 kt and a 6 km east wind at 20 kt does not equal a BRN shear of 10 kt.

In a three-dimensional context, shear is difficult to visualize and express. Therefore, we use two tools: vector math and the hodograph, the latter of which is more appropriate in a forecast setting. The hodograph is basically a worksheet for us to do vector math on, and it is marked with azimuths, representing direction, and rings, representing speed in knots (in research publication, this is sometimes meters per second). The center of the hodograph, or the origin, corresponds to a zero velocity relative to the Earth's surface. The first thing we do with a hodograph is plot the wind profile, a depiction that shows all the winds in the atmosphere above a given station. To do this, we simply look at the wind direction and wind speed at each level in the atmosphere, and plot this on the hodograph. Next to each dot, we plot a number for the level that it represents (usually this is a height in km, but can be mb or ft). We start at the bottom of the atmosphere and work our way up. The dot representing each level is connected to the dot representing the level above

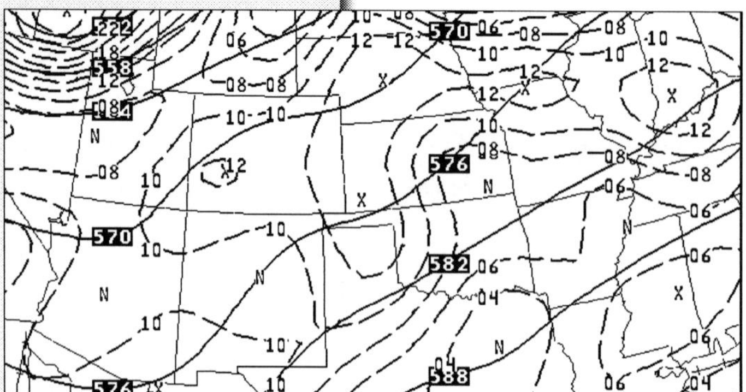

The 500 mb height/vorticity depiction has long been a favorite among forecasters for diagnosing lift. Locations where vorticity is increasing with time (such as downstream of high vorticity values) are favored for upward motion. Forecasters also look at tools such as Q-vectors, isentropic charts, and conceptual models such as the 4-quadrant jet pattern to find lift, as well as simple things such as orographics.

A long anvil cloud streaming away with the upper level wind, in this case toward the camera, is the most familiar manifestation of shear. The strong upper-level winds, contrasted with weak winds in the lower troposphere, create a strong quantity of bulk shear that helps separate precipitation from the updraft area and prolong the life of the storm. *(Tim Vasquez)*

and below it. The result is a wormlike shape, which itself is often called the hodograph.

Consider what would get plotted if the winds were calm throughout the entire atmosphere. All dots would be plotted at the center of the chart, and the hodograph line would have no length at all. Now what if the winds were calm at the ground and very strong aloft? We would have a line that stretches from the center of the chart to the edge. The longer this line is, the greater the shear in the atmosphere. Now what if the surface, 1 km, and 2 km winds are east at 50 kt, south at 50 kt, and west at 50 kt, respectively? We would have a long, curved line. The curvature of this line is a property known as helicity, and it has significant importance in thunderstorm forecasting. When compared to the storm motion vector, the larger the area swept out by the hodograph and the 0-1 or 0-2 km layer, the larger the storm-relative helicity (SRH). This is enhanced by a curved hodograph. The larger the SRH, the greater the potential for rotating updrafts.

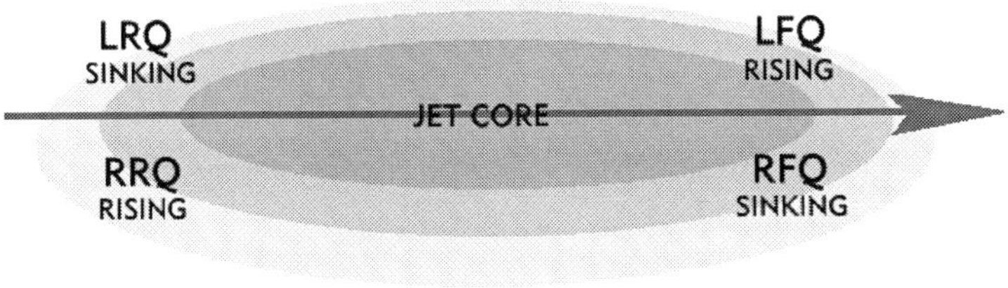

The conceptual model for lift and subsidence in various quadrants of an upper-level jet core due to ageostrophic (out of balance) flow. In general, the left front quadrant (LFQ) and right rear quadrant (RRQ) bring the strongest lift, which rapidly erodes caps and destabilizes the troposphere. The other quadrants tend to bring subsidence, strengthening caps and stabilizing the troposphere. If you use this model, always use it in conjunction with your other tools. Various factors may cancel each other out!

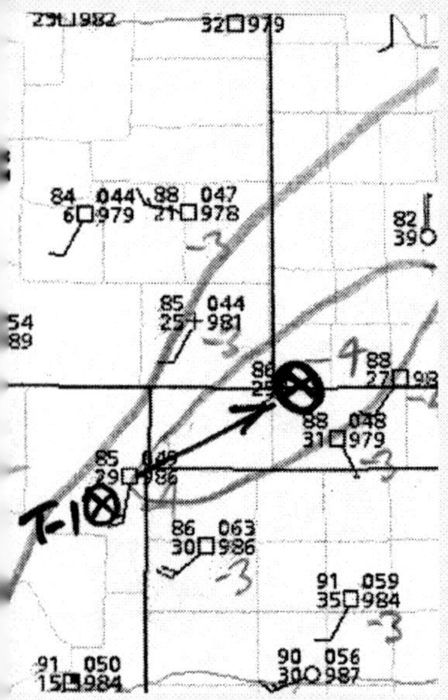

One excellent way of finding sources of small-scale upper lift is to watch 1-hour altimeter setting changes on surface observations. Here, the change values, written in hudredths of an inch, outline a core of moderate pressure falls over the Oklahoma Panhandle. The previous 1-hour pressure fall center has been plotted also, showing a progression with the upper-level winds. The standard 3-hour tendency changes of sea-level pressure should not be used unless nothing else is available. *(Tim Vasquez)*

SRH values through a layer containing a strong frontal inversion can be highly misleading. Just north of a strong front, where a frontal inversion is found aloft, the storm inflow layer is at and above the frontal inversion, which may be 1 km or more off the ground. However, SRH is almost always computed at layers whose base is at the ground. Thus, the cold northeasterly winds below the frontal inversion combine with warm southerly winds above the frontal inversion to produce nonsensical SRH values which are never realized by the storm. A little-known variation, called "effective SRH", attempts to calculate SRH above stable layers. So far this index has only been found in the SHARP software program, the SPC Hourly Mesoscale Analysis web site, and in BUFKIT. However it must be pointed out that SRH values north of a front or outflow boundary should not always be rejected. In certain cases, the "cool" air mass adjacent to the boundary is actually warm and unstable enough to be entrained into a storm updraft. In such cases, it is certainly possible to realize the standard SRH values that exist in these areas.

One thing that may become apparent to some readers is that these winds are considered in a ground-relative framework. To explain this, imagine that a weather station is reporting the low-level winds as perfectly calm. A storm is approaching this station, moving eastward at 30 kt. Fortunately you have the ability to saddle up with the storm and ride the cloud eastward. This gives you a unique perspective known as a storm-relative frame of motion. From the storm-relative perspective, the low-level winds are blowing out of the east at 30 kt! This very process is quite common, and when it occurs, we say that the storm is getting excellent storm-relative inflow. It can supply the storm with copious amounts of low-level moisture. Picture this on the hodograph. The wind dots stack up at the chart's center, and when you superimpose the storm's motion vector (east at 30 mph), a vector drawn from the tip of the storm motion vector to the wind dots illustrates the east-to-west storm-relative wind flow.

Picture a vector drawn from the tip of the storm motion vector to the dot representing upper-level winds, say at 15 km or 200 mb. This yields a quantity known as the storm-relative anvil-level winds. It indicates how fast the anvil material will blow away from the storm. For example, if the storm is moving toward the east at 20 kt and the upper level winds are from the west at 60 kt (i.e. blowing toward the

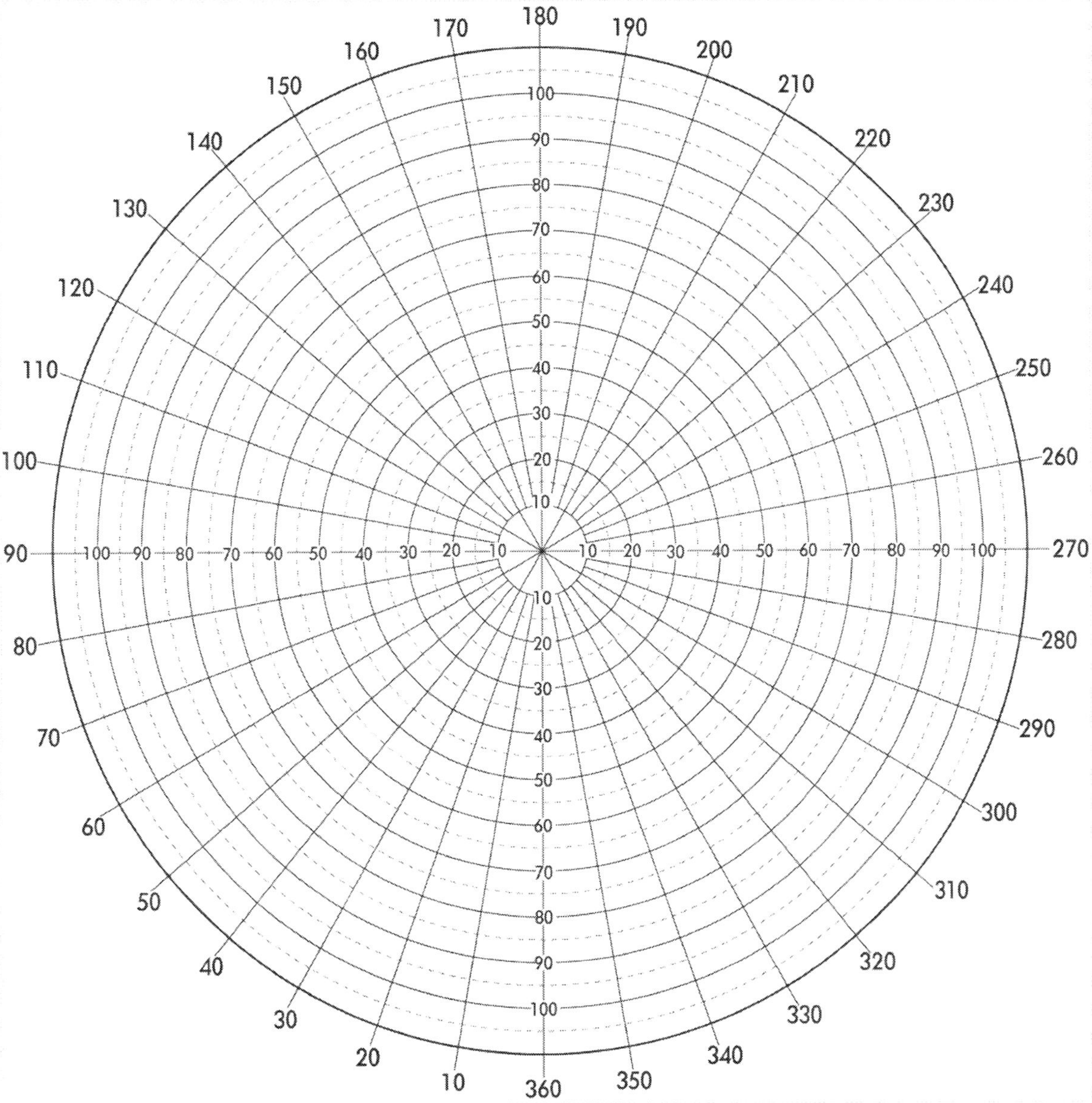

Blank hodograph. This page may be freely reproduced.

east), the storm-relative anvil winds are 40 kt. It is thought that in a storm with good anvil ventilation, the ice crystals tend to "blow" downwind away from the developing towers, preventing them from cycling back into the updraft. This lowers the efficiency of the precipitation process and results in a storm with less rain and a more "LPish" structure. Weak ventilation (common with weak upper level winds) is associated with HP modes, while strong ventilation (common with strong upper-level winds) is associated with LP modes.

Now picture a vector drawn from the tip of the storm motion vector to the dot representing mid-level winds, say at 5 km or 600 mb. This creates a quantity known as *storm-relative mid-level wind flow*. A value of at least 20 knots is thought to be important in sustaining a long-lived, non-elevated mesocyclone. Current theories hold that in a storm with strong storm-relative mid-level winds, graupel (larger ice particles) tend to get carried away from the storm. This reduces the efficiency of the downdraft, and dampens the mechanisms that occlude a cell's inflow.

Backing of the surface and low-level winds (where winds are more easterly than southerly) produces curved hodographs that are favorable for tornadic storms. Although a target area on the east side of large synoptic-scale low can be associated with such backing, the best chase days are associated with smaller scale lows called mesolows. Mesolows may not even be resolvable until hours before the

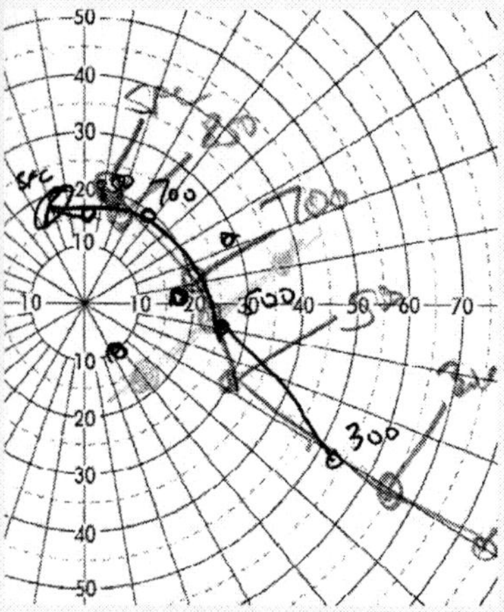

Actual working hodograph for a storm day. The afternoon wind field shown on the RUC2 model progs for a given location was plotted in pencil. A neighboring location was plotted using a pen. Using these profiles as a baseline, it is possible to understand how variations in the day's event will influence the anticipated shear and storm type. In this instance, backed surface winds would be most critical in boosting the storm-relative helicity. *(Tim Vasquez)*

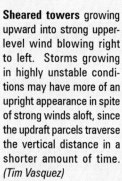

Sheared towers growing upward into strong upper-level wind blowing right to left. Storms growing in highly unstable conditions may have more of an upright appearance in spite of strong winds aloft, since the updraft parcels traverse the vertical distance in a shorter amount of time. *(Tim Vasquez)*

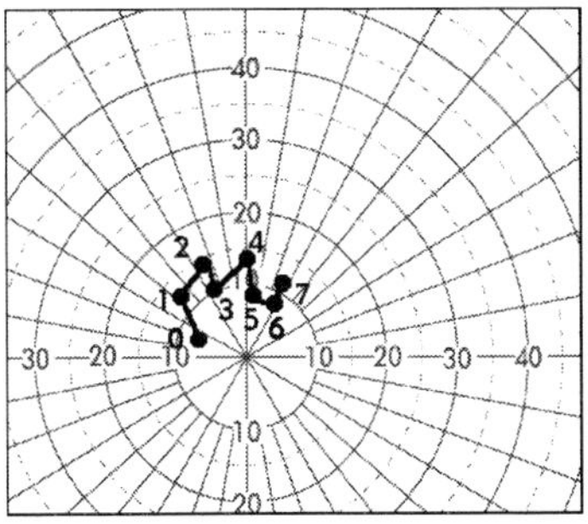

Poorly sheared environment. This hodograph plot implies that the wind changes very little from level to level.

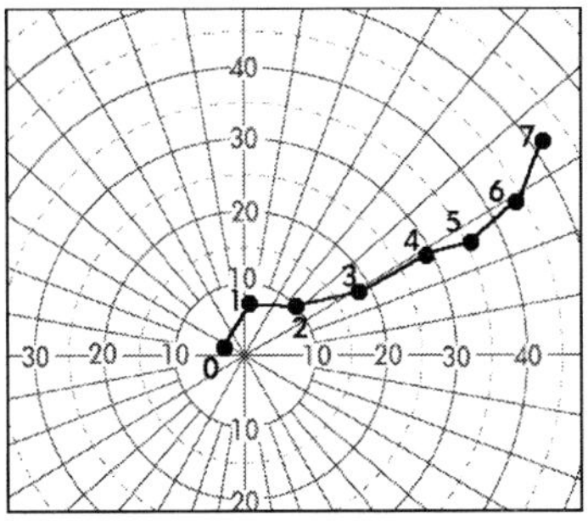

Highly sheared environment (straight-line hodograph). This hodograph shows strong change in wind speed with height, but relatively little change in direction. This is favorable for severe, nontornadic storms.

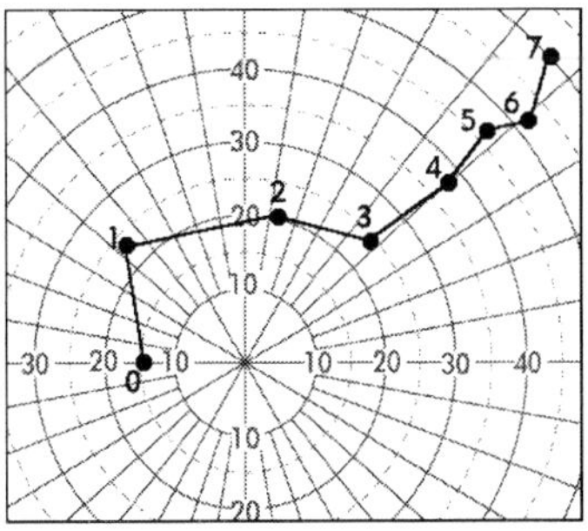

Highly sheared environment (curved hodograph). Note how there is rapid change in both the wind direction and speed in the lowest levels of the atmosphere ("turning of the hodograph"). This is favorable for tornadic thunderstorms.

weather event, and are usually not anticipated by numerical models.

Dryline

The dryline was recognized as early as the 1940s when forecasters found that "dewpoint fronts" were closely associated with areas of instability. Forecasting guidelines stipulated that storms were likely to develop along these features, however its mechanism for producing convection were not understood. The first three-dimensional picture emerged in 1956 when a P-51 Mustang airplane made measurements of the boundary as part of the Tornado Research Airplane Project (TRAP). This attracted considerable attention among researchers such as Robert Beebe, Theodore Fujita, Robert Miller, and E. McGuire, who combed through the results and published a flurry of findings beginning in 1958. This was followed in 1974 with a monumental paper by Joseph Schaefer that established the backbone of our modern-day knowledge.

In its simplest terms, the dryline is a sharp boundary that separates moist tropical air from dry continental air. The source of the moist tropical air is the Gulf of Mexico or recycled, humid eastern United States air masses, while the dry air source is in the elevated plateau region of northern Mexico, Arizona, and New Mexico. The dryline is most common during late spring afternoons in west Texas and western Kansas, though it may be found anywhere on the Great Plains depending on the weather regime. The

About forecasting

Forecasting is a love-hate relationship. You love it when you're right, you hate it when you're wrong; but the *most* important aspect is to understand why storms/tornadoes formed where they did when you were wrong.

SCOTT WEBERPAL
Janesville, WI chaser

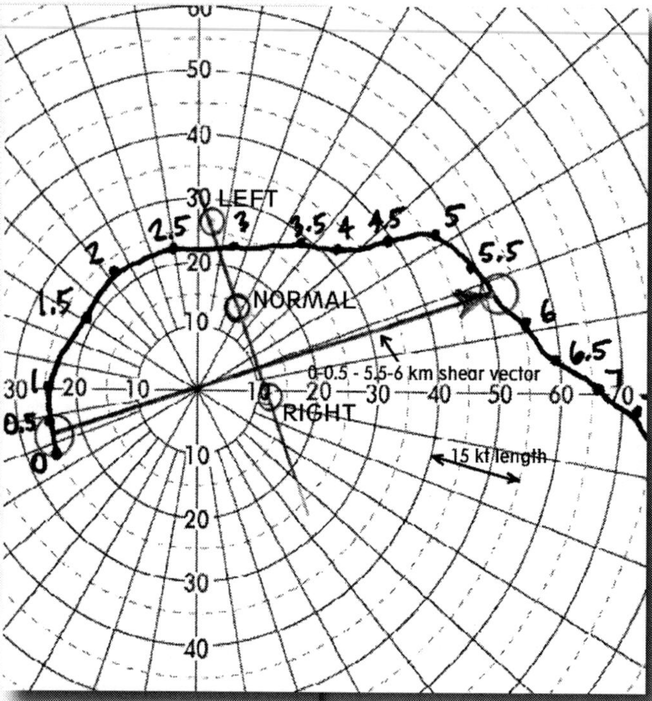

To calculate normal storm motion on a hodograph, one can simply eyeball an "equally averaged location" of all points from 0 to 6 km. The trick is then to determine deviant storm motion. The traditional rule of thumb developed by Robert Maddox in 1976 suggests that deviant right motion is 30 degrees to the right and 75% of the normal motion (in the above example, normal motion is toward 030/15 kt, so right motion would be 060/11 kt). According to a new method developed by Bunkers, Klimowski, Zeitler, Thompson, and Weisman in 1998, a shear vector is drawn from the average 0-0.5 km wind and the 5.5-6 km wind. A perpendicular line is drawn which intersects the normal motion point. The deviant storm motion points lie 15 kt on either side along this perpendicular line, as shown above. This suggests a right motion of 090/10 kt. *(Tim Vasquez)*

boundary is strongest when winds are out of the south and cyclonic flow is present: together this acts to bring trajectories from the Gulf and from the dry plateau areas to the same spot on the Great Plains.

The dryline is important because it coincides with the first spot where significant moisture can interact with upper-level lift approaching from the west. Another factor that often comes into play from an observational standpoint is theta-e: given a hypothetical moist sector of constant dewpoint and temperature value, the area closest to the dryline (i.e. in highest terrain) will have by far the highest theta-e values, and thus the most buoyant parcels with the best ability to overcome the cap.

More significantly, however, the dryline is a focus for wind field convergence, which is associated with lift. As with most linear boundaries, convergence also tends to be linear in nature, favoring multiple storms and even squall lines, unless there is a mechanism which can focus convergence more tightly in a specific areas. To find such mechanisms, forecasters look for small-scale upper-level disturbances, which are reflected in satellite pictures, profiler data, surface data (especially in altimeter setting pressure falls), and the related patterns that emerge, such as dryline bulges. Such

When looking for a dryline, a gradient of dewpoint temperature is the primary indicator. In some cases it is tempting to use wind direction as an indicator, however this should not be done unless justified by dewpoint changes (such as a fall during the past hour). Cloud lines and radar boundaries may be used to refine the position. Temperature readings, pressure tendency, relative humidity, and other indicators should never be used to place a dryline.

Front

A front is a boundary that separates two different types of air with differing temperatures. When analyzing a front, the boundary is placed on the warm side of the strongest temperature gradient. Wind shifts, pressure tendencies, and dewpoint gradients should never be used as a primary criteria for placing a front.

Outflow boundaries from thunderstorms can be thought of as fronts, though of course their source is of such a small scale that it has little impact on the synoptic-scale weather. Therefore for all intensive purposes they are grouped here with large-scale fronts.

The movement of a front is largely determined by the cool side's wind direction and air mass density. If winds in the cool air mass have a strong northerly component, the boundary will tend to move southward (either as a cold front or resembling one). If the the winds in the cool air mass have a strong southerly component, the boundary will tend to move northward (either as a warm front or resembling one). The density is largely a function of the temperature in the air mass: cold temperatures, such as from polar regions or from a recent convective system, will tend to push the boundary south, or at the very least will resist its northward movement. Strong pressure rises in the cold air mass will have a similar effect.

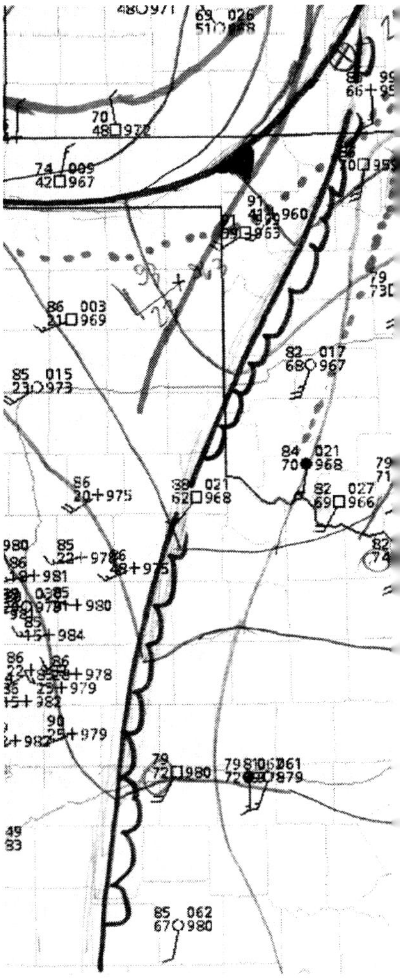

The dryline separates dry continental tropical air from moist tropical air. The line demarcated with semicircles above is the dryline. *(Tim Vasquez)*

Orientation of boundaries

The forecaster must get an idea of the expected storm movement, as well as the expected orientation of boundaries at that time. When storm movement is *parallel* to an existing boundary, this suggests that storms firing along the boundary can use it as a persistent source of convergence and possibly horizontal vorticity. If storms move *perpendicular* to a boundary, it must be assumed that the storm will fire on the boundary and then move deep into one of the air masses. If this air mass is cold and frigid, the storm will tend to weaken and die; whereas if it is warm and humid, the storm will tend to strengthen. Tornadic activity may not be likely, however, as the storm will be tracking into an area without boundaries.

The chaser must then evaluate storm-relative anvil flow. If this flow is oriented parallel to a boundary, it implies that the storm will be dumping its precipitation on other storms forming on the boundary. This is called "seeding" and it

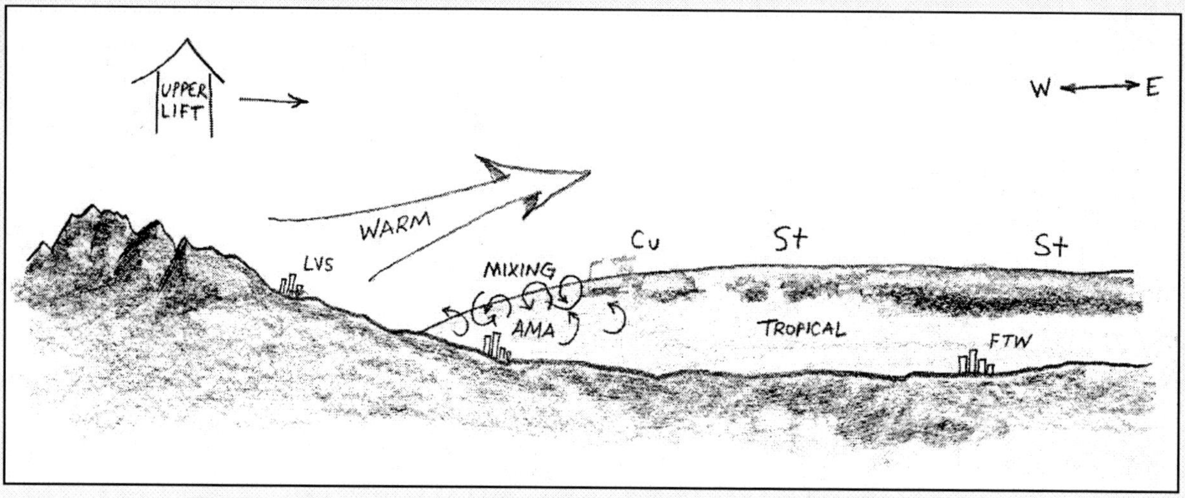

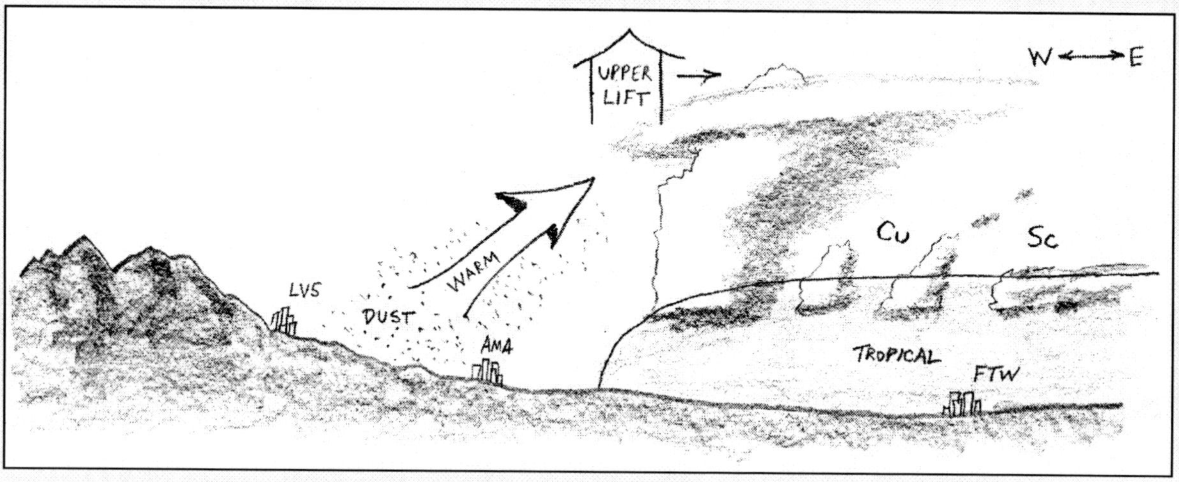

Top: Dryline cross-section in the morning hours. Note how the moist sector is like a pool overlying eastern portions of the Great Plains, with the dryline at its westernmost tip. Meanwhile warm air is being carried eastward off the higher terrain of the Rockies, riding atop the moist sector and causing a temperature inversion known as the cap, with warm air above the cap and cold air below it. The cap is located at the top of the moist layer. Vertical mixing is occurring wherever sunlight strikes the ground, and this is most prominent on the western fringes of the moist sector.

Bottom: Dryline in the late afternoon. Here we assume that a source of mid- and upper-level lift is emerging from the Rockies, and with fortunate timing it reaches the dryline at the time of peak heating. This allows the cap to break, much to the contentment of storm chasers. As the source of upper lift passes to the east, strong surface winds are ducted to the surface, raising dust through west Texas and eastern New Mexico.

weakens cells and causes the entire area of storms to consolidate into a solid, unchaseable line. This is why deep troughs with a strong southerly upper-level wind component, superimposed against a north-south dryline, are not favored among chasers. If the storm-relative anvil flow is oriented perpendicular to a boundary, it implies that the storm will be dumping its precipitation away from the boundary, preserving any storms that are occurring on the boundary.

Terrain

The role of terrain and topography in storm forecasting is often neglected in the age of pushbutton technology. Experienced chasers agree that the role of terrain is incredibly influential on a chase forecast. Terrain interferes with the atmosphere's ability to maintain a balanced, geostrophic wind pattern, and the response is through unusual accelerations and vertical motions. Most of all, an upslope flow forces parcels to rise, and if there is enough lift this can overcome a capping inversion which is are preventing initiation.

The primary topographic feature in the central United States, of course, is the Rocky Mountains. This north-south mountain range is a double-edged sword, because it helps channel good moisture northward. On the same token it allows detrimental cold air to channel far southward, particularly during the cool season, rather than diffusing across the northern United States. It can easily be seen why the Great Plains has such an unusually cold winter for its given

The gently rolling terrain that comprises most of the Great Plains. Shown here is the survey marker that identifies the northeast corner of the Texas Panhandle. Most of the photo and the background is Oklahoma; the two ocotillo plants at the right are in Texas. *(Tim Vasquez)*

A 1956 feature in Nebraska

- This instability line developed just ahead of a sharply defined low-level dewpoint front. This is in agreement with the findings of Fawbush and Miller.

- The line developed in an area of relatively high moisture content but some 100 miles west of the axis of the moisture ridge.

- The moisture at the 700 mb level in the vicinity of the line development was apparently increased from below, in agreement with findings of Beebe and Bates.

- The line developed in an area where the local temperature increase at 800 mb was not due to advection as evidenced from 0900 CST charts. This warming was not noted at 700 mb.

ROBERT G. BEEBE
An Instability Line Development As Observed by the Tornado Research Airplane, 1958

latitude, compared to warmer climates such as Morocco, Italy, Israel, and China.

The primary feature on the Great Plains is the Caprock Escarpment of west Texas. This north-south feature directly provides a source of enhanced upslope flow. The deep Palo Duro Canyon southeast of Amarillo, which is part of the Caprock Escarpment, is thought to act as a funnel for moisture or inflow which storms in the Panhandle often feed upon.

Numerical models

Needless to say, we can't go further without a discussion of numerical models. These forecast aids are actually quite useful in a proper context. They provide an unparalleled overview of what's occurring in data-sparse areas, and tend to do a good job at predicting the future location of temperature, moisture, and wind fields across a threat area.

Most numerical model forecasts in use by American forecasters are produced by NOAA's National Centers for Environmental Prediction (NCEP) in Camp Springs, Maryland. The agency hosts some of the most powerful supercomputers in the world and has been an innovator in prediction technology.

The basic NCEP forecasting system for the United States is referred to as the NAM (North American Mesoscale model). This is really a framework that hosts individual prediction models. Up until 2006, for example, the NAM was made up of the Eta model, but was replaced with the cutting-edge WRF (Weather Research and Forecasting) model. It is run four times a day and forecasts out to 84 hours in the future. It's used to get a general look at a forecast situation and evaluate severe weather prospects in the 12 to 72 hour range.

For fast-breaking mesoscale forecasting, NCEP offers a model called the RUC (Rapid Update Cycle). It was introduced in the mid-1990s and runs hourly, ingesting all of the latest data. As a chase day unfolds, the RUC is the model to turn to. The RUC is also run by the NOAA Forecast Systems Laboratory (FSL) which posts detailed maps on its RUC website.

Finally, NCEP runs a global model framework called the GFS (Global Forecast System), known as the MRF or aviation model in the 1990s. It forecasts out to 384 hours (16 days) in the future, and is preferred for looking at chase

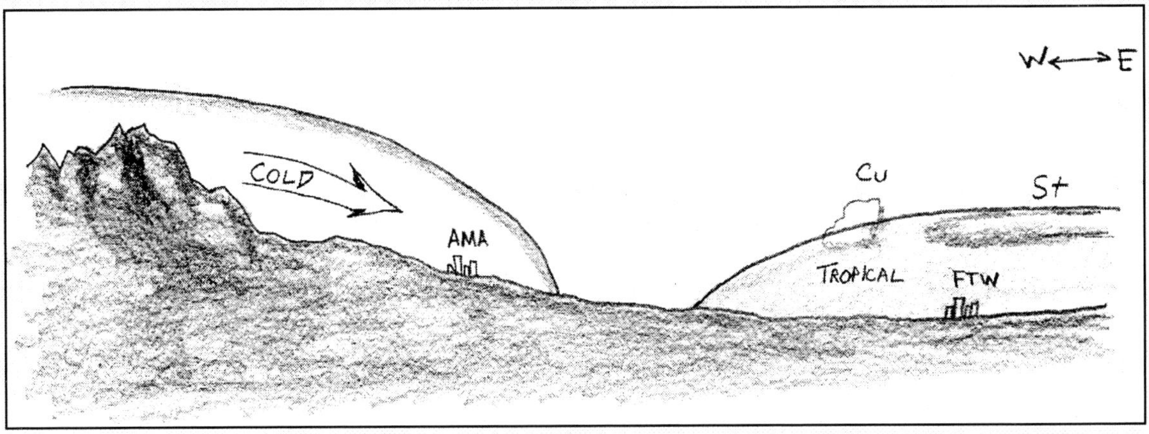

Above: A classic early-spring situation on the Great Plains, particularly in March and April, is when a strong Pacific cold front emerges from the Rockies. Quite often there is southerly flow ahead of the Pacific system, bringing tropical moisture and high dewpoint temperatures north through the Great Plains.

Below: About six hours later, the cold front reaches the dryline. The strong low-level convergence at the surface is now tapping into rich moisture, and the convergence is sufficient to erode the cap. This produces a linear "wall" of storms along the cold front: a squall line. This isn't the best scenario for storm chasers, who must then make the best of a 2-D squall line or head to the southern end of the line ("tail end charlie") where the cap strength dominates low-level convergence. A storm at this position isn't seeded by upstream storms and tends to have more access to moisture, so its odds of producing severe weather are somewhat enhanced, though not by much. At this point, the dryline has been overtaken and no longer exists.

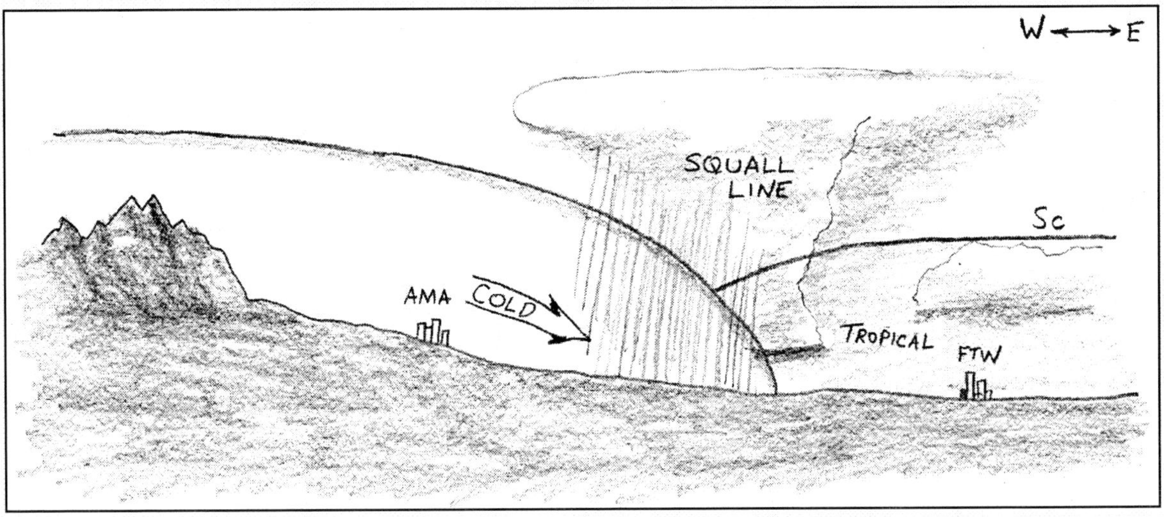

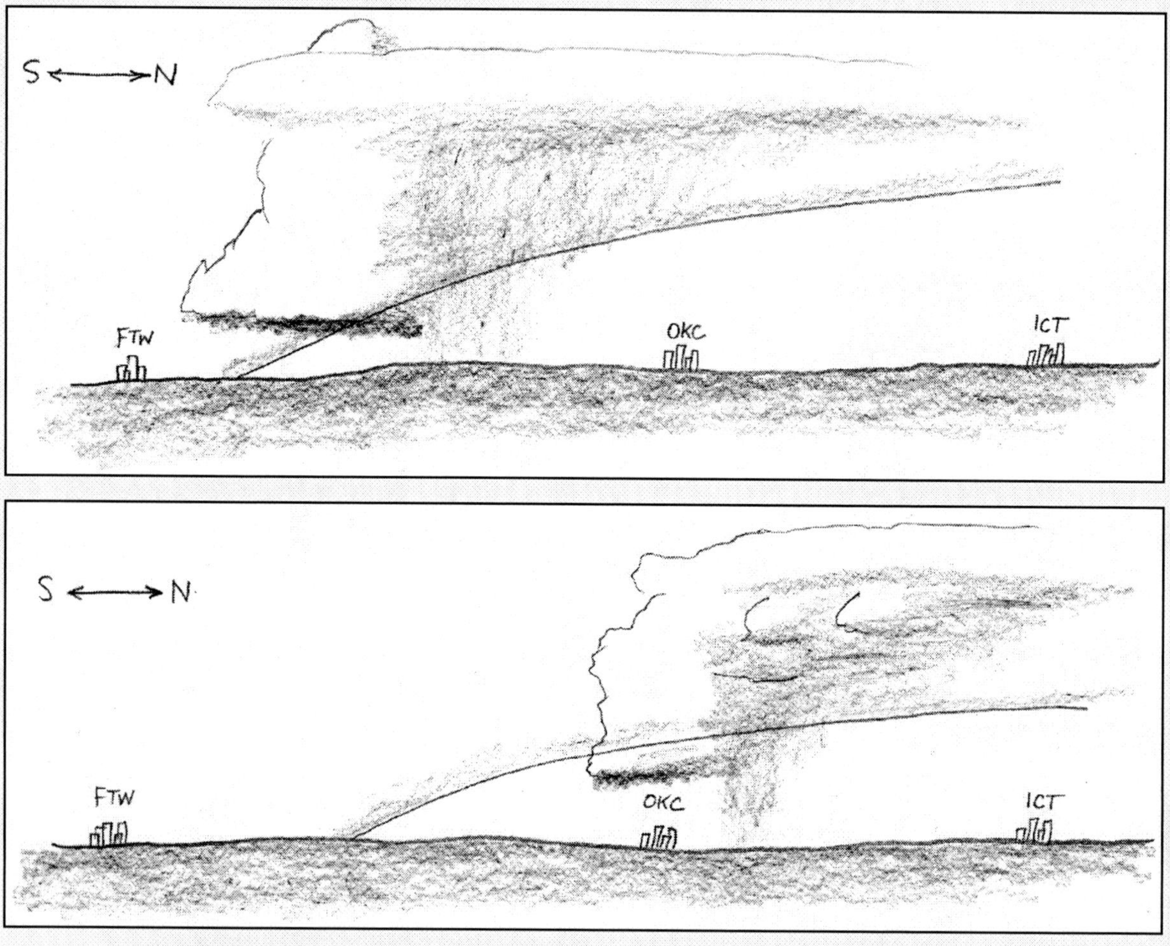

(Top) Cross-section along warm front in the afternoon hours, looking north-south along Interstate 35. Lift along the warm front has allowed a thunderstorm to form.

(Bottom) If mid- and upper-level winds are blowing south to north, the storm will tend to be carried rapidly northward. Riding into deeper and deeper cold air, the buoyancy of parcels entering the storm decreases and the storm weakens.

potential in the 3 to 16 day time frame. It should be noted, though, that accuracy for weather system placement diminishes rapidly beyond 5 to 7 days.

There are other sources of model data besides the NCEP products. Environment Canada runs its own model called the GEM (Global Environmental Multiscale), which has coverage well into the Plains. Output from the European ECMWF and British UKMET (or "Unified Model") is largely restricted but the hemispheric fields of height, thickness, and sea-level pressure are widely available and like the GFS are highly useful tools for planning a chase schedule a week in advance. Some research institutions run the MM5 and WRF for special areas of interest. Hobbyists can even run the WRF on a robust computer with Linux.

Model output, particularly in data-sparse areas, must be verified with actual data such as satellite imagery. Numerical models excel in the forecast time range beyond 12 hours, however as the convective event comes closer, forecasters must begin relying on actual observed data. And within a couple of hours of the model start time, model accuracy is poor due to the effects of "model spinup", the temporary mathematical noise which quickly dampens after the first few hours. This can produce spurious artifacts in the model charts.

Numerical models are good for evaluating upper level conditions on a chase day, but vertical products such as forecast soundings have, so far, proved theirselves to be poor tools, giving inadequate resolution. Forecasters must reach a healthy compromise between proper use of models and use of actual observed data or one's own intuition.

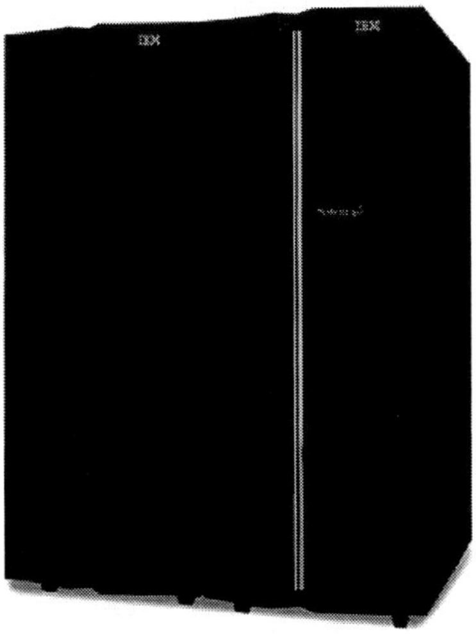

The IBM p5 supercomputer which currently runs most of the world's most powerful weather models, including at the National Center for Environmental Prediction where the NAM (WRF) and GFS are produced. *(IBM)*

The use of models

If I look at anything concerning models past 16Z (late morning) on Day 1, it is usually the surface pressure analysis from mesoscale models. The MesoEta and RUC often have a better forecast of sub-synoptic lows or mesolows than the regular ETA, AVN, etc. These models don't always catch these important mesoscale events, but they will do so far more often than the macro models.

For a few years, I was believing in looking closely at Day 1 instability and/or shear forecasts. I still look at them, but the mesoscale and macroscale models have misled me terribly at times. A good example was May 29, 2001 when I made a chase decision based on RUC2 output. The model was dreadfully wrong and had CAPE values much too high! Of course, we saw a great storm, but got skunked with the tornado being well north of us.

If I had done careful analysis, I (hopefully) would have seen an old boundary backing into the Panhandle from east to west during the morning, to the NE of AMA, and maybe would have had a chance at catching the Hwy 60 tornado that just missed White Deer. But I got lazy and wanted to believe the RUC model.

Although a chaser will invariably look at model data on a chase day, it is best to wrap things up with observational data, and stick to observations during the afternoon.

ALAN MOLLER
Fort Worth, TX chaser

Black Hills
Badlands
Shale Plains
Pine Ridge Region
Nebraska Panhandle
Sand Hills
Loess Hills
Till Prairies
Front Range
Palmer Divide
Central High Plains
Smoky Hills
Osage Plains
Flint Hills
The Ozarks
Raton Basin
Red Hills
Raton Mesa
Oklahoma Panhandle
Boston Mountains
Texas Panhandle
Wichita Mountains
Ouachita Mountains
Arbuckles
Mescalero Escarpment
Llano Estacado
Caprock Escarpment
Red River Valley
Northwest Texas
Texas Southern Plains
The Big Country
North Central Texas
West Texas
Far West Texas
Trans-Pecos
Pecos River Valley
Central Texas
Edwards Plateau
The Hill Country
Big Bend

It must also be pointed out that it is common for models to miss key details that become important at the time of storm initiation. The fault is not necessarily in the model but due to the lack of "hard data" in remote regions such in the southwest deserts and off the Pacific Coast. On May 3, 1999, for example, the Eta model failed to detect a strong jet max in New Mexico that became a key player in the evolution of the central Oklahoma tornado outbreak.

Long range chase forecasting

No aspect of storm chasing entails more black magic, witchcraft, and sorcery than the prediction of chase prospects greater than than 72 hours into the future. The atmosphere is a nonlinear system whose smallest motions cannot be resolved, so *even the best of numerical model forecast solutions always diverge from the real atmosphere.* The smaller details typically diverge in a matter of hours, while larger systems diverge in days.

Consider that it is a Sunday morning in Shamrock, Texas, and we are wondering about a possible storm at this location on Friday. At this time, the moisture that will arrive Friday is currently over Jamaica, the upper-level air is meandering through Korea, and the upper-level disturbance we are expecting will not be born until Wednesday west of British Columbia. It can be seen that assembling these ingredients with any degree of accuracy is a monumental undertaking, and requires an exceptional amount of accuracy in sampling the atmosphere across all of these regions! Unfortunately our sampling is spotty at best. Consider that an observation represents the state of a cubic kilometer surrounding it. Even within the dense observational network in the United States, there are 100 million cubic kilometers of troposphere above the nation, but only 2000 of these are being sampled, even including surface and radiosonde observations. It is clear we are putting very rough approximations into the numerical forecast models!

These approximations are further hampered by the effects of deterministic chaos, as theorized in 1963 by MIT researcher Edward Lorenz. For example, a camcorder box falls off a truck outside a Sony factory near Tokyo Sunday afternoon. The stir of air created by the falling box results in a chain of subtle atmospheric motions, which in this case is amplified into increasingly greater scales of motion. Finally, this motion imparts momentum into an upper-level

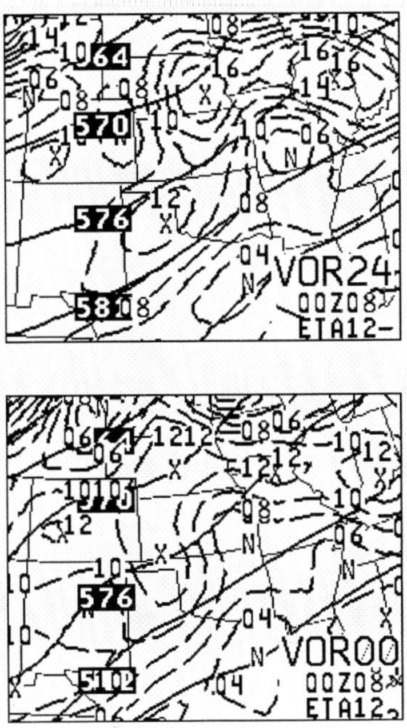

Comparision of 500 mb ETA model output for the May 7, 2002 supercells in southwest Kansas. The top panel is the 24 hour forecast and the bottom panel is the 00 hour forecast. The differences in the shape of the height field and radical differences in the vorticity contours hint at the difficulty the models have resolving and forecasting small-scale details.

Facing page: Physiographic regions of the central United States (sans-serif fonts) often used in meteorology references, and general geographic and cultural regions (serif fonts). The topography has been enhanced, revealing that the Great Plains is not washboard-flat. Texas' large size and irregular shape has produced a rather sizable number of geographical terms.

disturbance which arrives in Texas Friday. The increase in synoptic-scale lift wipes out the cap early in the day, resulting in squall lines! The disappointed chasers settle for this, patiently videotaping the squall line with their Sony camcorders. Farfetched? Probably. But trillions of subtle atmospheric motions all over the globe are constantly interacting with each other in ways that can't be accurately predicted or measured.

With that caveat made clear, there are long-term planetary-scale patterns which *theoretically might* make it possible to guess at the *general* type of chasing that can be expected over a given week, and what part of the country the target area might be in. This tantalizing prospect keeps many chasers busy swirling the tea leaves and gazing into the crystal balls as spring approaches. Since these techniques dominate conversations in the winter season and during bust periods, and may certainly one day unlock a few doors into the future, it certainly deserves an overview in this book. But once again, be warned — as of this writing there is yet no technique for reliably predicting chase weather!

The long wave pattern, which is the pattern of large-scale waves across the hemisphere, is responsible for the weather *regime* that affects a forecast area. When a large long wave ridge occupies the western half of the United States, the Rocky Mountain region is hot and dry. Cool air masses tend to move southward out of Canada through the Plains, providing northerly flow and keeping moisture out of the region. In weaker versions of this pattern, frontal boundaries may stall or good moisture may advect into the Plains, resulting in northwesterly flow storms. However when a large long wave trough

A random comparison of 12 hr NAM forecast sounding (top) and actual sounding (bottom) for the same time and place. The differences between the two are rather significant, with almost five degrees of temperature in the mid-levels and a drastic overestimation of forecast low-level moisture. This also sheds light on some of the errors that might be seen in the regular horizontal forecast fields. Errors like these can have a dramatic effect on storm prediction. It illustrates the importance of using models only as selective tools, and not as a template for the day's forecast. *(NCEP and CoD)*

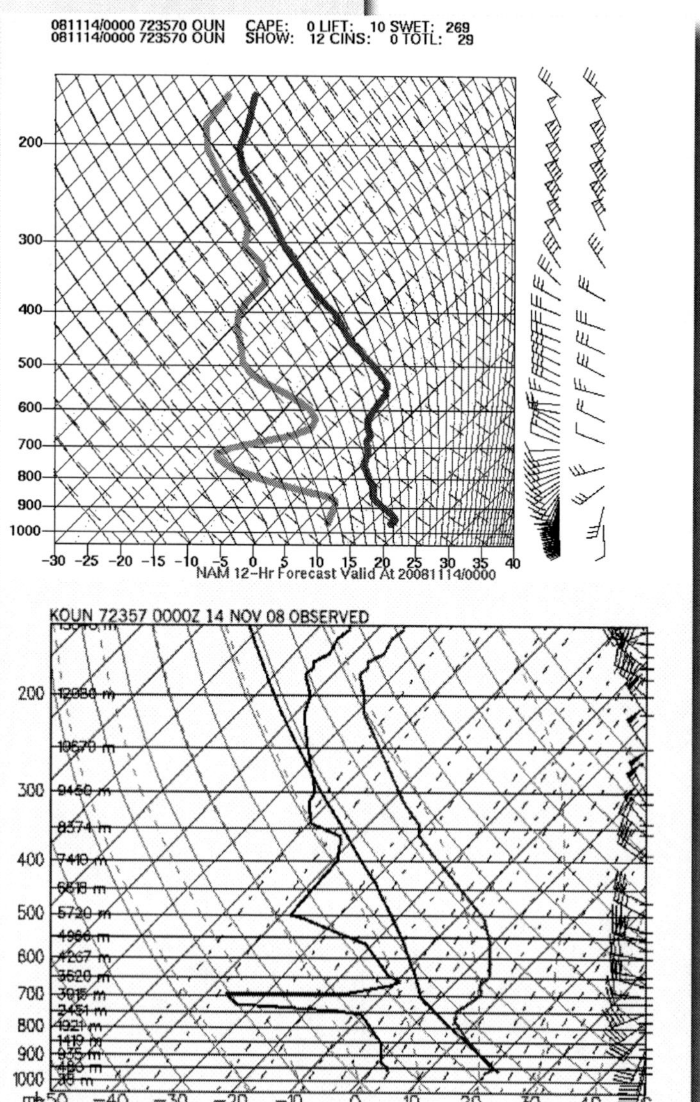

is in the western United States, the Rocky Mountain region is cool and stormy. Upper-level disturbances and warm moist southerly flow begin affecting the Great Plains.

Split flow jet patterns may degenerate into blocks. A block is any large-scale long-wave pattern that causes the normal west-to-east progression of long waves to become interrupted. Blocks can last for weeks or even months! One feature that is a signature of a developing block is the *Hudson Bay vortex.* This is a deep barotropic low, usually centered on northern Hudson Bay, which is produced by the occlusion of large frontal systems as they move northward along the Labrador coast. It is usually associated with a meridional pattern that results in slow progression and ultimately blocking of the long-wave pattern across North America. The *omega block* occurs when a cutoff high develops. The configuration of the polar jet, as seen on maps, resembles the Greek letter Ω (omega) as it circumvents this high. The *rex block* occurs when an upper-level high is north of an upper-level low. One common mode of occurrence is when a strong cutoff low over California retrogresses westward so that it is south of a cutoff high in the northeastern Pacific Ocean.

El Niño (warm episode, ENSO, El Niño Southern Oscillation) is the result of unusually weak trade winds in the tropics, which stalls the normal east-to-west fetch of equatorial Pacific water. This inhibits upwelling of cool water in the eastern equatorial Pacific. The result is warmer than normal sea surface temperatures in that area. El Niño years bring a strong, dominant west-east branch of the subtropical jet into the southern United States that skirts the Gulf Coast. Most forecasters agree that the enhanced upper-level flow does bring an increase in severe weather along the Gulf Coast into Florida. Preliminary research has shown no real correlation with El Niño and with Great Plains tornado numbers. A couple of studies have correlated a decrease in large, violent tornado outbreaks with El Niño years. There is also some unquantified speculation that: (A) during the onset of El Niño there are increased chase prospects; (B) during El Niño Great Plains chase prospects are generally poor, especially in the southern Plains; and (C) during a decline of El Niño, very bad chase prospects are in store.

La Niña (cold episode, LNSO, La Niña Southern Oscillation) occurs when unusually strong trade winds occur throughout the tropical Pacific. This creates a very strong

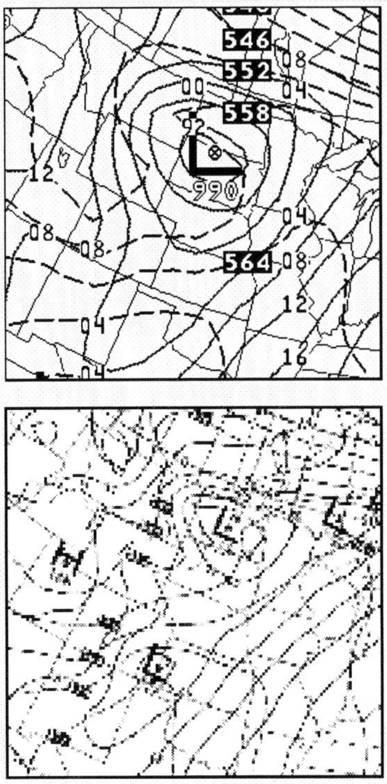

Comparision of 120 hr MRF forecast (top) with 00 hr initialized field (below) of surface pressure and 1000-500 mb thickness. What appeared to be a strong baroclinic low in South Dakota actually ended up being a slightly weaker system in North Dakota. Strong troughing in the southern High Plains actually turned into a well-defined closed low. Medium range models such as the MRF are often good at handling the overall pattern, but key details such as these don't emerge accurately until just before the weather event.

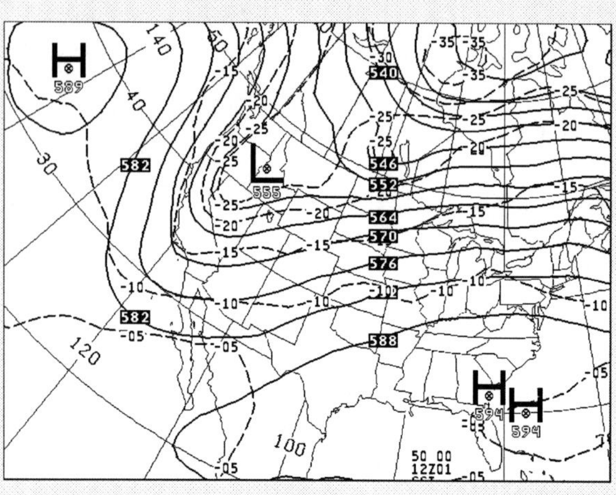

The "trough west ridge east" pattern as seen on a 500 mb chart. This type of long wave pattern is associated with a period of stormy weather on the Great Plains.

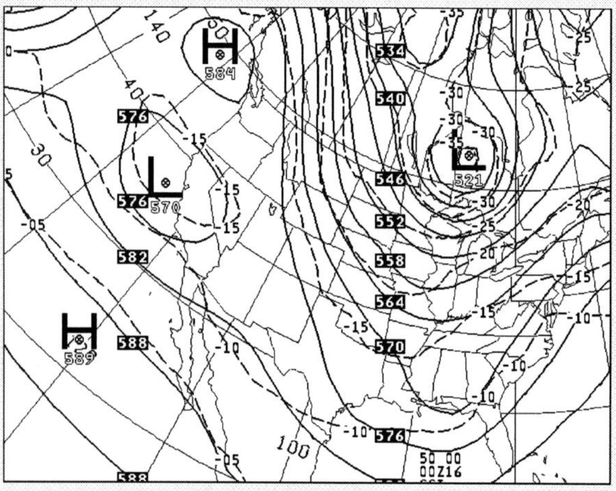

The "trough east ridge west" pattern as seen on a 500 mb chart. This type of long wave pattern is associated with a period of sunny skies, quiet weather, and lack of storms on the Great Plains. This chart also shows a blocking pattern: a rex block, signified by the broad low off the California coast and buried in the long wave ridge.

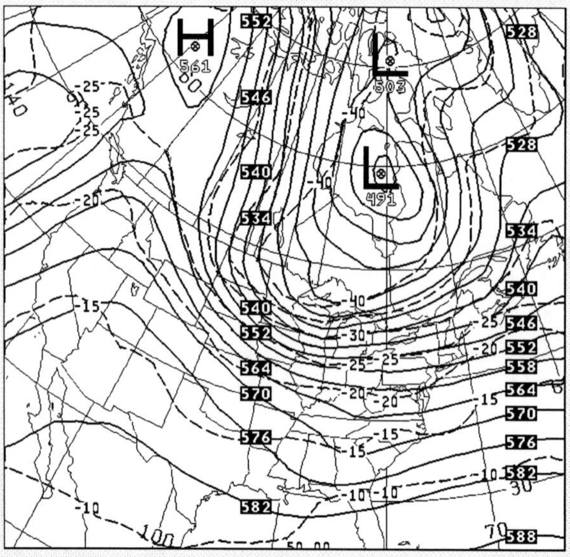

The dreaded Hudson Bay vortex pattern. It is usually associated with west coast ridging, and since it tends to remain stationary, it locks up the long wave pattern across North America. Poor chase prospects may continue for weeks.

east-to-west fetch across the equatorial Pacific that promotes very strong upwelling of cold water in the eastern equatorial areas of the Pacific Ocean. Preliminary research suggests that La Niña has no bearing on the total number of tornadoes that occur, however La Niña years seem to be associated with violent tornadoes and large tornado outbreaks. The mega-tornado outbreaks of Palm Sunday 1965; April 3, 1974; and May 3, 1999, were associated with a La Niña event. However this finding has not been well established.

Internet data sources

Once you have your Internet connection, what can you look at? Use your browser! The Internet is brimming with professional-grade weather charts if you know where to look.

For model data and surface maps, UCAR Weather Page <*www.rap.ucar.edu/weather*> is a longtime favorite, though College of DuPage Weather <*weather.cod.edu/analysis*> has rapidly gained popularity, especially for its high-resolution satellite with roads and isentropic charts. The place to go for your most demanding model needs is Earl Barker's Weather Page <*www.wxcaster.com*>. And SPC <*www.spc.noaa.gov*> has outlooks, discussions, mesoanalysis plots, event reports, and much more, especially at its mesoanalysis page <*www.spc.noaa.gov/exper/mesoanalysis*>. For model data, go right to the horse's mouth at <*www.emc.ncep.noaa.gov*> and get some cool high-res imagery at <*wwwt.emc.ncep.noaa.gov/mmb/mpyle/cent4km/v2*> (note the extra letter on the "www" part). OU's models can be found at <*downdraft.caps.ou.edu/wx*>.

A little money does make the forecasting process easier. WeatherTap <*www.weathertap.com*> ($7/mo) has been a longtime favorite of storm chasers since its radar pages are fast, refresh regularly, and take up little bandwidth. They offer a cutting-edge data viewer called RadarLab HD, but its bandwidth requirements do not make it well-suited for 2G cellular connections.

For those that want power capabilities, look to on-board software programs. GRLevel3 <*www.grlevelx.com*> ($80) and its high-res brother GrLevel2 ($80) are simple but powerful radar viewers, arguably the best out there. SwiftWX <*www.swiftwx.com*> is another radar viewer offers many more bells and whistles, but has recurring charges ($13 to $15 per month).

A personal favorite

My favorite resource for forecasting weather is the College of Dupage numerical models. Everything is laid out very nicely, easily able to switch between products, and the products are very easy to read.

DEAN BARON
New Brighton, MN chaser

To view high-resolution surface and upper-air weather maps, a good jack-of-all trades program is the author's own Digital Atmosphere software *<www.weathergraphics.com>* ($89 to $199), a sort of "gentleman's AWIPS system". Though not as proficient with radar as GRLevel3 and SwiftWX, it is the heavyweight of surface and upper-air chart creation. It can produce ultra-high resolution skew-T diagrams for precision cap forecasting, and can import radar from places like Canada and Mexico. It can also get you started on new upper air chart packages during the 1300-1400 UTC period, a time that many Internet sites still have old upper air charts. Digital Atmosphere data is downloaded automatically from a variety of free sources.

For detailed sounding analysis, see RAOB *<www.weathergraphics.com/raob>*. It offers not only interactive skew T diagrams, a major step up from the old-school SHARP program,but also provides unbeatable hodograph analysis. Prices start at $100.

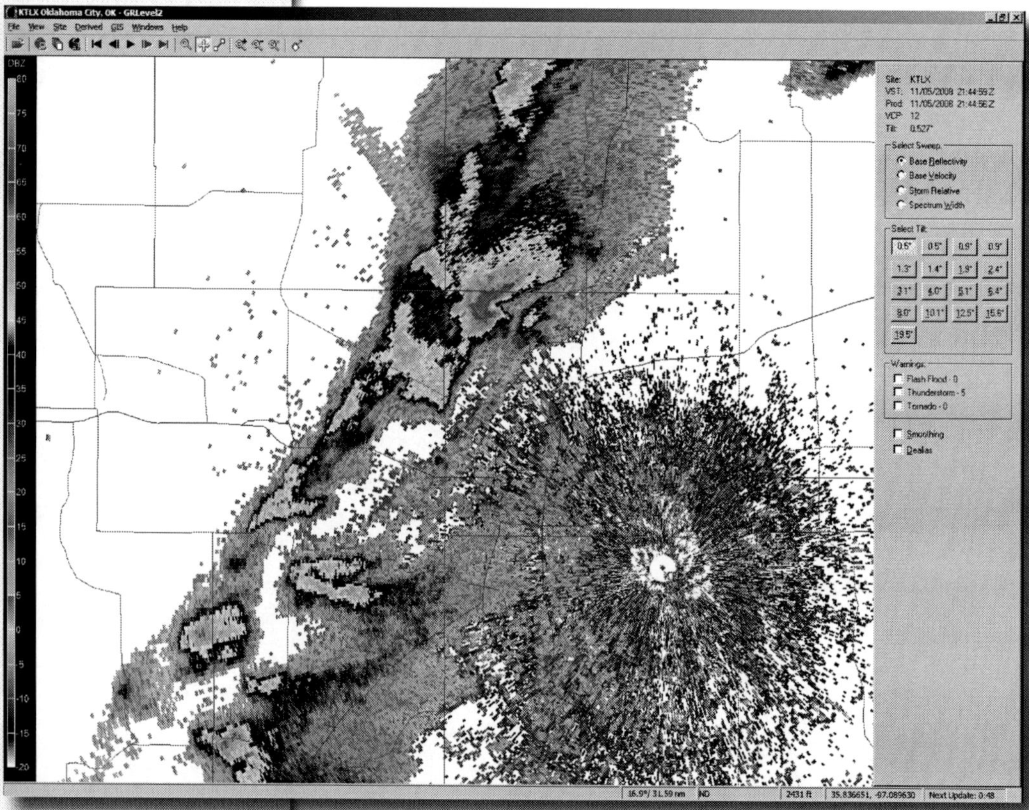

GRLevel2 (shown here) and GRLevel3 are two tools widely used by chasers. The GRLevel3 software lends itself to bandwidth-friendly performance at the cost of coarser imagery.

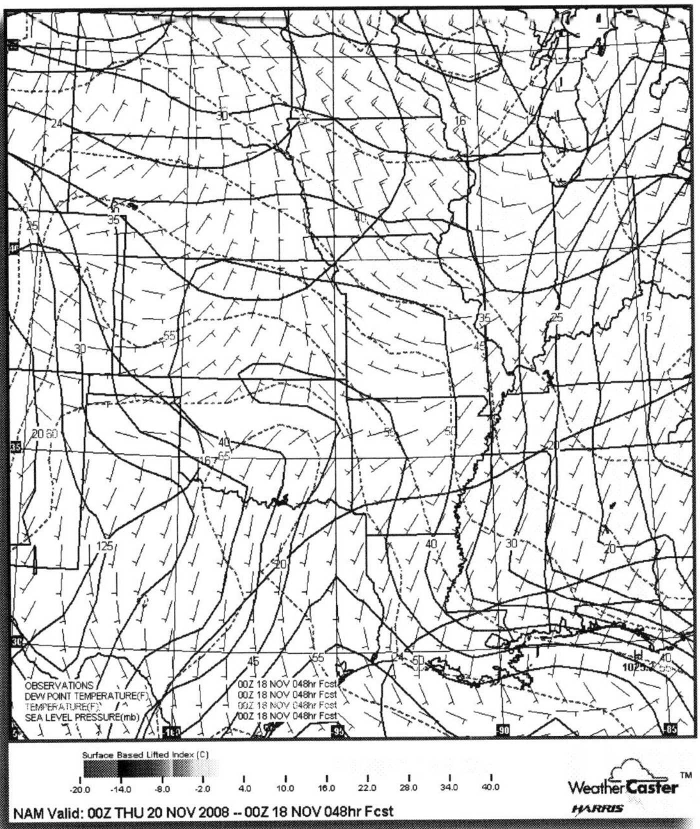

Earl Barker's model website (www.wxcaster.com) has rapidly become a favorite of storm chasers, and a good alternate to NCEP's website. It features numerous extremely detailed numerical model charts.

Chasers Allan Rosenberg and Casey Crosbie stop to evaluate the sky. Visual analysis is very much a part of the forecasting process. *(Chris Kridler/skydiary.com)*

CHAPTER FIVE
STRATEGY

Even with the best forecasting knowledge, the best data in the field, and with years of experience in the field, a chaser is doomed to failure without a good grasp of field strategy. The Merriam-Webster dictionary defines strategy as "the art of devising or employing plans or stratagems toward a goal". Indeed, being on the road requires chasers to think ahead, devise plans, and use clever techniques to get the safest and most spectacular view possible. Questions must be considered such as, "does the atmosphere look right?", "is this the best road?", and "how will the storm evolve while I am near it?"

Chase area targeting

After the last glance at hard data, the chaser is usually on the road, without access to further data, and must immediately be a careful observer of the sky. The information gleaned from that look at hard data must be remembered and integrated with what is being seen. For many chasers, much of this draws on years of intimate knowledge of meteorology. However even beginners can pick out skies that don't look good for chase activity. All that remains is to compare these observations against the building blocks of thunderstorm development.

Moisture. Are cloud bases relatively low, even during the afternoon? This indicates that there is plenty of moisture in the boundary layer. Do you have a sling psychrometer? Calculate the dewpoint and see if it's consistent with the readings you expect in your locale. Is the dryline moving faster or slower than expected? A slow dryline movement indicates that the moist sector is still quite deep. Can you see hills thirty or more miles away? If you're in the moist sector, a lot of your moisture is likely getting mixed out!

Instability. Are cumulus towers rising vigorously during the afternoon? This is one of the foremost signs of good instability. Are cumulus clouds shrinking? This probably

Favorite chase spot

Selecting a favorite spot when chasing is like choosing your best cat, child, or song. It is difficult to do. I will say that traveling on open roads with great views and no telephone poles are my favorite. Here is my top ten list of favorite roads I have chased on:

1) Rt. 72 from Folsom to Raton, NM

2) Rt. 207 from Post to Spearman, TX

3) Rt. 10 from La Junta to Walsenberg, CO

4) Rt. 249 from Hagerman to Malijamar, NM

5) Rt. 160 from Medicine Lodge, KS to Trinidad, CO

6) Rt. 27 from Elkart to Wheeler, KS

7) Rt. 70 between San Angelo and Perryton, TX

8) Rt. 214 from Seminole to Adrian, TX

9) Rt. 94 from Childress to Matador

10) Rt. 23 from near Canadian, TX to Meade, KS

This list does not include all the great vacation roads that I have been on.

TIM MARSHALL
Flower Mound, TX chaser

indicates a loss of heating. Are high clouds invading the sky? They may cut down on heating.

Lift. Synoptic-scale lift can't be seen, but its presence is often revealed by the appearance of altocumulus castellanus (or "accas" for short). These look like miniature cumulus clouds at a much higher level in the atmosphere than regular cumulus clouds, and are a sign that large-scale lift is taking place, eroding the cap. Can you find a dryline, an outflow boundary, or a front once you're out in the field? Sometimes you can detect these features as you drive, however most of the time it takes sharp eyes to find clues to their existence. In many cases the boundaries are revealed by a cluster or a line of enhanced cumulus growth, especially during the afternoon hours. This can be spotted many miles away and lead to to your target area.

Shear. Are cumulus clouds breaking off at the tops, with these bits blowing rapidly eastward? This indicates that there are strong winds aloft. This is a good sign, though too much of this for a given amount of instability and forcing can keep the atmosphere completely capped all day. Compare the surface winds, the movement of the bottom of the cumulus, and the movement of the top of the cumulus. If they are moving different directions at different speeds, this indicates strong helicity is present in the atmosphere. It can serve as a visual confirmation that wind fields are excellent for severe storm development.

Another consideration is whether the patterns have *changed*. Morning convective outlooks, model forecasts, and chaser expectations may become outdated by the afternoon

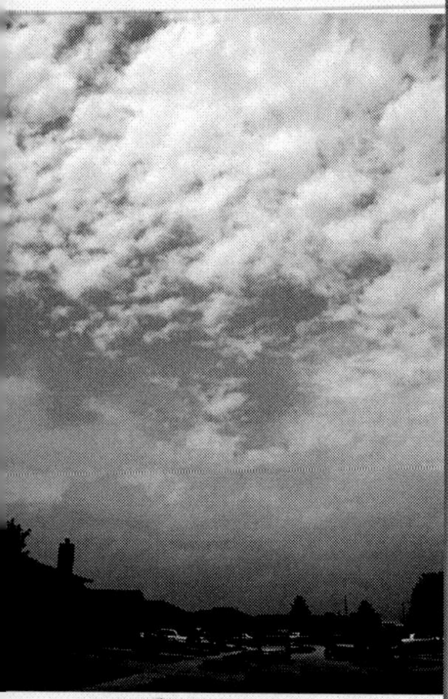

Altocumulus castellanus, often called by its abbreviation "ACCAS", is a sign that there may be strong instability above the capping inversion. In the distance is a layer of lower stratocumulus, representing the low-level moisture field, which is beginning to break up in the late morning hours. *(Tim Vasquez)*

Sounding success. Being familiar with the essentials of stability is a key to good forecasting. *(art by David Hoadley)*

hours. Keep close tabs on wind directions, moisture, and cloud layers to see how the atmosphere may be changing. This is even more important when you didn't get a good look at any data. Don't get caught waiting for a storm to fire, ignoring the dry northwest winds that have been ruffling your hair all afternoon!

Finally, be attentive to wind direction! If you can't stop, keep an eye out for flags, which are most common near car dealerships, apartment complexes, and public buildings. Debris blowing across the road may also yield directional clues. Wind backing with time (i.e. originating from the south, then the east) across a threat area suggests increasing shear, strong pressure falls, and increasing moisture depth. Conversely, veering winds suggest decreasing shear, weak pressure falls, and a decline in the moisture. Strong veering of winds may require repositioning to the east.

Finally, if there is a choice of target areas, you may want to consider rooting for the underdog and taking a chance on the less-favored area. While this presents more opportunity for failure, it allows you to avoid the chase crowds and, in some cases, you'll get to document something that very few others will!

Picking a local viewing site

On a day where you have a lot of free time, scout out the local area for rural viewing spots. Look for spots on ridges that are far away from houses and trees, away from traffic flow, and which are not fenced in at night. Gravel access roads to pumpjacks, microwave towers, and crop fields work quite well. From then on, anytime a storm rolls into the local area, you have a selection of perfect viewing sites to choose from.

TIM VASQUEZ

Approaching the storm

When the stratified mass of an anvil cloud begins spreading across a blue sky, it represents a turning point in the events of the day. It means that a cumulus cloud has broken the cap long enough for it to grow into a massive cumulonimbus cloud: a giant updraft, its tops glaciating and being carried off by the upper-level winds. This does not guarantee thunderstorms — in some cases insufficient shear or forcing can allow the cap to choke off the updraft, causing the cloud to dissolve from the ground upward. Instead of targeting the first cumulonimbus cloud that develops, a chaser should examine the cloud and its anvil cloud for important clues.

Look at the main updraft of the cumulonimbus cloud (not the anvil) — are

A potentially dangerous updraft base, complete with a large, low updraft area and a tail cloud. This particular storm, however, did not go on to produce any significant severe weather. Extreme vigilance is required when approaching well-developed updraft bases. Photographed 28 July 2007 near McCook, Nebraska. *(Dean Cosgrove / chasetours.com)*

its tops soft and mushy or are they rock-hard? A rock-hard top indicates a healthy cumulonimbus cloud. Is the anvil showing some signs of backshear, where it tends to spread *into the upper-level flow*? This indicates a strong updraft that is spreading in all directions, even into the prevailing upper-level wind. Is the cumulonimbus cloud growing in a viable target area? If you're positioned along a warm front, just south of a frigid air mass, a cloud that is growing to your north does not represent a wise chase opportunity. How large and bulky is the anvil? This can give you a good idea of how much moisture is being lofted by the updraft. A thin, narrow anvil that is translucent does not indicate a healthy updraft, while a solid anvil with mammatus clouds suggests a very strong updraft is present.

Underneath the storm

Even an isolated storm is a large entity: in many cases it can be 20 miles in diameter or more. A successful chaser cannot simply point the car at the storm and drive to it. Three out of four sides of the storm are dominated by amorphous shafts of rain, and crisscrossing through the storm to seek out something to look at can be an extremely dangerous undertaking that even seasoned veterans would

The approach to the updraft yields a tremendous number of visual clues about the storm's characteristics, in some cases more than can be obtained by chasers parked directly underneath. It truly gives the big picture. *(Tim Vasquez)*

The art of navigation

Navigation is a critical chasing skill. A van packed with chasers is doomed for failure if none of the individuals can read road maps, remember where north is, and estimate distances to cloud features.

Are you in a region with "grid roads"? All of the Great Plains except Texas uses the rectangular survey system, which tends to cover the area in a checkerboard of roads and fencelines one mile apart and aligned with true north. If you're driving perpendicular to "grid roads", you can anticipate a turn by noting the tenths place on the odometer at any major road. Then each successive grid road will be one mile further at the same tenths place (e.g. 471.6, 472.6, 473.6). This can help you find an important turn.

Another way to find a crossroad is to look at the electrical poles ahead of you. A road is usually found where you see several electrical lines leading perpendicular away from the main road. Sometimes these lines cross the main road.

Are you trying to find a place to park? The most dangerous spot to park is alongside the roadway! A much smarter option is to find a turnout for a cattle gate or a little-used dirt road. Some chasers prefer to travel down these dirt roads a few hundred yards to soak in more of the scenery and avoid electrical wires obscuring the photograph or collapsing onto the vehicles. On the other hand, wires overhead are considered to provide a "cone of protection" from lightning strikes.

TIM VASQUEZ

shudder at. Therefore a chaser must give careful attention to which portion of the storm to drive to. In most cases, this portion is the storm's updraft area. This is the area directly beneath the tallest, hardest portions of the cumulonimbus tower, and is usually on the south side of the storm. As the miles to the updraft area diminish, the wise chaser is thinking hard about two things: what type of structure the storm has taken, and which way it is moving. These two considerations provide a framework for how things will evolve during the first hour underneath the storm.

As you see the type of storm that you are approaching, give thought to how you want your photos to appear, and compare this with the time of day, the illumination, and the road network. For example, by positioning yourself east of the updraft base, you will have a front row seat on tornadic activity and storm structure, but backlighting from behind the storm can steepen contrast in such a way that makes the storm difficult to photograph, and tornadoes and wall clouds look like sihouettes. Less harsh contrast occurs with the sun at a right angle, implying that locations southeast and south of the updraft base should be considered. Unusual, highly illuminated scenes can be found west of the updraft base with the sun to your back, but the tones are often more flat, the storm is moving away, and it is impossible to see structure and developments on the forward flank.

In unusual upper-level flow, such as when upper winds are out of the northwest or exceptionally weak, the entire storm structure framework will be oriented in an unusual direction. In northwesterly flow, for example, the updraft base will tend to be on the west side, and you may be chasing southward rather than westward. A common mistake novices make in northwesterly flow is to get immersed in the forward flank downdraft, meanwhile catching brief glimpses of a tornado to the distant northwest.

Core-punching is the controversial technique of penetrating rain shafts in order to get to the updraft area. This typically occurs when the chaser approaches a storm from the north, and

Awareness of the sky

One of the most frustrating things we've done chasing is stop at a convenience store that blocked our view to the east. While we tried to get data ... and talk with other chasers we failed to see a storm go up east of our target zone and move away from us. Game over!

DAPHNE & JIM LADUE
Norman, OK chasers

Busts. Documenting the bust as well as the big day, whether by video narration, email exchanges, or casual conversation, is an essential skill for clarifying mistakes and perfecting future chases. *(art by David Hoadley)*

less often from the west (in HP storms) and east (in northwesterly flow). While core-punching provides a convenient shortcut, it's also very dangerous because tornadic activity and large hail occurs very close and sometimes within the storm's rain shafts. Beginners should never core-punch under any circumstances. Chasers should divert to make as much of a south-to-north approach as possible.

Once you're near the updraft base, the storm's structure and health are readily apparent. Large, circular updraft bases with fast cloud motions are associated with tornadic activity, while smaller, linear updraft bases with poor cloud motions are associated with weaker outflow-dominant storms. Keep close tabs on the winds. A southeasterly wind is the fuel that feeds the storm; the stronger, the better. Wind from other directions may be associated with the main downdraft or from a supercell's rear-flank downdraft wrapping into the circulation. Downdraft air that spreads rapidly underneath the updraft base may indicate an outflow-dominated storm.

Rotating wall clouds, which are large lowerings underneath the updraft base, are often thought to be the focus for tornado development. However it has been found that as many as half of all tornadoes are associated with a weak wall cloud or none at all. Therefore it is important to watch for other clues, such as the presence of a clear slot, dust whirls, good inflow, and other such signals.

Chasers should never get into the habit of listening to the radio and "chasing warnings". Understandably, some beginners have the impression that this is proper field strategy. However warnings typically give a chaser little or no time to get to the warned area. Successful chasing requires being in the right place *before any warnings are issued*. Chasing a warning may also result in abandoning a good storm to chase a cell that only has radar indications. A warning often *does not* mean that any photogenic weather will occur, or that a circulation will intensify further!

Being out of position dramatically increases the chance of encountering a law enforcement *roadblock*. These are usually found on major highways leading into the path of a tornado. It's very rare that chasers are permitted through a roadblock, and it's best to stay well ahead of the updraft track to avoid them. If delayed

Using radar

When chasers are evaluating a radar velocity image for a "couplet" to identify the existence of a tornado, they should be aware of the following limitations of radar. The operational radars, such as the WSR-88D, do not have the spatial resolution to resolve a tornado's circulation. Instead, the radar senses the larger "mesocyclone" circulation which is typically broader and weaker than the tornado vortex.

The radar senses information across a "sample volume" by averaging the change in the phase of the reflected wavelength for a number of sample pulses (typically 32 or 64 pulses). The received energy is a reflection of the "average" information within the sample volume, and the size of the volume becomes larger at greater ranges from the radar. Finally, at far ranges from the radar, the radar beam is much higher above the ground, and the circulation is not at the ground level.

Why is this useful? Scientists have collected statistics on over 100,000 detection signatures and have found that stronger signatures are generally more likely to be associated with tornadoes than not. However, reports of tornadic and non-tornadic signatures are distributed across the entire spectrum of radar signature strengths. There are cases where tornadoes have been observed with weak radar signatures and cases where strong radar signatures have resulted in no tornadoes. It is a best practice to correlate signature strength with the probability that the signature is tornadic, rather than using a "magic threshold" above which all signatures could be considered tornadic, and to never rule out the possibility that a weak signature, or sometimes no radar vortex signature at all, might still result in a tornado!

GREG STUMPF
Norman, OK research meteorologist and chaser

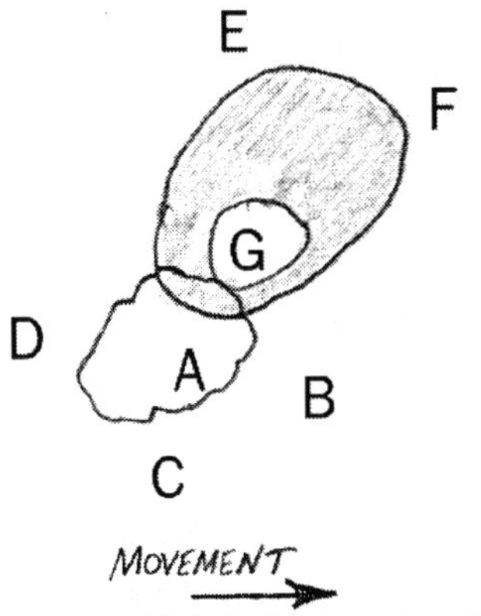

Low-precipitation (LP) supercell

This storm makes an excellent practice target for inexperienced chasers due to high visibility all around the storm. However it is not without fangs, as it can contain very large hail in a small precipitation core. Location A offers a good view of the updraft base, but the low tornadic potential and spectacular structure makes B, C, and D the best targets. During the evening, location C actually provides the best photographs since the sun is usually perpendicular to the storm and the three-dimensional striations tend to stand out. Chasers at E and F should divert around the storm, while those at location G should drive west then divert around the storm unless visibility is good and hailstones are small.

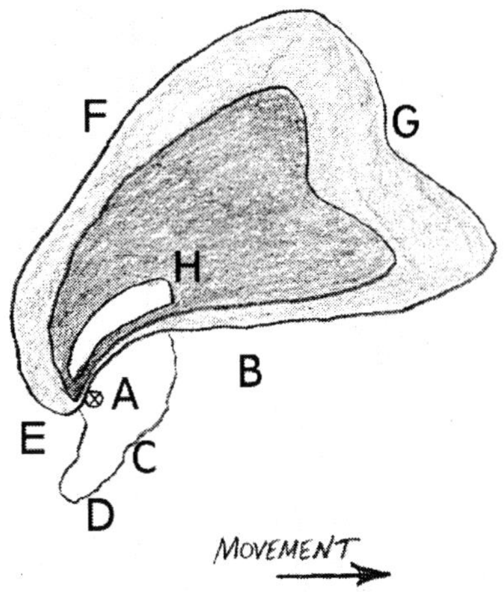

Classic (CL) supercell

Classic supercells can be difficult for new chasers because of the rapidly changing stages in the storm's life cycle. Towards the early stages of the storm's development, it may look like an LP supercell, then as the core collapses, it may take on HP characteristics. Although A is the best position for experienced chasers, B is the best for new chasers, offering excellent contrast, but close attention to the storm's movement is necessary because of the proximity of the forward flank downdraft. Position C and D are quite safe but may yield poor contrast, while position E is safe and may offer excellent views of the tornado's rope stage as it moves to the back of the storm. Chasers at F and G should divert around the storm, while those at position H should drive north then divert around the storm.

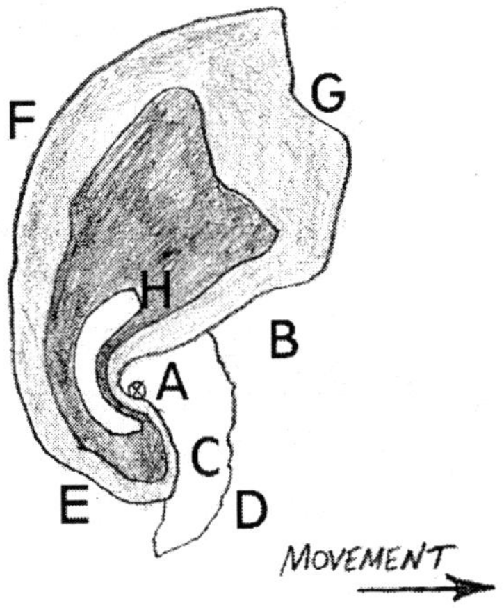

High-precipitation (HP) supercell

The HP supercell is one of the most dangerous types of storms and should be avoided by beginners. Location A corresponds to the "bear's cage", or "notch", and while it offers the only view of any tornadic activity it is also extremely dangerous. Less-experienced chasers should stay far ahead of the bear's cage at position B. Location C can be dangerous due to the potential for high straight-line winds and hail. Positions D and E offer little photographic potential and chasers will need to move east then north to take up position B. Chasers in positions F and G will need to divert around the storm, while those in position H are within the core and should drive north then divert around the storm.

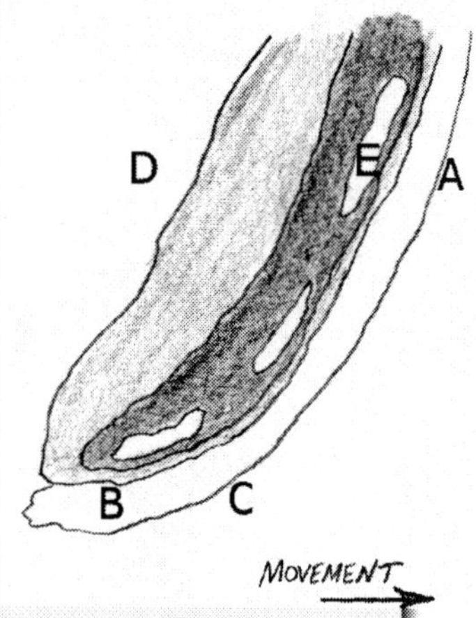

Squall line

A squall line offers very little in the way of chase potential. Chasers at location A have the option of either staying ahead of the line to look at cloud formations, or to let the line pass to take up position D. Position B, at "tail-end charlie", offers the best potential for any severe weather development, though inexperienced chasers should keep a short distance ahead of tail-end charlie at position C. Position D offers some excellent opportunities for anvil lightning after dark — providing that low clouds aren't tailing the squall line (a typical occurrence along strong cold fronts). Chasers at location E should drive west or sit tight and allow the squall line to pass.

Navigation errors

I was chasing a tornado-warned cell northwest of Minneapolis on May 31, 2008. I started driving east when in reality the storm was moving southeast. The wall cloud ended up passing right over my head and I got stuck in the hail core which added a few nice dents to my car. Lesson learned: ALWAYS know what direction the storm is moving.

DEAN BARON
New Brighton, MN chaser

Cancelled warning

On May 25th, 2008, while chasing a tornado warned supercell in Kansas, we received on our cell phone a call from the Wichita NWS WFO. They were using spotter network and wanted to know what was the behavior of the storm. We explained that the storm was strongly outflow dominant. The tornado warning was canceled.

JEAN-FRANÇOIS MASSICOTTE
Chambly, Quebec chaser

by a roadblock and there's no possibility to sidestep to an alternate storm to your west or south, then it's time to map out a complete re-intercept of your storm by using minor unblocked roads that lead parallel to or to the right of the storm track. Use the opportunity to get well ahead of the storm to prevent further problems.

Reporting severe weather

Chasers are invited by all NWS offices to make reports of severe weather. This includes specifically tornadoes, large hail (0.75" inch, penny size, or greater), or winds of 58 mph or greater. Do you have spotter affiliation? If so, find a local ARES net or use eSpotter <*espotter.weather.gov*> or SpotterNetwork <*www.spotternetwork.org*> if you have mobile Internet. If you do not have spotter affiliation, check the appendix for the area NWS office and use the designated phone number. The 911 number can be used under all circumstances, but since they deal with the general public it can be more difficult to get your report through when chasing near large towns or cities.

Before you start typing or talking, get your facts straight. Determine your exact location with respect to what part of the city or county you're in, identify the intersection you're near, and orient yourself to true north. If you're reporting hail size, it's strongly recommended that you actually measure the hailstone diameter with a ruler; not only is it

Roadblocks are a common obstacle, as seen here on 23 May 2008 in Kansas. Don't attempt to talk your way through one: it makes the officer personally accountable for your safety, and permission is rarely granted anyway. Simply find an alternate route, wait it out, or select another storm cell to chase. *(Andrea Griffa)*

the right way to report but a "measured" hail size gets more attention. Eyeballed hail sizes can be very erroneous.

Then it's time to make your report. Be clear and concise. First briefly state your **credentials or affiliation**. Then briefly **describe** what you are seeing. Next, report location information. If you're reporting a tornado, do not attempt to provide its location unless the debris cloud is at an obvious landmark. Instead, state **your location** ("I am located at...") and the **direction** of the phenomena. You may also add **distance**, which is the most likely part of your report to contain an error. Be judicious about your ability to estimate distance, and use ambiguous words like "distant", "several miles", or "nearby" if necessary.

Do not be the one who unwittingly called in a false report. If you're unsure of what you're seeing, it's better to not call it in, as the forecaster will often not be able to clear up the confusion for you. If you have grave concerns, though, you can call in the report, but be sure to communicate the fact that you're unsure about what you're seeing and be prepared to explain why.

On the same token, it must be noted that a few weather offices are asking experienced chasers to call in reports of obvious *non-tornadic* activity when this can be positively confirmed on a tornado-warned storm. Do not report such an "anti-verification" unless the entire updraft area has been plainly visible for some time and you have seen neither a debris cloud nor a condensation funnel.

Lessons learned

By far my biggest intercept mistakes have involved dirt roads in the presence of storms with heavy rainfall. An aggressive maneuver to peer into a rain-wrapped mesocyclone, with a history of tornadoes, ended in near disaster when we were overtaken by a broad, weak tornado. The single escape route turned out to be a muddy quagmire, leaving us no choice but to experience the full fury of the storm from a lonely county road.

I recently missed most of an impressive tornado due to an attempt to get close too early on a road that turned to mud. We ended up having to double back for fear of getting stuck, and this wasted enough time to get us stuck in a police roadblock many miles from the tornado crossing I-70.

RICH THOMPSON
Norman, Oklahoma meteorologist and chaser

Night hazards

In the pre-dawn hours of May 26, 2000, I was alone and driving north from Amarillo toward Dodge City in extremely heavy rain. There were flash flood warnings on the radio and visibility was limited due to darkness and rain.

As I drove down a hill, my car suddenly plunged into water that was crossing the road. I felt the front of the car start to shift from the water. I managed to quickly back up the car and escape the flooded road. I am very lucky that I was not swept away by the water. I learned new respect for the dangers of flooding, darkness and poor visibility that morning.

BILL HARK
Richmond, VA chaser

Remember, your safety is more important than getting the report out, so continue to be attentive to proper safety practices in regard to weather and traffic.

Finally, it's bad form to ask questions on reporting networks or reporting numbers. The person on the other end of the line is usually dealing with a high workload. If you have questions, monitor the radio-based spotter weather network to maintain awareness. Sometimes the NWS point of contact will use the frequency to give all spotters an update.

Nighttime

As dusk falls, the chaser has a dilemma. Keep pursuing the storm? Chasing often becomes extremely hazardous because of the inability to follow the storm visually. Chasers are highly dependent on lightning activity in the cloud to figure out what's taking place, and weaker, outflowish storms may be almost unobservable. Furthermore, the likelihood of bagging a fantastic wall cloud or tornado photo diminishes significantly at night, and road hazards, downed lines, and debris can create a highly unsafe driving situation. It's usually better to break off from the chase, rest, and recharge.

But if you can't bring yourself to do that, a relatively safe option is to seek out lightning photography. Some of the best anvil lightning is found 20 or 30 miles from the storm's core. Astonishing lightning displays are often best seen behind a squall line or multicell cluster, assuming stratiform precipitation has not filled in behind, so it may be wise to point the vehicle slightly west. A lawnchair in a dark field with a few refreshments and lightning arcing in the distance can be a perfect way to end the day.

But planning does not end at dark. It's important to keep tabs with the weather if another chase day is scheduled. The SPC Day 2 outlooks should be checked early enough in the evening to avoid the dreaded "overnight haul". This happens in a progressive pattern where a chaser might find the center of action shifting from the Texas Panhandle to north-central Kansas the next day. Being six hours out of position at 9 p.m. is always a dismal discovery. For the night owls, this is where a well-rested chase partner comes in handy, to take a shift of driving and give the driver a much-needed break.

At some point in the evening it comes time to select the hotel. Weekends are always a busy time, so it's smart to actually reserve a room on Fridays, Saturdays, and Sundays as early as possible in the day if you know what town you'll be in. If not, call the motel before arriving to make sure a room's open. If you need data, ask about WiFi availability and test it out from the parking lot before checking in.

Dusk is when tough decisions are made: stick with the storm, get in position for tomorrow, or return home with extra time to spare? *(Tim Vasquez)*

The night chase question

Night chasing has taken off with the availability of real-time radar imagery. Unfortunately, you lose most perspective at night and you can become dangerously reliant on the radar data. Delays in updates and a false sense of precision can leave you in a dangerous spot with little time to react and no clear "right" choices.

A storm like the Greensburg supercell (4 May 2007) can produce simultaneous tornadoes in a variety of locations a few miles apart in poor visibility. Sooner or later, someone will literally get carried away by one of these storms when they miscalculate their margin for error and find themselves within a strong tornado.

RICH THOMPSON
Norman, OK meteorologist and chaser

The big scare

One chasing memory that does stand out — and I can't say it's positive — was back in 1996 while watching a developing storm in southwest Oklahoma. A local man drove up and asked what was going on.

We told him, "Not much," and walked over to his truck. He had no pants on! *Yikes!*

He blubbered, "Storm scared me so much I forgot to put my britches on."

Possibly the best quote I have ever heard while chasing!

ROB SATKUS
Oklahoma City, OK chaser

CHAPTER SIX
SAFETY

Chase safety is a significant issue as the hobby by its very nature places the chaser in harm's way. Safe practices often run counter to popular media depictions on cable TV which imply that chasers meets death in the face every week. There is little doubt that this is a natural product of sensationalist journalism and a tendency to pepper stories with yarns spun by "local yokels" and thrill-seeking yahoo chasers.

The clear reality is that most storm chase threats are quite predictable and recorded chaser fatalities within the actual thunderstorm are still zero. Granted, if a chaser is trying to drive right up to a tornado there will be colossal and life-threatening risks, but such practices are widely condemned within the hobby. What follows is a clear set of guidelines, consistent with safe and rewarding chase objectives, which draws upon three decades of experience among veteran chasers.

Safety in numbers

When multiple chasers occupy one vehicle, this is the true definition of a chase team. The team can work together to improve safety and coordination, especially since chasing is sometimes a stressful and dangerous activity. One ingredient unique to chasing is that chasers travelling together are occasionally just acquaintances. Occupants might not feel free to complain or speak their mind about an issue. All of these issues are the very basis for cockpit resource management (CRM) principles developed by NASA and now in widespread use by airlines.

The main goal of CRM is to improve situational awareness and safety by removing barriers that impede communication, leadership, and decisionmaking. Interestingly, aspects of CRM were addressed as early as 1981 in an operations guide established by the Texas Tech University chase

A March 2007 chase scare

I decided to call it a night, but I was briefly able to observe a strong updraft developing on the storm I was driving into. I began encountering very heavy, blinding rain. A couple minutes after that, hail began to fall. I decided to turn on the radio and found a local station.

"At 10:35 p.m. Central Time, law enforcement officials reported a large tornado on the ground two miles northwest of Bird City." I was five miles northwest of Bird City! I spotted a farmstead immediately to my left and started making preparations to run for my life.

I jumped out of the truck and narrowly missed getting crushed by the door as the wind slammed it shut. There was no time to look for the basement, so I dove under an old kitchen table. By that point the whole house was shaking violently, and I could hear debris hitting the side of the house. Upstairs I heard the shattering of glass.

My prayers were answered, as the house gradually stopped shaking and the sound gradually got quieter. I learned to never drive blindly into supercells at night during a tornado outbreak. It's like teasing a pit bull tied to a tree with a fraying rope - you're just asking for serious trouble.

MARK FARNIK
Glendale, Colorado chaser

Roadside stop

Veteran chasers take advantage of chaser convergence to exchange notes and get a few shots of a linear multicell storm. Note how even though the road is obviously empty and flat, the vehicles are parked away from its surface out of habit. This is a safe chaser convergence. *(Tim Vasquez)*

team. Some professions such as medical trauma teams have begun adopting CRM in their operations.

The chase vehicle driver's primary responsibility is to insure complete safety of everyone while on the road. This is equivalent to the aviation rule of thumb: "Fly the airplane!" Thus the driver concentrates exclusively on traffic, road hazards, and operating the vehicle within its safe limits. Tasks like evaluating weather hazards, photography, navigation, digging up toll money, and planning chase strategy take away from the task of safe driving and should always be delegated to other passengers unless the vehicle is parked safely.

Passengers take on personal tasks and any subdivided group tasks such as working the radio or laptop computer. At the same time, all passengers should assist the driver by pointing out road hazards such as road debris at night and by identifying unsafe situations. There must be a flow of information and a cooperative, comfortable relationship between all members. Individuals resolve not to take issues personally. Solving problems becomes a team effort.

Unfortunately this cooperative situation may be affected by personality conflicts, ego, or stubbornness, such as the driver who is dead-set on following through with a certain plan. This can create safety issues that do not get resolved. CRM techniques suggest a five-step assertive process that works effectively to address safety issues. This is outlined in the margin and can be of great help in resolving an urgent situation with chase partners you don't know well.

Safety assertiveness

The five-point model for cockpit resource management used by airlines consists of an opener, a statement, a detailed statement, a solution, and a buy-in. Addressing a situation in this manner can help break down communication barriers and raise a call to safety with any stubborn or distracted chase partner.

- **An opening** addresses the individual. "Hey, Bill?"
- **State the concern** without adding emotion. "I don't like the look of that dust plume near that circulation."
- **State the problem as you see it**. "We're sitting a mile east of that circulation and it's moving this way."
- **State a solution**. "If we move east, we can get clear of its path and be in position for some good shots."
- **Obtain an buy-in**. "Does that sound good to you, Bill?"

A major hazard of chasing in rain, in traffic, and at night is the risk of emerging into a tornadic circulation. Shown here is the dissipating 2008 Quinter tornado, against backlighting and poor contrast, crossing a road. This is what a chaser might see emerging from a rain core. *(William Hark / harkphoto.com)*

Driving

The biggest danger to chasers is surprisingly not the storm, but traffic and other people. Developments in the storm take dozens of seconds to evolve, while road dangers materialize in fractions of seconds. The best way to avoid traffic and people dangers is to be prepared! Defensive driving is all about total awareness while behind the wheel.

• **Night driving is dangerous**. Many chasers start their day at 7 am, and by dark they've been up at least 15 hours. Exhaustion and drowsiness can lead to dangerous driving and veering off the road. One veteran chaser admitted to a nighttime experience in the early 1980s where he zoned out returning to Lubbock and drove at 55 mph through an entire town. To combat fatigue, get a good night of sleep, take regular breaks every two hours, drive with companions, take a catnap, play loud music, open the windows, and play an entertaining audio book.

• **Do not speed or break traffic laws**. Yahoos, "local yokels", and a few experienced chasers will routinely break traffic laws to get to a good storm. When a chaser's selfish motives are put above the safety of other drivers, a key tenet of ethi-

First chaser fatality

The first known storm chase fatality occurred on April 26, 1984, when OU student Christopher Phillips hydroplaned and lost control of his vehicle in Logan County, Oklahoma. The car rolled over into a ditch. Fortunately his two passengers survived. Unfortunately, the odds are that hydroplaning will claim the lives of more chasers in the decades ahead.

cal chasing is violated. On the other hand, when a chaser stays below the speed limit, they spend more time enjoying the sky and the setting, rather than looking for cops and seeking out passing zones. It allows a more introspective experience to emerge. If you haven't done so already, just try it once: you may be amazed at how the entire experience changes!

• **Driving too slow is often dangerous**. When you are driving far below a reasonable speed, you are technically blocking traffic. This can invite accidental collisions and encourage dangerous passing maneuvers. If you must drive slow to find a usable turnout and traffic is behind you, use your turn signal as much as possible. This will invite patience from the driver behind you, and perhaps will give you some extra room.

• **Never obstruct traffic lanes**. Obstructing any lane of highway traffic is a selfish action that puts travellers, other chasers, and local residents in danger. Never park on a lane, leave a car door opened into a lane, or use a lane as a surface for standing or setting up tripods. Use your options: in a single mile of highway, you can find dozens of turnouts, parking lots, and lightly-travelled gravel roads that serve as excellent spots for temporary parking. They may even allow you to get away from the power lines along highways which tarnish photographs.

• **Don't congregate near chase crowds**. Chase veteran Roger Edwards has made an important distinction between convergence and crowds. *Chaser convergence* is a meeting of safety-minded chasers in a secluded spot, such as a parking lot, a picnic area, a gas station, or even a gravel road off the

A sudden diversion

My worst brush with chase safety was while I was driving on a nicely paved asphalt highway, with lots of reflection working off of it after a recent storm. Suddenly I encountered, most unexpectedly, several inches of water over the roadway that completely blended in with the otherwise black and reflective asphalt. The vehicle I was driving went out of control, and after several gyrations and some tense moments I found myself still on the hard road surface unscathed.

I guess that my emergency vehicle driver training, as well as some high school hot rod experience taught me to not panic when faced with sudden vehicular adversity! After this incident, I have tried to do a better job of remembering some of the basic rules of chase safety. The last place you want to get in real trouble is 45 miles west of Nowhere, Texas. Just who is going to bail you out?

ROBERT WILLIS
Fort Worth, TX chaser

Chase crowds are a common traffic hazard. *(David Hoadley)*

main highway. A *chaser crowd* refers to people congregating directly on a highway. It's common for participating vehicles and chase equipment to partially block lanes. Surprisingly, *most chase crowds do not contain experienced chasers but are composed largely of inexperienced chasers and "local yokels".* Keep your speed to the bare minimum when navigating past a chaser crowd, since participants are often distracted.

• **Beware of hydroplaning.** Layers of water only fractions of an inch thick can cause the tire to "ride up" the film of water and lose contact with the pavement. This can result in disastrous loss of control. Some roadways are poorly surfaced without grooves or camber, and constitute the worst danger for hydroplaning. Excessive tread wear on your tires, underinflation, and poor vehicle alignment can contribute to hydroplaning trouble. Even if you are careful, bear in mind that many other motorists drive too fast for road conditions and they may lose control, colliding with you no matter how carefully you handle your own car. A huge dose of defensive driving is essential to your survival on rain-slicked roads.

• **Avoid watching the TV or computer while driving.** It is illegal in several states to have a television screen visible by the car driver while the car is on a public street. Entrust weather and navigation decisions to a passenger.

Hydroplaning physics

A civil engineering rule of thumb for rural highways is hydroplaning can be expected for speeds above 45 mph where water ponds to a depth of 0.10 inch or greater over a distance of 30 feet or greater. It's largely a function of water depth.

Red clay roads, such as this one near Wanette, Oklahoma, can be notoriously treacherous when wet. In some cases they may hide a deep layer of soft sand. Consider not only current precipitation activity but whether the weather pattern has been dry or wet in recent days before using a dirt road. Use extreme caution where the road leads into depressions and be prepared to turn around. *(Tim Vasquez)*

Every chaser has probably had an uncomfortably religious moment at one time or another. Keep your distance if you do not have a perfect understanding of the situation at hand. *(David Hoadley)*

• **At night, be vigilant for livestock and deer.** Loose cattle are very common on smaller farm-to-market and county roads, congregating at night on warm road surfaces. They can be almost undetectable in the headlight beam. The condition of fencing along the road and livestock warning signs can alert you to the magnitude of the danger. Fortunately deer is primarily a fall and early winter problem, with central Texas the most problematic area of the Great Plains, but deer collisions can occur at any time.

• **Be alert for storm damage**. When you are approaching a tornado or the path carved out by a severe storm, be alert for debris, limbs, poles, and wires that have fallen into the roadway. At nighttime, electrical wires can be almost invisible and present a significant danger to unwary travellers.

• **Dealing with yahoos.** If you get a chance, jot down the license plate of anyone troubling you, just in case you need it for the police or insurance company. Chase roaches, unknown individuals who follow chasers without their permission, tend to drive recklessly and have caused actual accidents with chasers. Some drivers have had success with confronting the individual politely but firmly. Others have shaken them off by taking an extended tour through a congested town. Chasers who keep a low profile rarely have a roach problem.

• **Avoid forming chase caravans**. If you must chase as part of a large group, give your followers a margin of safety and

Getting out of the mud

Avoid spinning the wheels at all costs; this digs the tire pit and lubricates it with soil moisture. First, try to use the vehicle power to gently rock the vehicle out. If that doesn't work, try to park either as far forward or as far back as you can go or jack the vehicle up, and fill the rut with boards, branches, and rocks, then drive out.

If that fails, bleed the drive axle tires by about 50-75% until the part that contacts the ground looks fat and squishy. This will drastically increase traction and is a method widely used by beachgoers. But letting too much air out will risk the tire coming off the rim, so do not overdo it, then once out limp slowly to a gas station to reinflate.

Expect significant vibration at highway speeds anytime mud is still stuck to the tires, since it will throw them out of balance. An unscheduled stop at the car wash may be needed!

TIM VASQUEZ

don't outrun them. Followers must never make dangerous maneuvers to stay with the group.

Navigation

The task of planning a route is not a light undertaking. Road surfaces, construction, and congestion must be accounted for. Depending on the weather, all of these can impact the safety of the vehicle and its occupants.

• **Keep your gas tank full**. Significant tornado outbreaks damage power transmission and distribution grids. This will cause power outages over a multi-county area, making it impossible to buy gas. Always make sure you have at least a half tank of fuel by the time storms are developing.

• **Avoid unpaved roads**. Throughout much of the Great Plains, unpaved roads are composed of packed dirt and gravel. However, erosion by traffic or from crop fields can rapidly soften the surface, producing a pure dirt road

Kansas hospitality

Many decades ago while driving my mother's dated Oldsmobile, the fan belt broke with a great rattle and I coasted to a stop on the shoulder. Miles from any town or farm (before cell phones), I wondered how to get help. It was almost 11PM and not a car in sight. I turned off the lights and started to bundle up for a long, cold night.

Well, in the next 20 minutes, five out of the six cars and trucks that passed me stopped and asked if they could help. One southbound driver told a garage, and they sent a tow truck. I was broken down by the roadside in western Kansas, late at night, and never before had so much company. Just one more reason, why I love the Plains and the good people that live there.

DAVID HOADLEY
Falls Church, VA chaser

Always have an escape route!
(David Hoadley)

surface. With rain or field washout, this can make the road impassible. Arguably the worst kind of mud to drive in is red clay, the type found in the Ustalf soils of north Texas and Oklahoma, as its particle size is much smaller than sand or loam and it creates a very slick surface.

• **Try not to chase in metropolitan areas**. Traffic and road construction creates a frustrating and occasionally dangerous situation for the chaser. Furthermore the cap usually breaks at rush hour. One problem that plagues the city is the tendency of travellers to park underneath overpasses to protect their vehicles, blocking lanes of traffic. This can leave chasers stuck in traffic with no escape route. If you must chase into a city, you must be exceptionally attentive of your navigation plan, as you often sacrifice the luxury of turning around or taking an alternate route!

Weather safety

Fortunately, the thunderstorm is not as much of a hazard as the general public thinks. Avoiding the tornado is a relatively simple task, though it requires awareness, common sense, and some basic knowledge of the storm.

• **Lightning is an extreme hazard!** Stay in your car as much as possible! A good rule of thumb is when the thunder follows the lightning by less than ten seconds (a two-mile distance), or when the very first fat drops of rain hit your car, typically indicating the descent of a negatively-charged downdraft core, you need to be inside. Do not stand on wet ground or in water puddles; these will conduct charge to your feet. If your skin tingles or your hair stands on end, a lightning flash is imminent — crouch down immediately! If a lightning strike does occur nearby and you were electrocuted, seek medical help! There have been cases where bone marrow has been damaged from electrocution, resulting in coma or death in several days due to lack of blood cell production. Dr. Mary Ann Cooper, one of the leading experts on lightning injury, has more advice on her site at <*www.uic.edu/labs/lightninginjury/*>.

• **Don't core-punch**. Core punching, the act of driving through a core of the precipitation in order to get to the updraft area, is a very risky maneuver due to the dangers caused by reduced visibility. Tornadoes often enshroud theirselves in rain and may not be seen until you are a few hundred feet away. Beginners should never core punch under any circumstances.

The overpass problem

Even in Virginia, I have seen roads partially blocked from people taking shelter under an overpass during a tornado warning. Many of my friends have asked me if I have hid under an overpass during a chase. Despite recent documentaries now advising people to avoid hiding under overpasses, the practice is still very common.

BILL HARK
Richmond, VA chaser

Keeping others safe

In Eastern Nebraska I was forced to physically restrain a chase tour guest from trying to climb a radio tower. She was a bit of a daredevil and not happy I had to enforce a safety (and legal) issue, however, I'm sure she understood as we've chased together a few times since the incident.

SCOTT WEBERPAL
Janesville, WI chaser

• **Keep an eye on all parts of the storm.** Even if you are in the middle of observing a tornado, a new circulation could be developing underneath the updraft base: overhead!

• **Do not remain focused solely on the tornado.** It's easy to forget that a storm can destroy a chase vehicle with large hail and high winds. A good understanding of storm structure and evolution, as well as constant observation, is essential to stay safe. All passengers should constantly monitor what they can see out their windows.

• **Have an escape route.** Thunderstorms can evolve rapidly and in unexpected ways. Always make sure you have a plan for getting away from the storm immediately. Know the roads immediately around your present position (your "road options") and whether they dead-end.

• **Keep an eye on power lines.** When you're near a tornadic storm, keep in mind that both high-tension (transmission) and local (distribution) power lines tend to fall over in a domino fashion, sometimes miles away from the tornado or the RFD winds that decimate them. This is exceptionally important if you find yourself within a mile of any tornado. Roads with very close parallel power lines on the *south or west side* are the most dangerous. If you actually observe poles falling down, take immediate action.

• **Do not take refuge underneath freeway overpasses.** Engineers and storm researchers have been aggressively warning the public about the dangers of freeway overpasses, citing a large body of evidence. These efforts are constantly being undone by endless broadcasts of a 1991 media clip in which a news crew films a near-miss from underneath an overpass. In 1999 three people were killed in Oklahoma hiding underneath overpasses in Newcastle, Moore, and Mulhall. To compound matters further, freeway lanes are often blocked in severe weather by drivers who shelter their vehicles underneath bridges, blocking lanes of traffic! This is an amazingly selfish act that leaves hundreds of other motorists trapped in the tornado's path. One person in the 1999 Oklahoma event was killed after being unable to get past vehicles blocking I-44 at an overpass near Newcastle. Chasers should plan on encountering this type of behavior on freeways and always have a way out.

Across the pond

Our team made an effort to meet up with some first-time chasers from Denmark in 2006. We met them via Stormtrack and joined them for a chase on their next-to-last day in the US. After that somewhat successful day in a dreadful chase season, their team decided to return again, and they have been teaming up with ours each year since with quite a bit of success.

But what is important here is that we forged a very close friendship with our Danish counterparts and would find it difficult now to imagine chasing without them. I look forward to seeing them and sharing stories almost as much as chasing itself.

The chase community truly is worldwide, and our commonalities often far overshadow any differences we have, even cultural ones. The friendships we've forged at the National Storm Chaser Conference in Denver the last two years are similarly valued.

PAUL AUSTIN
Gainesville, FL chaser

Health considerations

The intent of this book is not to make chasers healthier and live a longer life, but maximizing comfort and increasing stamina while in the road is an important consideration. What follows are some tips that will help you stay in peak condition for the daily grind of chasing.

• **Hydration.** The constant exposure to warm weather and abundance of car time means you should keep well-hydrated and drink fluids at regular intervals. Pure water, of course, is the best bet. A supply of extra drinks is also good insurance in case of an unforeseen breakdown.

• **Don't succumb to a poor diet.** Chasers, unfortunately, are exposed to the "road food" problem: an endless supply of burgers, burritos, sodas, energy drinks, chips, and candy. These are all extremely high in carbohydrates and energy, but the body burns through them rapidly and within hours it's often followed by a "carb crash" with the symptoms of brain fog, tiredness, and irritability. For peak physical condition and maximum mental energy, it's wise to increase the proportion of protein and even fat in a road food diet. Include cheese, nuts, peanut butter, canned tuna, deli meats, or beef jerky in your snack stash. The old health standby, fruit, is squarely in the carbohydrate category but it is low in junk sugars and it contains healthy fiber. Inspect labels for surprise sugar and syrups, as well as excessive sodium, which can cause its own set of immediate and long-term side effects.

• **Food poisoning.** Lots of road food, much of it from questionable establishments, means an increased risk of food poisoning. When you set foot into a restaurant, keep your eyes and ears open for clues hinting at the quality of the establishment. Be extra careful at buffets: hot food trays should not be merely lukewarm, and staff should be seen rotating out food frequently. But most importantly, trust your gut feeling about your food and stop eating if something doesn't seem quite right. A bitter taste, sour smell, or strange sogginess might be the only warning sign you get. An old rule of thumb holds that it's better to walk away from the table than to gamble with one's health.

• **Deep vein thrombosis (DVT).** A dedicated chaser who spends two weeks on the Great Plains chasing all day is likely to spend about 120 hours sitting down with little room for movement. This can result in deep vein thrombosis (DVT), a condition that occurs when blood flow stagnates and clots in a vulnerable or damaged area of the vein. It is just now being recognized as an important safety issue in ultra-long airline flights, where the affliction is known as *economy-class syndrome.* Symptoms include unusual

An unconventional solution

I had a very close call with deep-vein thrombosis (DVT) on June 9, 2008, a few days after returning from my chase trip. Small clots broke off from this DVT and showered into both lungs. I am recovering well and am on Coumadin for a few months, but it was a very close call. Chasers are at risk of developing DVTs because they spend long hours sitting. DVTs can be easily prevented - you just need to be aware of what can happen and behave accordingly.

CHERYL CHANG
Indian Harbour Beach, FL

pain, swelling, and redness in the leg. DVT symptoms may subside but can progress to a pulmonary embolism with breathing pain and circulatory failure if the clot is dislodged. Formation of DVT can be prevented by regular rest stops, regular hydration, and regular in-place muscle exercises. Compression socks and stockings are available at drugstores for about $15 which have been clinically proven to reduce DVT risks. The occurrence of DVT is an urgent matter, so see a doctor as soon as possible. If any chest pain develops, it's a bona fide emergency.

Environmental safety

Chasers are not well-known for clinging to the comfort of chase vehicles, restaurants, and tourist traps. Most avidly immerse theirselves in the Great Plains, exploring abandoned structures, wandering out into fields to get video, and watching storms from desolate locations at night. This book would not be complete without itemizing some of the hazards that might reasonably be encountered. And what the heck — it makes for an entertaining read.

• **Snakes.** "Snakes on the Plains" could be a great name for a Samuel L. Jackson film, but it's a real chase safety matter. Rattlesnakes are found throughout all of the Great

Local food is one of the great delights of chasing on the Great Plains, but since local restaurants don't subscribe to corporate-controlled food preparation procedures, there's more of an opportunity to pick up a stomach bug. A little awareness of quality can go a long way to preventing an unscheduled down day from chasing. Shown here is the retro Donald's Serva-Teria in Pratt, KS, which the photographer said was "very good". *(William Hark / harkphoto.com)*

Serpentine encounter

One afternoon in 1993, I stopped next to a field in the northwest Texas Panhandle to videotape a building storm line. The wind was blowing through dry grass, so when I heard a "TSSSSSS" sound, I assumed it was just that: wind.

Shortly after my taping, I looked down at the base of a utility pole. Five feet from where I stood was a four-foot West Texas rattlesnake — and he was not happy!

DAVID HOADLEY
Falls Church, VA chaser
(art by David Hoadley)

Plains, but are most numerous in the southern Caprock region of Texas south to the Rio Grande. One record from 19th century Shackelford County, northwest of Abilene, described the killing of 1200 rattlesnakes on a 15.6-square mile rangeland. Along the I-35 corridor there tend to be more sightings of the well-mannered but venomous copperhead snake. Storm chasers over the years have encountered rattlesnakes. Caution is mandatory when you set foot into unkempt grass. If you are bit, keep the wound below the level of the heart, do not cut it or suck for venom, do not use ice or tourniquets, apply antiseptic if available, and get immediate medical care at the largest hospital that can be reached. Many bites have minor effects, but envenomations with rapid symptom onset can develop into major emergencies. *Snakes are avoided by using caution in rocky, grassy areas and, at night, on warm road surfaces; always being attentive of where you are stepping; and being alert for suspicious hissing, rushing, or leaking sounds.*

• **Fire ants.** Fire ants deserve brief mention as they are extremely numerous along and east of I-35 in Texas. Some sparse populations can be found west to Midland and Lubbock and north to Oklahoma City. Most sting problems are caused by inattentively standing on a fire ant mound. If you get significant stings, wash the skin to clear any residual venom, disinfect if you can, and use ice for relief. Some claim to get relief from meat tenderizer, calamine lotion, and insect sting treatment. Antihistamines will help with swelling. Seek medical help for any serious symptoms.

Can you find the copperhead snake? These snakes are found around the I-35 area of Oklahoma and Texas eastward to the Atlantic. It's a common species around the Norman, Oklahoma chase mecca, but is rarely seen except when it moves out onto warm road surfaces in early spring. The snake appreciates a little caution when running into brushy areas for better shots of the tornado. *(Tim Vasquez)*

Scorpions are not simply a thing to be reckoned with in the deserts. This three-inch individual was found in a building in Norman, Oklahoma searching for prey. Be careful overturning rocks and debris when roaming the Great Plains. *(Tim Vasquez)*

To avoid fire ants, watch where you stand when chasing in Kansas or Oklahoma.

• **Killer bees.** While Africanized bees have not lived up to their reputation from 1970s horror movies, they do exist in the southwest United States, including all of Texas and Oklahoma except in the wooded eastern regions. According to U.S. Department of Agriculture charts published in 2008, the region from Childress, Texas south to Fort Stockton and Ozona is particularly hospitable to killer bee colonies. Many storm photographers seek out old trees, junk cars, and abandoned structures for interesting pictures and unfortunately these are the habitats favored by Africanized bees. *Unwanted encounters can be avoided by simply being alert for buzzing sounds indicating the presence of bees. Leave the area quietly and calmly if unusual bee activity is noticed.*

• **Scorpions.** These creatures are not just convenient props for Arizona cowboy movies. The striped scorpion, *Centruroides vittatus*, is extremely common in the rocky, rolling terrain extending from northern Oklahoma fanning southwestwad to Del Rio and the Big Bend. This crustacean comes out after dark, with dozens often found scavenging clearings, junk piles, sandy river banks, and rocky terrain for crickets and other small insects. Daytime chasers will probably never encounter one, but lightning photographers working on warm nights in rocky terrain might pick up one in their camera bag or clothes. If you get stung, immediately apply ice or the surface of a cold beverage container, which will provide immediate relief. The pain will subside in a couple of hours and may itch for a day or two. Seek medical

Wayward tick

When walking through tall grasses to get a good view or photo angle, always be careful of ticks. While chasing in Oklahoma in May 2008, I walked through some bushes to set up a tripod where trees wouldn't get in the way. While on the road after the storm gusted out, I felt something crawling up my chest, and shook out my shirt to discover a tick that was trying to bite me! I lost him in the folds of my shirt, but managed to shake him out on the side of the road a few moments later.

CONNOR MCCROREY
Plano, TX chaser

help if any symptoms other than localized pain and numbing develop. *Scorpions are avoided by using caution when sitting on or rummaging through loose rocks and boards. Keep out of sandy/clay soils and off rocky terrain at night.*

• **Ticks.** Ticks, particularly the Lone Star tick *(Amblyomma americanum)*, are extremely common in the grassland areas of the eastern Great Plains, especially near paths used by livestock, deer, opossums, and skunks. A chaser is likely to get them when wandering through lush knee-high grass, especially in the late spring. Though the Great Plains does not have the Lyme disease problem that the East Coast has, Rocky Mountain Spotted Fever is endemic in some parts of the Plains. To remove a tick, pinch it as closely to the skin as possible with fingers or tweezers and pull slowly but firmly until it lets go. Be patient. Pulling too hard may separate its head, which is even more difficult to remove and may require medical help to avoid infection. Some recommend flipping the tick on its back. Once it's out, always use antiseptic! *To avoid ticks, do not wander out into lush grass and brush, especially after April, particularly in the eastern Plains. Immediately investigate all tickling sensations. Inspect your body as soon as possible if you think you've been exposed.*

• **Chiggers.** Chiggers are the microscopic larval stage of the harvest mite (*Trombicula alfreddugesi*) which feed on skin cells and cause intense itching. The condition is mostly an annoyance, manifesting itself as a mysterious itch that goes away after a few days. There is no disease threat; simply keep the itch clean, scratch minimally, and the chigger will leave the skin on its own; in fact by the time symptoms appear the chiggers are often gone. *To avoid chiggers, keep out of tall damp grass, especially where it can come into contact with skin.*

• **Burr grass.** Knee-high stands of burr grass, *Cenchrus spp.*, are quite common on highway shoulders and along the borders of irrigated fields. Burr grass is endemic in any kind of sandy, well-drained soil. The spiny seeds lodge in clothing and deeply in skin, which can be a problem as they're often encountered by the dozen. *Never walk through any weedy or wild grass areas barefoot or in socks or sandals. Pay attention to where your pets step and don't let them wander!*

Worst of nature: Honorable mention

Poison oak is common in wooded areas of Texas and Oklahoma. These shrublike plants have three oaklike leaves to a cluster. They can be avoided by staying out of shady, brushy wooded areas, especially if you're wearing shorts. Poison oak creates powerful itching starting around one day after exposure and lasting over a week.

Prickly pear cactus plants are small football-sized plants which are extremely common in central and west Texas and are a nuisance for ranchers. Never pick up a prickly pear. Even handling the smooth faces will give you Mother Nature's equivalent of fiberglass particles embedded in your hands.

TRAVEL GUIDE

Great Plains
TRAVEL GUIDE

Remembering those who came before — DAVID HOADLEY

Half of the storm chase experience is absorbing oneself in the lore and legend of the Great Plains. Unless a chaser sticks to metropolitan chasing, it's virtually impossible to chase the region without coming into contact with its culture and history. And without an appreciation for it, chasing becomes a series of excruciating eight-hour drives interspersed with occasional chase action.

Some travellers may reach for iPods and DVD movies to shut out the monotony, but a good argument can be made that disociating from the experience closes off of the mind, squelching situational awareness and dampening forecast success. It's certainly noteworthy that most successful veteran chasers are scholars of Great Plains lore.

Unfortunately, ordinary travel guides barely suffice for the true Great Plains connoisseur. Much of what's published emphasizes "sensible" tourist attractions, the history of a town's wealthy gentry, and a focus on shopping, dining, and golf. One town is painted in exactly the same Chamber of Commerce brush as the next. Here we try to focus on attractions that inspire, conveying some element of the unique heritage and nature of this part of the country.

Furthermore, storm chasers tend to be limited to *short diversions lasting a couple of hours or less before convection breaks*. Unless it's a down day, chasers don't have time to immerse theirselves in structured activities. Most of the attractions presented here require only short attention spans.

This travel guide is an interactive primer for the deep introspective knowledge that many chasers are destined to accumulate roaming the Plains. For the traveller who needs more than what's presented here, I recommend the excellent *Roadside Geology* series that will have chasers chiselling at a roadcut a few hours before convection. There's also the *Off the Beaten Path* series, though the treatment of the Great Plains is somewhat inconsistent, ranging from pedestrian to reverent depending on the book. In spite of this, the series is a safe bet for those demanding less adventure and more creature comfort on the road.

Road choices

If I chose all the roads frequented by storm chasers, this book would be well over 600 pages! I've had to narrow down the selection to several dozen trunk routes, and have tried to confine these to the most frequented areas of the Great Plains. The roads listed here are *familiar long-haul routes that a chaser typically uses from 9 am to 3 pm to reach a target area.*

I've also aligned the direction of flow to provide the most likely afternoon routing; this usually heads toward the axis of highest tornado potential on the lower High Plains, but I may invert the routing if it starts in a poorly populated area. For example Denver's larger severe weather potential suggests the book should contain a Cheyenne to Denver routing, but a Denver to Cheyenne route serves a larger number of chasers.

GPS coordinates

You won't have to worry about wasting time criss-crossing town and pulling up Google Maps to find your way around, because all significant destinations here carry the latitude and longitude coordinates down to the thousandth of a degree. Just program the coordinates into your GPS as a destination and enjoy the ride.

Off the Beaten Path

At the end of each section is Off The Beaten Path, which lists many great ideas when you're looking for a place to kill some time, yet keep an eye to the sky. There are several criteria we use in choosing a destination:

- a great setting in which to relax and meditate in the hours before convection occurs
- doesn't require a big time commitment and having to wait on a tour schedule
- easy to get in and out of when convection breaks with no traffic congestion
- conveys some aspect of the Great Plains' culture, history, science, and nature
- is of traditional interest or significance to storm chasers.

If you don't like a choice, or have one of your own to be considered, please write! It may be added in the next version.

GREAT PLAINS TRAVEL GUIDE

West Texas

West Texas, in the opinion of the author, is truly the last frontier of the Wild West. Most American travellers remember it for the ten hours of their life they'll never get back — ten hours of sheer monotony between the cosmopolitan comforts of El Paso and San Antonio. Yet beneath the veneer of sparsity is a surprisingly rich history and geology, a secret glossed over by most recreational guides due to the sparsity of golf courses, antique shopping, and tourist attractions.

Erratic rainfall, poor natural resources, and distance from transportation networks have allowed southwest Texas to escape the tentacles of any significant human activity and land development, isolating it culturally. The region offers the chaser endless miles of mesquite scrubland, rocky terrain, and unique geological corners to explore, along with a surprising number of settlements that faded into ghost towns, unable to eke out an economic existence. There is perhaps no finer area for travellers to reflect on what this subtropical desert was like before the dawn of man, and to contemplate what its future will hold, perhaps as it one day becomes gridded with suburban sprawl from San Antonio and Austin.

The geography of Southwest Texas is divided into three portions by the Interstate highway belts. The area north of Interstate 20, particularly to the northeast, harbors a sizable population. For example, agriculture, particularly cotton production, is a major industry in the Lubbock and Abilene area. This in turn promotes a large rural population. In contrast, the region between Interstate 10 and Interstate 20 has an economy based heavily on oil production, so the population is condensed into urban centers and several small towns. Along and south of Interstate 10, the drier climate, rugged terrain, and weaker capacity of the land leaves a very thin assortment of cattle and sheep ranching as the only profitable activities. Ranching is generally associated with very low population figures. These regions indeed contain some of the lowest population density figures in the United States, comparable to the vacant realms of eastern Montana and northern Nevada.

In terms of driving, distances are vast and the long haul can be quite monotonous. Interestingly, west Texas has the highest speed limits in the nation: 80 mph (130 km/h).

Storms on the frontier

June 11, 1882, Seminole Cave [between Del Rio and Sanderson]: At 8:00 pm last Sunday night a terrific storm came upon the railroaders in camp at the Pecos, sweeping everything before it. It lasted nearly an hour, during which torrents of water fell. The thunder and lightning were wonderfully severe. One of Hall's tents was struck and one man was killed and three sent swirling out of the tent in a senseless state. Henry and Dilley had their entire headquarters and camp, and over 100 tents at their works blown down.

San Antonio Daily Express, 1882

Climatology of wildflowers

Wildflowers are an often-overlooked treasure of southwest Texas. The best displays peak in late March south of I-10, in early April along I-10, and in mid April along I-20. A wet fall, followed by a brutally cold winter and a wet spring are precursors to an explosive bluebonnet displays

TIM VASQUEZ

The majestic Pecos River, one of the most significant geological features of west Texas. Here we see the river carving into Cretaceous limestone, the remains of an ancient sea bed. The river and its culture were featured in a September 1993 issue of National Geographic magazine. *(Tim Vasquez)*

These daytime limits were signposted starting in summer 2006 on Interstate 20 westward from Monahans and Interstate 10 westward from Kerrville in the Hill Country.

Meteorology

Among some chasers, common sentiment is that southwest Texas is too far, too desolate, too devoid of roads — a prickly fringe area of the Great Plains; and that any real storm action remains north of Midland and Abilene. Although some of these facts are true, the weak storm climatology is skewed by the fact that the area south of Midland is sparsely inhabited. Hailstorm damage is measured in terms of broken cacti and toppled ant hills, while tornadoes simply tear up range fences and scatter native vegetation.

Chase tactics in recent years have painted out southwest Texas as an excellent target. Every March, the opening bars of the Great Plains chase season are trumpeted loudly in this region. As Gulf moisture begins making its cyclic advances northward, it encounters upper-level patterns that focus on these southern regions. Low-level winds become easterly with the strong early-season dynamics, and the tropical air mass rises rapidly on the steep terrain. Powerful thunderstorms develop. Many of these are supercell storms. In March and April, the Sierra Huacha range west of Del Rio is often a focus for strong upslope flow that breaks the cap and sends powerful supercells drifting eastward into Del Rio and the U.S. 90 corridor towards dusk.

Later in the spring, the region tends to be far south of the polar front jet and becomes strongly capped. It merely becomes a conduit for moisture to move through. Nevertheless, backed winds occurring in poorly-sampled regions can produce unexpected surprises. Veteran chaser Tim Marshall has pointed out "Old Faithful": the rogue supercell that pops up southwest of Fort Stockton on a May afternoon at a time when the dryline is drawing chasers to the Texas Panhandle.

Unfortunately storm chasers, uneasy about remaining under a strong cap and near a marginal road network, are rarely around to sample the buffet that Old Faithful offers. When chasers congregate on the Caprock, who are the brave ones waiting in Saragosa?

The allure of West Texas

As a sixth generation Texan, I have grown to love the "Great Southwest". The great geography of Texas, and the Southern Plains always leaves me with some sort of serendipitous experience. Although many think that the Southern Plains are just that, plain, I love the stark contrast of the often rugged terrain coexisting with beautiful plant life and the occasional glimpse of native wildlife.

My family's roots are in Texas and Oklahoma. My Grandfather was legendary western swing artist Bob Wills' piano player back in the years before World War Two. Those guys spent alot of time driving the back roads of west Texas playing dances. When I am traversing the countryside I cannot help but think what it must of been like for the pioneer settlers, and my grandfather, years ago. It is for me is a spiritual thing...

ROBERT WILLIS
Fort Worth, TX chaser

West Texas storms

I would have to say West Texas is an underrated chase area. A dryline event initiating on the TX/NM border can lead to several hours of chasing on some of the best road networks in the country! And you can't beat the visibility! We also may not have as great of tornado concentration as Oklahoma does, but we do get awesome storm structure and some of the best chase day sunsets!

DAVID DRUMMOND
Lubbock, TX chaser

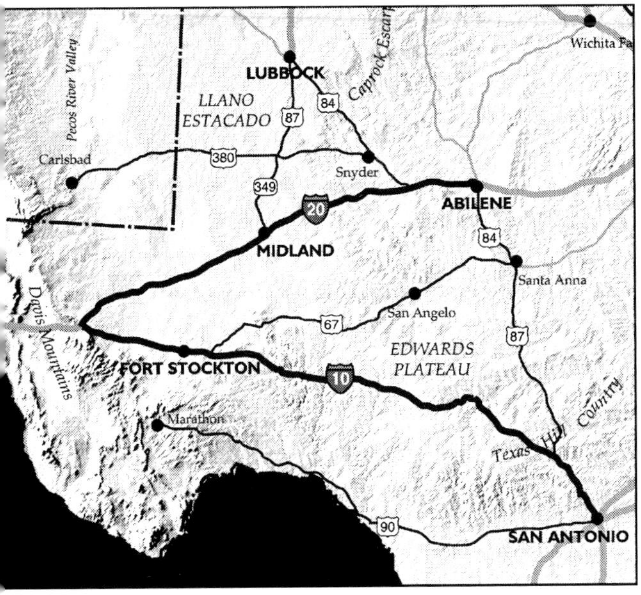

Road Guide

■ San Antonio - Del Rio - Marathon TX

U.S. 90 (326 miles; 5.0 hours)

Driving out of **San Antonio**, the road passes through rolling mesquite forest, then suddenly enters a series of rich cotton and hay fields. **Castroville** is famous for its Alsatian (northeastern French) colonialists who arrived in 1844, fashioning a town that was considered positively "un-Texan" by an 1850s-era visitor. Immediately past town, the road ascends 150 ft, climbing into the Texas Hill Country. Rolling terrain is densely populated with mesquite. **Hondo** is passed. Three miles west of the longtime agricultural center of **Sabinal**, a roadcut [N29.312 W99.531] exposes a layer of grayish-green volcanic rocks. At the mining town **Knippa**, the highway angles between two volcanic hills that loom 290 ft above the surrounding terrain [N29.290 W99.657]. These were underwater volcanoes that were active during the Cretaceous period. The southern one is mined and is a major source of basalt for road pavement, railroad ballast, and decorative stone. About 20 miles west of **Uvalde**, the vegetation begins transitioning from mesquite to desert forms: ceniza, blackbrush, and creosote. About eight miles short of **Brackettville**, you pass next to the unmistakable Del Rio WSR-88D radome (DFX) [N29.273 W100.281]. Brackettville was home of Fort Clark (1852-1946), an Army post where WWII figures George S. Patton and George C. Marshall once served. Terrain here is mostly alluvial (river deposits) but there are some outcroppings of ancient Cretaceous limestone as well as a few volcanic hills. The dusty border town of **Del Rio** is based on international trade and is home to an Air Force pilot training base. Many Vietnam War pilots got their first rides on fighter planes here. From Del Rio, you head northwest. The road passes through carved limestone cliffs around **Lake Amistad** and reaches **Comstock**. Roadcuts are teeming with fossils. The road then traverses the majestic Petry Bridge, the highest in Texas, which crosses the Pecos River 273 ft above the waterline [N29.709 W101.351]. The chaser enters the barren, remote country of Old Roy Bean and historic **Langtry**, the Southwest Texas Wild West. The ceniza and blackbrush disappears past Langtry, leaving mostly creosote and prickly pear. Cattle and sheep grazing are the local trade. The near-ghost town **Dryden** can be found at the TX 349 junction. Finally the road wanders into the ranching town of **Sanderson**, which was nearly destroyed by a flash flood on June 11, 1965 due to torrential storms west of town. A long-gone ghost town is along the way: **Longfellow** [N30.162 W102.638], about 5 miles into Pecos County; it thrived at the turn of the

20th century as a railroad pickup point for livestock then declined in the 1940s; the railroad buildings still remain along the track to the south of the road. Near **Marathon**, old volcanoes and mountain peaks loom in sight and the scrubby vegetation gives way to dry grama grasslands with rich outcroppings of ancient, white novaculite rock. A sizable area of the region has been overgrazed, with desert creosote and tarbrush replacing the native grama grasses.

■ San Antonio - Fort Stockton - Davis Mountains TX

Interstate 10 (386 miles; 5.5 hours)

Driving out of **San Antonio** past Loop 410, you enter hilly terrain that rests on top of the Balcones Fault Zone. There are numerous underground faults that fill the area from Loop 410 all the way past Loop 1604. As the **Fiesta Texas** amusement park passes by on the left, the road immediately leaves the fault zone and enters the Texas Hill Country. This is an area of geologic uplift that has been carved out by widespread stream erosion. Hills tower 450 ft above the freeway. Limestone outcroppings are common, allowing for a thriving quarry industry, and forests of Texas oak and hackberry flank the freeway. Near **Boerne**, Cascade Caverns offers a good stop for the geology-savvy. Such caverns within the limestone throughout the Hill Country are part of the Edwards Aquifer Recharge Zone, which collects much of San Antonio and Austin's drinking water. From here onward for about 150 miles, you are in the densest white-tailed deer population in North America, so be vigilant, especially at night! **Comfort**, lying along the Guadalupe River in a region of upslope flow with southeasterly winds, is a name often associated with flash floods, including the August 1978 flood that nearly destroyed the town, the July 1987 flood that killed 10 on a church bus, and yet more flooding in July 2002. West of Comfort the freeway ascends dramatically from 1600 ft to 2030 ft MSL, before reaching the cultural and ranching haven of **Kerrville**. West of town, deep road cuts rich with fossils are frequent. Some of the limestone rock strata are even folded, suggesting a collapse into large caverns below the surface. The road soon tops out onto the Edwards Plateau and becomes relatively flat [N30.163 W99.241]. At **Segovia** the road descends into the highly eroded Johnson Fork Valley, and six miles later descends once again into the Llano River valley as it skirts the ranching town of **Junction**. [See Off The Beaten Path: TELEGRAPH] The freeway then crosses eroded terrain, then ascends onto the Edwards Plateau again about thirty miles west of Junction. Land here is generally unused except for grazing. Mesquite and juniper brush begins replacing the oaks, allowing for good sky visibility. The largely sheep-ranching town of **Sonora**, nestled in an eroded valley, was promised railroad service in 1908, but 22 years would pass before the first train would roll into town. The town's prosperity peaked in the 1970s with an oil boom but has been in a slow decline since, partly due to the rail stop closure in 1984. The area's rounded hills are replaced with barren mesas. These west Texas mesas are actually identical to the hills further east, but the weathering mechanisms are harsher due to the lack of soil moisture, giving them their sharp edges. Near **Mile Marker 371** just north of the freeway is Crockett Heights, the remains of Ozona Air Force Station which had a long-range defense radar during the 1960s. **Ozona**, another sheep and goat ranching town, was founded during the 1890s with the hope of turning it into a tourist haven due to the "healthy" ozone that was supposedly in the air. The road descends nearly 650 ft into the Pecos River valley, brushing **Sheffield**, which during the mid-19th century was a major Pecos River crossing point for California-bound settlers, protected by troops at nearby Fort Lancaster [See Off the Beaten Path: FORT LANCASTER]. The freeway ascends out of the valley and onto a dramatic expanse of the Edwards Plateau, studded with vast mesas. The region is oil-rich, and the number of pumpjacks multiplies. The near ghost-town of **Bakersfield** did not exist until the oil boom of the 1920s. By 1930 it had a hotel, pool hall, restaurant, and a population of 1,000; the population now is barely two dozen. Immediately west of Bakersfield, north of the freeway, is 300 ft Squawteat Peak, a rich archaeological site that uncovered a Native American city which flourished as recently as the 14th century. The mesquite trees are gradually replaced by scrubby creosote bushes, signifying the deep immersion into the Chihuahuan Desert. Mesas towering to 400 ft fill the horizon. You then reach the large city of **Fort Stockton**, which originally protected the southern route to California in the 1850s but grew into a regional ranching hub. [See Off the Beaten Path: SIERRA MADERA ASTROBLEME] The Davis Mountains begin looming in sight. The sister towns of **Balmorhea** and **Saragosa** share runoff from a series of springs south of Balmorhea which have cultivated a rich cradle of agriculture here for centuries. In modern times cantaloupe and dry onion are the favored crops. Balmorhea swelled to a thousand residents in the 1930s, dropping gradually due to urbanization and mechanized agriculture. Saragosa was the site of a deadly tornado in May 1987 from an "Old Faithful" type supercell, killing or injuring over half the town's population. As I-10 meets I-20 [N31.090 W104.053], the road enters the Davis Mountains [See Off the Beaten Path: DAVIS MOUNTAINS AREA]

■ San Antonio - Abilene TX

U.S. 87 to U.S. 84 (249 miles; 4.0 hours)

NOTE: See San Antonio - Fort Stockton (Interstate 10) for the first fifty miles of this drive.

This route starts in the hilly Balcones Fault Zone in northern **San Antonio**, crossing into the Texas Hill Country south of **Boerne**. Leaving Interstate 10 at **Comfort** the road begins a gradual ascent from 1500 ft to 2080 ft into rugged limestone hills, laid here as ocean floor sediment in Cretaceous times 100 million years ago when a vast sea covered this area. This region has a rich deer population and is a favorite haunt for hunters during the autumn months. **Fredericksburg** was settled by Germans in 1846. For sixty years almost no one in town even spoke English! It still retains its rich German heritage with a booming tourist economy. **Cherry Springs** was also a German town which took advantage of being on the San Antonio to El Paso route in the 1850s. Past Cherry Springs there are some unique road cuts through reddish Cambrian sandstone and limestone, deposited half a billion years ago. Six miles further is the near-ghost town of Loyal Valley [N30.576 W99.008]; take the FM 2242 spur to see it. The town was an overnight stagecoach stop between San Antonio and El Paso during the 1860s and 1870s. The picturesque **Llano River** crossing [N30.661 N99.109] is then reached; it can be enjoyed from a turnout on the north side. The road then descends into **Mason**, which grew up around an Army fort during the 1850s which provided protection against Indian raids. Many older buildings are made of the reddish sandstone found to the south. Further along is **Camp Air** [N30.901 W99.282], situated in broad fields that were maintained by Comanche tribes and used as grazing land. **Brady** is a town with surprisingly young roots, dating back only to the 1870s, but it rapidly grew into the region's livestock shipping hub. Leaving town, the road passes through **Cow Gap**, flanked by 400 ft hills, which channeled mid-19th century cattle trails. From Cow Gap, if visibility is good you will be able to see northward 50 miles! The road passes **Fife**, half a mile to the west, which had 200 residents and two stores in its 1910s heyday but has dwindled to only about a dozen residents. You then cross the **Colorado River**, whose waters ultimately leads to Austin; it must be noted that this is *not* the same river that carves the Grand Canyon. [See Off The Beaten Path (North Texas): TRICKHAM] The road soon leads to the silica mining town of **Santa Anna** with its Cretaceous limestone hills. Northwest of **Coleman** are several road cuts into Permian limestone and shales, which are rich with fossils. You then pass through the town of **Lawn**, a town that shifted once with a new railroad routing. Just 10 miles short of **Abilene** is the Callahan Divide, which towers 450 ft (140 m) above the surrounding countryside.

■ Santa Anna - Fort Stockton TX

U.S. 67 (244 miles; 3.8 hours)

Leaving **Santa Anna**, the terrain becomes composed of Permian limestone and sandstone. **Valera** and **Talpa** were small ranching towns that grew along the GC&SF railroad. Short live oak forests continue all the way to **Ballinger**, which has one of the only operating Carnegie libraries in Texas, built in 1908. The town benefited from access to the Colorado River, and grew overnight in June 1886 with extensive promotion of town lots and the arrival of the GC&SF railroad. Farming was surprisingly profitable and cotton became an important crop in the region during the 20th century. Terrain becomes quite flat, but mesas poke out on the western horizon, indicating where tougher limestones resisted weathering action. **Rowena** was another town that grew only with the arrival of the GC&SF railroad, settled mostly by Germans and Czechs; the town is the birthplace of Bonnie Parker of the Bonnie & Clyde outlaw duo. **Miles** was also a railroad town, containing an opera house that is on the National Register of Historic Places. A mixture of wide open sorghum fields and mesquite tracts are found approaching **San Angelo**. The city was hit by two big weather disasters: a tornado on May 11, 1953, killing 13 and injuring 159; and a massive hailstorm on May 28, 1995 that produced $120 million in damage. Dimpled cars can still be found crawling around town to this day. Leaving town, the highway passes by the 150 ft Twin Buttes. **Tankersley** [N31.350 W100.642] is a near ghost town that formed along the railroad, eventually peaking at over 70 residents in the 1940s. Descending into a rugged valley, the highway enters **Mertzon**, a ranching town spurred by the Kansas City, Mexico & Orient (KCM&O) railroad, which soon took up petroleum in its economy. Just out of town, the highway skirts the Mertzon Oil Field. Barnhart is another KCM&O railroad town that got its start in 1910. Approaching **Big Lake**, the road passes through the Price Oil Field, which led to the town's rapid growth in the 1920s. **Rankin** also expanded during the 1920s oil boom, having two 46-room hotels. It had a population of over 1500 in its heyday, and has levelled off to 1000. The road winds through flat terrain, between mesas, reaching **McCamey**, which grew entirely due to oil, not the railroad. **Girvin** is a near-ghost town that flourished along the KCM&O railroad, sporting hotels and saloons during the 1910s. Just outside of town, south of the road, is the 350 ft Girvin Butte, then passes through a gap between East Mesa and Big Mesa before reaching the junction with **I-10**. From here you continue to Fort Stockton. [See Off the Beaten Path: SIERRA MADERA ASTROBLEME]

■ Abilene - Pecos - Far West Texas

Interstate 20 (283 miles; 4.1 hours)

Leaving **Abilene**, the countryside is saturated with a mix of cotton and wheat farmland and red, iron-oxide rich Permian soil. The town of **Tye** is located along the approach path to Dyess AFB to the south, and it's common to see sleek B-1B bombers cross low over the freeway during weekday mornings and evenings. Native vegetation is dominated by short mesquite trees and lotebush. Like **Tye**, **Merkel** is yet another town along the freeway that is home to Texans working at Dyess AFB. Just past Merkel, cuestas begin dotting the landscape. They are similar to those seen in eastern Kansas: leaning, wavelike hills that form due to differential erosion where layers of sandstone tilt eastward and upward out of the ground. During the 1880s, **Trent** and the larger town of **Sweetwater** were railroad stops, the former being exactly 430 miles from Texarkana and El Paso. The ranchland surrounding Sweetwater was so infested with rattlesnakes by the 1950s that folks from town pitched in to help pare the numbers down. The Rattlesnake Roundup festivities eventually grew out of this, hosted annually on the second weekend in March. Sweetwater is also the site of a rare morning tornado, at 7:15 am on April 19, 1986, which killed one person and injured 100. At a spot immediately west of Sweetwater [N32.450 W100.483] the freeway ascends a shallow piece of the Caprock Escarpment onto the Llano Estacado, crossing from older Permian sandstones onto a new blanket of Quaternary sediment that originated from the Rocky Mountains. The town of **Roscoe**, from 1908 to 1978, thrived because of its unique connection from the Texas & Pacific Railway to the Santa Fe railway barely 50 miles northwest in Fluvanna; it was said to be one of the most profitable short lines in the country, and the town has held a surprisingly steady population through the years. Six miles past Roscoe at **Exit 230** is the ghost town of **Brownlee**, developed in 1908 in expectation of a Lamesa to Sterling City railroad spur; although two stores and a school were built, the town withered away by the 1920s. **Loraine** grew slowly as a loading point for cotton and cattle; like many towns on the Plains it has been in a very slow decline since the 1950s. **Colorado City** (this Colorado instance rhyming with "tomato") grew in the 1880s as a major ranching city, having an astounding population of 6,000 that was barely matched again in the 1960s. **Westbrook**, flanked by the 150 ft Morgan Peak just west of town, was a typical prosperous railroad town that peaked in the 1910s. The road then leaves the Caprock, descending into an eroded river basin. The 1890s ghost town of **Iatan** [N32.335 W101.134] had well over a hundred residents, a post office, and a school, but almost nothing is left now. It is located just south the freeway near mile marker 200. Two miles past the county line, the freeway begins ascending 100 ft back onto the Caprock. The annual rainfall becomes too small to support agriculture, and fields become heavily irrigated, containing mostly cotton. **Coahoma** grew in 1881 as a small railroad town, then prospered during the 1920s and 1970s oil booms. Near **Exit 181** is the sprawling Alon USA refinery, which processes 2.5 million gallons of crude oil per day and supplies nearly all of the gas sold at Fina and 7-Eleven stores throughout Texas. Nestled in an eroded valley in the Caprock is **Big Spring**, the site of battles between the Comanche and the Shawnee, and eventually grew into a cattle trail campsite during the 1870s, followed by railroad growth in the 1880s. [See Off the Beaten Path: BIG SPRING STATE PARK] **Stanton** was a religious colony run by German Catholics in the 1880s; the weather was too harsh for grain farming, forcing the Germans to move away in the 1890s, and the town embraced a more successful ranching economy. The soil type from here on gradually changes to aridisol, the type native to Arizona and Nevada. Farmland begins vanishing, giving way to flat, grassy terrain populated by short mesquite shrubs. You then reach **Midland-Odessa**, the pair of oil production cities. **Midland** is the regional center of oil business and banking, while **Odessa**, 20 miles further west, is a manufacturing and production center.[See Off the Beaten Path: ODESSA METEOR CRATER] Only 16 miles past Odessa is the near ghost-town of **Penwell**, an oil boom-town from the 1920s that supported an area population as high as 3,000, but rapidly decayed during the 1940s. At **Exit 86** is Monahans Sand Hills State Park, where you can climb over wind-blown sand dunes [see Off the Beaten Path: MONAHANS SAND-HILLS] The ranching town of **Monahans**, which later grew during the 1930s oil and carbon black boom, holds the official record for hottest temperature in Texas, at 120 deg F on June 27, 1994. Past the the town of **Wickett**, you cross an underground fault zone that stretches north-south [N32.547 W103.042]. Very weak earthquakes are common in this region. Oil pumpjacks to the south of this spot specifically take advantage of oil trapped along the fault line. At **Pyote** you can leave the freeway to get a look at what is essentially a ghost town; the Pyote population reached 10,000 after WWII but is now 75, with only a museum and crumbling buildings left. The freeway soon begins a gradual descent into the Pecos River valley. On the west side is **Pecos**, originally serving as a cattle trail camp in the 1880s; by the next decade it had railroad service and an astounding reputation for frontier violence. Fifty years later it was an important WWII aircraft training base. Desert creosote bushes begin dominating the landscape. Twenty miles further is the town of **Toyah**, a ranching hub during the 1880s that prospered when the railroad came in 1910. The town has been in slow decline since the Great Depression, with only about ten percent of its original population left. The freeway then approaches the Davis Mountains through Ninemile Draw, with the Texas & Pacific railroad following faithfully only a mile north into Moody Draw. The junction with **Interstate 10** is reached [N31.090 W104.053]. [See Off The Beaten Path: DAVIS MOUNTAINS AREA]

■ Abilene - Lubbock TX

U.S. 84 (166 miles; 2.5 hours)

NOTE: See Abilene - Pecos (I-20) for first 50 miles of this trip.

Turning northwest from **Roscoe**, you encounter several ghost towns that attempted to prosper along the Roscoe-Fluvanna railroad, just west of the highway. The first is half a mile north of FM 1982: **Wastella** [N32.510 W100.649]; the second is at FM 4196: **Inadale** [N32.540 W100.682]. Both had stores and post offices during the 1920s, but declined after the Great Depression. Two miles past the town of **Hermleigh**, which fared better due to a steady ranching economy, the Caprock ends and the road descends into eroded terrain. Triassic sandstones are exposed here. **Snyder** was an 1870s buffalo hunting center that later embraced farming, ranching, and petroleum. The small town of **Dermott** moved with the railroads in 1915, merely a cattle pickup station and oil boom town in the late 1940s, and is now a ghost town. Descending into the Mountain Fork Brazos River valley and crossing the river, the road brushes past the tiny but slowly growing railroad town of **Justiceburg**. **Post** was designed by cereal entrepreneur C. W. Post as a model town; saloons were kept out and its streets were lined with trees. It became a major cotton and textile producer. Just north of town you can see the bluffs northwest that mark the Caprock Escarpment. Leaving Post, in only 3 miles (5 km) the terrain rises from 2600 ft (790 m) to 2950 ft (900 m). At the top is the flat Llano Estacado [N33.215 W101.426], a blanket of young erosional sands from the Rocky Mountains. It serves as a rich agricultural bed for cotton, wheat, and sorghum farmland that seems to stretch into infinity. This part of the plains also has rich oil fields, and many pumpjacks are in sight. **Slaton** was intended to be a community for a railroad servicing depot, and its streets were laid out in the fashion of Washington, D.C.; the characteristic radial pattern is still present, centered on City Hall. You then reach **Lubbock**.

■ Snyder TX - Carlsbad NM

U.S. 84/180 (203 miles; 3.3 hours)

Leaving **Snyder**, the road weaves through the eroded terrain of the Colorado River system. Driving into the town of **Gail** is like going back in time: it sits in an oil-poor region on rocky terrain unsuitable for farming. The town has never had a population greater than 250 since the Great Depression, and the entire county has less than 1,000 inhabitants! Surrounding Gail are mesas rising 300 ft above the valley floor. These mesas are part of the Llano Estacado, composed of tougher rock that refuses to erode. About 16 miles west of Gail, the road ascends the eroded Caprock Escarpment [N32.742 W101.734] and rises dramatically onto the pancake-flat, uneroded Llano Estacado. All the signs of thriving agriculture suddenly appear. The source of the Colorado River, the grand waterway that passes through Austin, is about four miles south of this point, and many of the dry creeks between the Caprock and Lamesa feed into the river. **Lamesa** is a town built on wealth from cotton. Fifteen miles west of Lamesa is the tiny town of **Sand**, a young town appearing on maps in 1935 and serving as a local nucleus for farming and ranching. Approaching **Seminole**, the appearance of pumpjacks hints at the economy's reliance on petroleum rather than agriculture, some of which includes irrigated watermelon farming. The town holds the official record for Texas' coldest temperature: -23 deg F on the snow-covered morning of February 8, 1933. [See Off The Beaten Path: SHAFTER LAKE] Twenty-four miles west is the **New Mexico state line** [N32.727 W103.064] dividing rural State Line Street. Approaching **Hobbs**, very complex underground topography creates subterranean pools of crude oil, allowing oil and natural gas to replace cotton as the main source of income. In places, the air is thick with the aroma of petroleum. A mile west of the split with S.H. 8, the road leaves the western edge of the Llano Estacado [N32.684 W103.407]; this edge forms a New Mexico Caprock called the Mescalero. The terrain becomes rugged and begins a slow drop, the result of about 3 million years of carving by the massive Pecos River system found further west. The highway then reaches **Carlsbad**. The famous caverns are not actually located in Carlsbad but are 25 miles southwest by road, near Whites City.

■ Midland - Lubbock TX

TX 349 to U.S. 87 (118 miles; 2.0 hours)

The flat terrain around **Midland** is used mostly for grazing. However, rugged underground topography allows for vast pooling of oil, making for a healthy petroleum industry where the pump jacks outnumber the cows! The drive angles north across the Llano Estacado, a huge, flat blanket of very young, sandy Quaternary deposits that consist of accumulated erosion from the Rocky Mountains during the past few million years. Very little of the land is developed, and agriculture is poor because of a profound lack of much-needed winter snowfall which helps hydrate the topsoil. Past the junction with TX 176, the road curves northeast and descends into eroded, rolling terrain. The town of **Patricia** was formed in 1923 as a land sales town, becoming a minor nucleus for scattered cotton farming operations throughout southeastern Dawson County. Approaching **Lamesa**, cotton fields rapidly fill the landscape. This area gets some snowfall during the winter, contributing to soil moisture, and has the single highest density of cotton fields in North America. Planting activities are usually in full swing in early May. Rolling farmland punctuates the drive. The town of **O'Donnell** was developed during the 1910s as a community for cotton farmers in the northern county area, and still serves this purpose. **Tahoka** has similar roots to Lamesa but also emphasizes cattle production, being in proximity to grain and corn agriculture that produces feed. Cotton in the crop fields diminishes and is gradually replaced with sorghum and wheat, much of which is used for livestock feed. You then reach the sprawling city of **Lubbock**.

Texas Caprock near Post, Texas. Contours are drawn every 10 meters. Note the dramatic transition from low rolling terrain (east side) to a flat plateau of agricultural land (west side). The flat terrain is the Llano Estacado, a vast carpet of sands and soils eroded from the Rocky Mountains. *(USGS)*

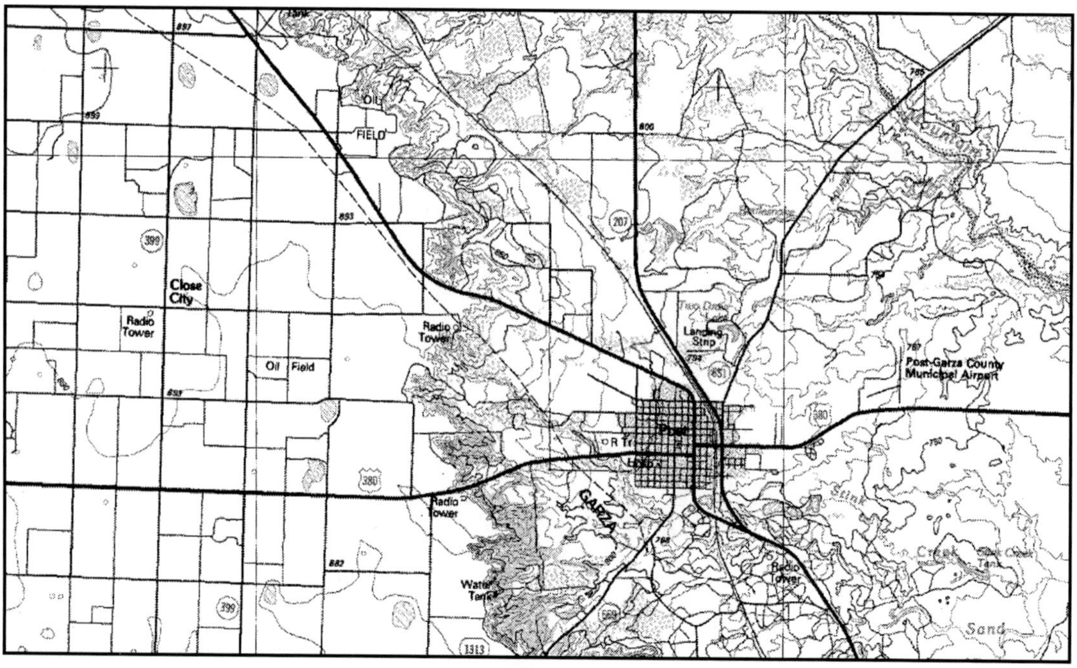

Off the beaten path

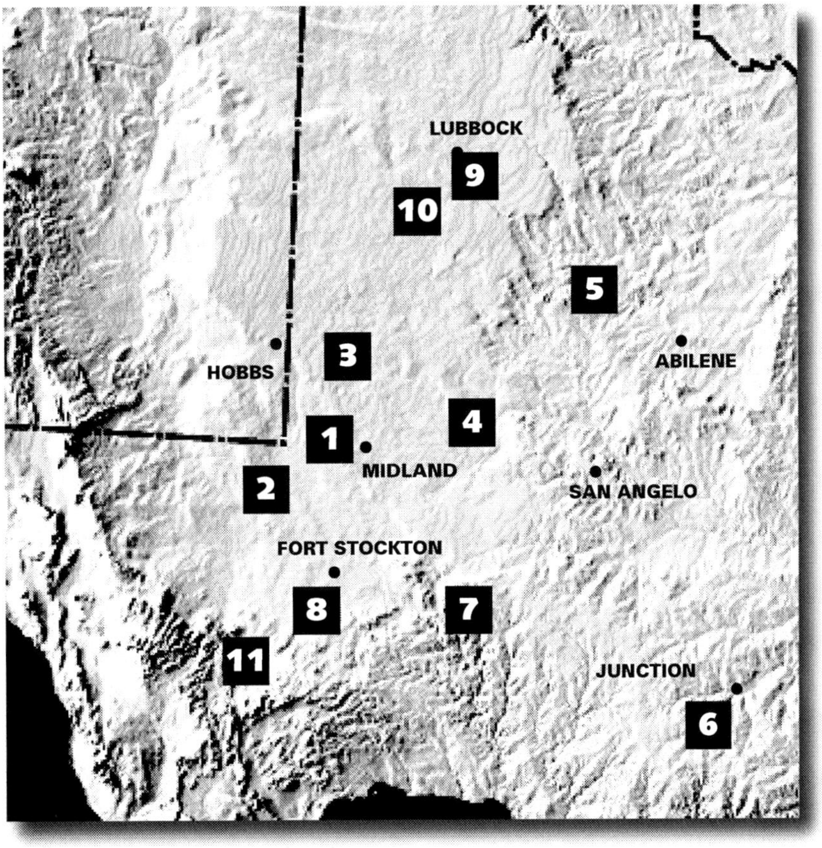

Interstate 20 Corridor

1 Odessa Meteor Crater. West of Odessa at Exit 108, then 3.4 miles to the south is the free-admission Odessa Meteor Crater [N31.756 W102.479]. At 500 ft wide, it is only a shallow 15 feet deep, though it was originally much deeper until it filled it in. The crater occurred about 20,000 years ago, the result of an aerial meteor disintegration rather than a direct impact. Many meteor fragments have been recovered in a plume northwest of the crater.

2 Monahans Sandhills State Park. Monahans, surrounded by sand, saw the hottest temperature in Texas, 120 deg F, set on June 28, 1994. Along Interstate 20, Sandhills State Park [N31.616 W102.811] gives you a chance to clamber and roll around on Sahara-like dunes rising to more than 50 ft tall. This is part of a vast belt of sand that extends northward through much of Winkler County, blown from the Pecos River Valley and deposited here during the past one million years. Just southwest of Pyote is the WWII facility Pyote AFB, nicknamed Rattlesnake Field due to the numerous rattlesnakes uncovered during its construction. It housed hundreds of retired B-29 Stratofortress aircraft after the war. The ruins are still accessible.

3 Shafter Lake. Near Seminole, Shafter Lake [N32.413 W102.648] is a peculiar ghost town, being located on the north shores of a natural lake. Speculators had great success selling lots in the 1900s as West Texas lakefront property! The town reached the lively population of 500 with a bank, churches, a store, and a stone schoolhouse. Unfortunately it lost a county seat bid to Andrews in 1910, and began a slow death spiral. Only a few ruins are left. The cemetery [N32.381 W102.661] is on the south side of the lake and requires some circuitous routing on dirt roads. To get to Shafter Lake, take US 385 south from Seminole 20 miles to FM 1967, then head west 3 miles.

4 Big Spring State Park. On the southwest side of Big Spring is Big Spring State Park [entrance N32.229 W101.481], a true jewel in the I-20 corridor. You can drive right up 300 ft Scenic Mountain and park to observe convective developments and get a suntan, then wander around on marked nature walk trails. The visitor center has a display of fossils and Indian artifacts. To get there take Business I-20 to the west side and look for FM 700; the entrance will be adjacent to a large hill.

Caprock Region

5 Rayner ghost town. From Aspermont, head eight miles east on US 380 to the ghost town of Rayner [N33.123 W100.085]. Vying for the Stonewall county seat in the 1890s, it had 250 residents, a business district, and a stone courthouse. Unfortunately in 1898 Aspermont won the vote for county seat, and the town slowly dissolved to virtually nothing. The cemetery is a couple of miles south at [N33.093 W100.092]. Driving a few miles east on U.S. 380 you reach the tiny town of Old Glory, which dates back to the 1880s but was hit hard by urbanization in the 1930s and drought in the 1950s. At the turn of the century, very few residents remained.

Hill Country

6 Telegraph ghost town. If you're in the Junction area along I-10, head 13 miles southwest from town to visit the ghost town of Telegraph [N30.327 W99.906]. Located in a rocky valley, the town got its start in the 1890s as a nucleus for area ranching operations. During the 1920s it evolved into a getaway for hunters and campers, with a park, a gas station, a store. It was a favorite destination of many affluent Texans, and its resident population soon reached 60. The town slowly dwindled into obscurity.

Edwards Plateau

7 Fort Lancaster historic site. A short excursion on TX 290 (I-10 Exit 343 or 325) brings one to the Fort Lancaster historic site [N30.667 W101.696], an Army post (1855-61) nestled in the Pecos Valley region a little east of Sheffield which protected settlers bound from San Antonio for El Paso. There's a nature trail, historic ruins, and exhibits.

8 Sierra Madera Crater. Meteor Crater near Winslow, Arizona is often thought of as the biggest meteor crater in the United States. This is not true. South of Fort Stockton, you can see an exposed impact crater 8 miles in diameter and actually drive into the basin on a major highway! The crater was produced by a meteor that hit in the post-Cretaceous era (about 65 million years ago). NASA has studied it as an analogue for the Moon's Copernicus crater and used it to train astronauts. Be aware that the Sierra Madera Crater is shallower and much less satisfying than Arizona's Meteor Crater but with a little imagination its presence is simply awe-inspiring. Seventeen miles south of Fort Stockton on U.S. 385, you ascend a hill at [N30.642 W102.942] with a natural gas plant just past the summit. You have driven onto the very rim of

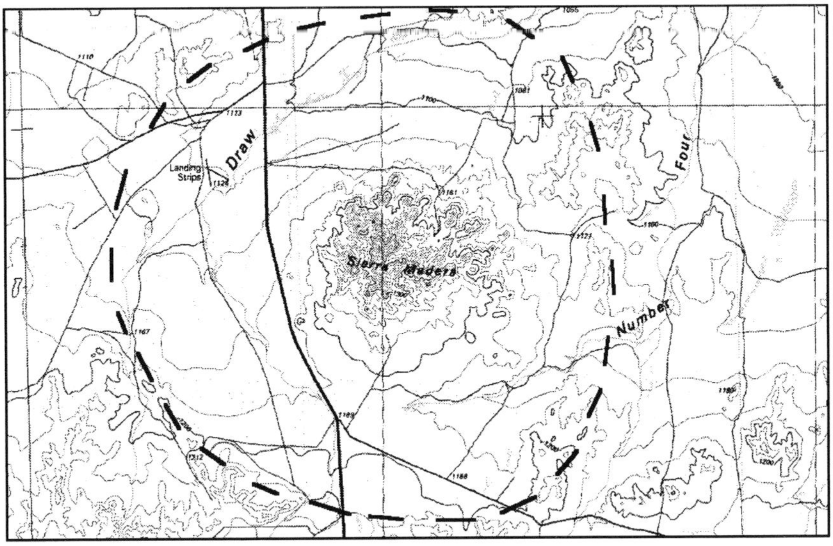

Topographic map of the Sierra Madera Astrobleme south of Fort Stockton. The 8-mile diameter crater wall (dashed) surrounds a 2-mile diameter area of uplifted rocks, essentially consisting of molten rebound from the meteor impact. Highway U.S. 385 is the north-south road in the left center of the illustration.

Set your odometer in downtown Marathon or Fort Stockton to figure the following locations:

Northern rim is 17.4 miles from Fort Stockton; 38.3 miles from Marathon.

Uplift area: 21.4 miles from Fort Stockton; 34.3 miles from Marathon.

Southern rim: 24.5 miles from Fort Stockton; 31.2 miles from Marathon.

(USGS)

this crater and entered the impact zone! Straight ahead and to your left is a group of hills 2 miles in diameter and up to 793 ft high. This is the scar of a massive central uplift caused by impact rebound. Geological strata have been shifted upward nearly a mile here, exposing older Permian rocks!

South Plains

9 Lubbock Lake. The Lubbock Lake Landmark State Historical Park [N33.627 W101.905] is a 336-acre treasure trove of nature and archaeological exhibits. It's located northwest of Lubbock outside the loop. There's a four-mile nature trail, a one-mile archaeological trail, and an indoor exhibit hall. When you're in the chase target area, it's a relaxing place to spend time when it's too late to stay in the hotel and too early to chase. Open Tue-Sat 9-5; Sun 1-5.

10 Gomez ghost town. Just west of Brownfield is the ghost town of Gomez [N33.174 W102.377]. At the turn of the 20th century, three visionaries saw it as the seat of Terry County, and during the 1900s they had it surveyed with grand designs for a public square and courthouse. In the mid 1910s, Brownfield wooed the railroads with free right-of-way, and in 1917 the new railroad track visited Brownfield and bypassed Gomez, sealing its fate. The old townsite, up until 1918, is half a mile south of the new town [N33.182 W102.378], and its cemetery can be found a mile to the east [N33.176 W102.360].

Far West Texas

11 Davis Mountains. When the dryline is tucked back into the mountains of West Texas and you're waiting on a helping hand from orographics, a jaunt around the Davis Mountains can be quite fun. If you enjoy taking a swimming break, Balmorhea State Park near Toyahvale [N30.945 W103.786] has a unique 2-acre artesian-fed swiming pool, 25 ft deep, 72-76 deg F year round, and populated by various fish and turtles. The UT McDonald Observatory [N30.672 W104.023] northwest of Fort Davis has plenty to offer during the day: not only cool temperatures at 6700 ft MSL, but a great visitor center and gift shop open 9-5 daily, with solar viewing at 11 am and 2 pm and guided tours at 11:30 and 2:30 pm (877-984-7827 / 915-426-3640; call for night programs).

GREAT PLAINS TRAVEL GUIDE

North Texas

North Texas was where the cradle of American civilization, with all its comforts and traditional values, rested firmly against endless prairie. Oklahoma and the Panhandles were still an eerie place, a vast land populated by buffalo hunters, Army soldiers, and powerful, dangerous tribes of Plains Indians. While towns like Gainesville, Denton, Dallas, and Fort Worth grew rapidly as agricultural centers during the 1840s and 1850s, settlements to the west struggled. Some towns in Clay and Jack County were wiped out by Kiowa and Comanche raids. These attacks were meant to instill a reign of terror against invaders of the hunter-gatherer Indian homeland.

It worked for awhile. In the end, familiar names such as Abilene, Wichita Falls, and Seymour would not appear on maps until 1880. In fact, nearly every town, big and small, in these western regions was founded during the 1880s, in sharp contrast to their East Texas cousins which appeared generations earlier! And it was during the 1880s that railroads built their spiderweb of steel into the Great Plains, transitioning the region from a Native American homeland into agricultural belt.

Since those early days, agriculture has perpetually dominated the economy of north Texas. The history books of the region became rather devoid, punctuated mainly by chapters such as the oil boom of the 1920s and the Great Depression and Dust Bowl eras of the 1930s. Tornadoes, however, have left very deep impressions on North Texas history: at least ten were killed in tornado disasters in Cisco in 1893, Sherman in 1896, Zephyr in 1909, Waco in 1953, Dallas in 1957, Paris in 1982, and Jarrell in 1997. The list of minor tornadoes is vast, and stories of them would fill volumes. Just after the turn of the century, a series of hailstorms raked North Texas with billions of dollars in property and agricultural losses, with 2003 a notorious year in the record books. Forecasting North Texas weather is no trivial matter.

Meteorology

North Texas storms are described by one very simple adjective: *massive.* Close proximity to deep, rich Gulf moisture, as well as favorable upper level wind fields, make the region a prime breeding ground for severe weather.

Chasing North Texas

When I am out on a storm chasing expedition , the experience is very spiritual for me. When I go out it is like taking a walk with an old friend. You will recount old memories, but of course there is always something new to discuss as well. Even in the familiar territory of North Texas, routes west on I-20, northwest on 287, or north on I-35, do not matter.

I will see familiar sights that I have probably experienced many dozens of times, then something inserts itself into the picture, and in that lies the true beauty of the experience. An old windmill, a "roadrunner", a speeding freight train running parallel to the highway, maybe a lonely old farmhouse. One cannot help but think about the history of the Plains, its indigenous inhabitants, and the early settlers. I think of the matter-of-fact way that these rural people deal with storms (a "bad cloud" is a common colloquialism).

I have learned to take a lawn chair with me, and if the opportunity presents itself I will stop, pull out the chair and just sit, enjoying whatever and wherever I happen to be. I don't have any one particular spot that I really enjoy over another, although there are some spectacular views to the west in Wise County, TX that I am fond of. I am just thankful when I have the privilege of getting a front-row seat to the real "Greatest Show on Earth".

ROBERT WILLIS
Fort Worth, TX chaser

Powerlines leading into the distance along U.S. 287 near Vernon, Texas in May 1999. *(Tim Vasquez)*

Behind Texas brawn

In 1995 I stopped at an entrance to a huge Hill Country ranch to have a look at the atmosphere. Mind you, I didn't cross into the property; I just stopped in the turnout. In the corner of my eye I caught a plume of dust, being stirred by an old pickup truck driving up from the ranch house. I decided to stay put, and figured the landowner was just running an errand.

Well it wasn't the case, as this old pickup pulled right up to my bumper and this 6' 6" monster of a man stepped out with long blond hair down to the small of his back. With a sweat-soaked old cowboy hat and his gunrack stocked nicely with rifles, this man did not look happy. I was outside my vehicle when he walked right up to me, pointed his dirty finger in my face and said: "Boy, what the hell are you doing on my property?" I quickly apologized, playing ignorant even though I was actually outside his cattleguard.

After I told him that I was chasing storms he looked at my vehicle plates, then his stern face broke a smile. He said, "You chasing storms all the way from Colorado?" At that point, we had a terrific conversation. He talked about the storms that went through his ranch in the past, and mentioned that he too is a storm lover. Towards the end he asked me to stay for dinner, but I politely declined. I needed to press on to the west just a bit more.

TIM SAMARAS
Denver, CO chaser

From a chasing standpoint, North Texas offers a mixed bag. The path to powerful storms are often snarled by road congestion and urban sprawl. Eastern regions, east of a line from Paris to Mexia, are blocked by tall oak and pine forests. The entire Dallas-Fort Worth area itself is a major bottleneck during weekday afternoons. Chasers need to step up their situational awareness when planning chases near Dallas suburbs and eastern wooded fringes.

The first rumblings of severe weather usually occur along the Gulf Coast. Warm-front episodes and strong upper-level dynamics are usually the focus for development in February and March. As spring arrives, severe weather events tend to spread westward toward the San Antonio and Del Rio area. Warm fronts remain the favored mechanism, with upslope flow on the Texas Hill Country taking on an important role in many events. April brings a shift northward into the Austin area, and to Dallas-Fort Worth late in April and early May. These mid-spring events are associated with an increased incidence of dryline activity as weather systems sweep rapidly eastward out of Colorado and New Mexico.

The most significant characteristic of North Texas is one shared with Oklahoma: a heavy diurnal-nocturnal bias from west to east. Storms have a strong tendency to form in western parts of the region during the afternoon hours. These then propagate into the I-35 corridor just after dark, and into the Piney Woods of east Texas after midnight. This characteristic has not been quantified to any significant extent in professional journals, but it is a very real effect, probably the cumulative result of many instances of diurnal development in high terrain along the dryline's favored west Texas position.

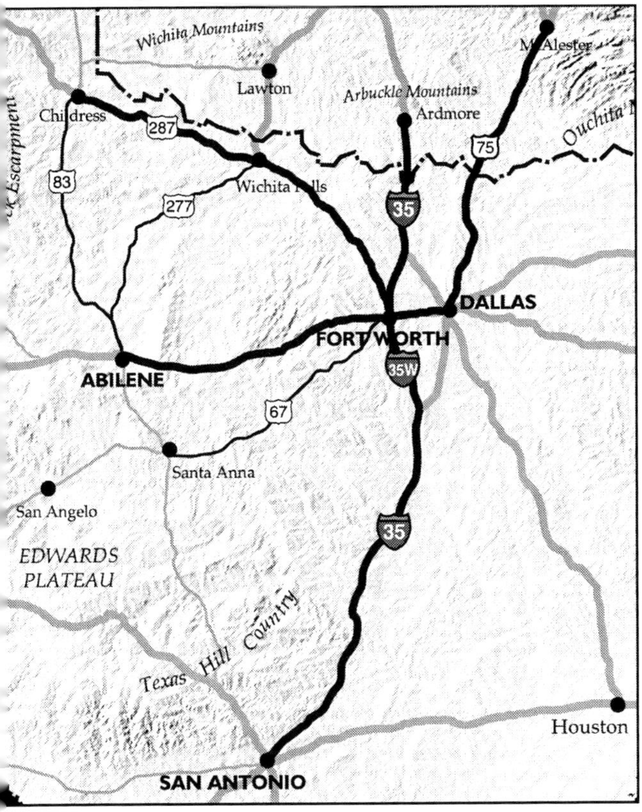

Road Guide

■ Fort Worth - Childress TX

U.S. 287 (217 miles; 3.5 hours)

This route closely follows the Fort Worth & Denver (FW&D) railroad, built in 1881-1888 to connect its two namesakes. The routing was highly unique for its time, in an era when existing railways only led from Kansas southward and westward. Leaving **Fort Worth**, the road passes one of the largest grain storage buildings in the world, a third of a mile long, 150 ft tall, and visible for 20 miles! Meandering into mixed grasslands and post oak forest, the terrain becomes somewhat hilly near *Decatur*. Oil is under this terrain, and a few pumpjacks may be spotted, leading to the town of **Alvord** which was a major railroad loading station. North of town, the old Fort Worth and Denver Railroad, constructed in 1882, follows the east edge of the highway. Its original 1920s-era telephone poles are still intact. Near **Bowie**, the oak gives way to scrubby mesquite vegetation and the terrain flattens. A few miles past Bowie the traveller passes by a hill north of the highway known as **Brushy Mound** [N33.590 W97.918]. During the 1980s this 140 ft (42 m) hill was often climbed by Dallas area chasers to get better reception of National Weather Service weather radio. The town of **Bellevue** began in 1882 with the railway, thriving until a tornado nearly levelled the town on April 26, 1906. **Henrietta**, a much older town, was prosperous until its militia went to fight in the Civil War; Kiowa raids gradually decimated the town, and it stood as an abandoned shell for nearly ten years. Only until the 1882 railroad did it thrive again. **Wichita Falls** is the biggest city on the route, having suffered through two devastating tornadoes: in 1964 and 1979. [See Off the Beaten Path: RIVERBEND NATURE WORKS] Past town, agricultural land mixed with mesquite stands dominates the land. The clay soil becomes a bright red color due to the abundant iron oxides. **Electra**'s name had nothing to do with electricity but the name of a rancher's daughter; it became an oil boomtown and peaked in 1936, declining as with most small Texas oil towns due to urbanization and diminished drilling. The road leading out of Electra, though, still shows hundreds of pumpjacks with rich oil reserves still being tapped. **Oklaunion** is a town whose namesake reflects its dreams of getting the Oklahoma railroad connection; unfortunately for Oklaunion, Vernon got it in 1903. It persisted for awhile as a farming community, but at this point it is in danger of becoming a ghost town. The stretch northwest continues through rich red soils, skirting a major wheat production area. **Vernon** comes into view, which grew rapidly in the 1880s with the railroad and has had a relatively steady population since the 1940s. **Chillicothe** is another 1882 railroad town, peaking in 1950 but slowly shrinking since. It is called the Iris Village, due to the numerous iris flowers found throughout the town. **Quanah** is yet another town that developed along the FW&D line in the 1880s, hit hard on June 4, 1890 when 14 inches fell in 24 hours and decimated the wheat crop. [See Off the Beaten Path: MEDICINE MOUND and COPPER BREAKS STATE PARK] A little further and just across Groesbeck Creek is **Acme**, a gypsum-mining ghost town that had a hotel, school, and post office in the 1890s; the town is gone but a Georgia Pacific plant continues the work. Cotton fields begin appearing near **Childress**, and it is here where the chaser reaches a strategic crossroad.

■ Wichita Falls - Abilene TX

U.S. 277 (152 miles; 2.3 hours)

About 19 miles past **Wichita Falls** is the first of three near-ghost towns whose fate was marred by 1920s-era tornadoes. At the junction of TX 25 is **Mankins**, a near-ghost town that peaked in the 1950s due to ranching, but was lost due to urbanization and control of much of the town land by private interests. A tornado hit the town in 1938. About eight miles further at the junction of FM 2846 is **Dundee**, which during the 1890s had a three-story hotel, numerous stores, and peaked in the 1920s until a tornado struck in 1929, followed shortly after by the Great Depression. **Mabelle**, at the U.S. 283 junction, was a modest trade center until a tornado hit in 1923; its population gradually scattered during the 1950s and 1960s. About four miles north of the agricultural center of **Seymour** the land suddenly flattens out, emerging into flat cotton and wheat fields, and occasional stands of mesquite. Seymour held the record for Texas' hottest temperature, 120 deg F, set in August 1936, until it was matched in 1994 in Monahans, TX. The near ghost-town of **Bomarton** is found at the FM 1152 junction; during the 1920s its Saturday baseball games were legendary, and its population swelled to 600 before 1950s urbanization took hold. Continuing through **Goree**, fields consist largely of cotton, wheat, and corn. The highway bends southward at **Munday**, a town known for its high vegetable production due to well-irrigated fields and local skill. A research center was established by Texas A&M University in 1971 that studied vegetables, but now focuses on cotton and wheat. Past **Weinert** is the diminutive ghost town of **Josselet** [N33.234 W99.704] almost hidden without a GPS; it attempted to prosper along the Burlington Northern Railroad, still seen east of the highway, but only peaked at a population of ten in 1945 with one business. The large agricultural centers of **Haskell** developed in the 1890s. **Stamford** has one of the only remaining Carnegie libraries in Texas, built in 1908 with funding from steel magnate Andrew Carnegie. **Anson** is home to the "Anson Lights", a local legend, said to be easily visible at night looking north from a spot south of a graveyard [N32.737 W99.869] along U.S. 180. The most likely explanation, however, may be due to the fact that U.S. 277 north of town aims at this spot over a four mile stretch. Near **Abilene**, the rich history of petroleum is quite evident in the fields lining the roadside.

■ Dallas - Abilene TX

Interstate 20 (184 miles; 2.9 hours)

As with many major Texas routes, this one follows a historic railroad: the Texas & Pacific (T&P), which was built in 1873-1881 to connect Marshall, TX with San Diego, CA, and many of the towns grew along this line in the 1880s. The route leaves **Dallas**, which sits atop Blackland Prairie topped with deep, clayey soils that once harbored prairie grasslands. It reaches **Weatherford**, the chaser enters rolling terrain and a mix of post oak forests, with grasslands composed of bluestem and wintergrass. [See Off the Beaten Path: CLARK GARDENS] The freeway crosses the **Brazos River** [N32.665 W98.032] near **Mile Marker 395**; the river has its roots in the Caprock Escarpment east of Lubbock. Near **Strawn**, the terrain becomes hilly, and mesquite becomes the dominant vegetation type. The Pennsylvanian rock outcroppings are associated with a period of rich deposition, which spawned a lucrative limestone, coal, and clay mining economy in this area. Just take **Exit 367** and at the stop sign you'll be in the remains of **Thurber**, which had a population of 10,000 in the 1900s and was the single biggest city between Fort Worth and El Paso! Past **Exit 361** the freeway makes a sudden climb from 1100 ft to 1400 ft MSL. The top of the hill [N32.472 W98.640] at **Exit 354**, marked by a 470 ft radio tower, proves a longtime favorite vantage point for Dallas area chasers. The road continues through short, scrubby mesquite forests. The railroad town of **Eastland** has roots going back to the 1880s in cotton, and later, oil. The slightly larger sister city of **Cisco** is just ten miles further. The first major tornado disaster in Texas occurred here on April 28, 1893, with 23 dead and 150 injured. The T&P railway leads through the north side of town and follows the Interstate about a mile north. The rock composition begins changing from yellow Pennsylvanian to red Permian sandstones. **Putnam** was an 1882 railroad town which eventually tried to compete with Mineral Wells as a health resort, but with failure; petroleum and some agriculture have persisted, but the town has been in slow decline since the 1940s. Approaching **Baird** the freeway enters a valley carved out by streams leading into Mexia Creek. The Texas & Pacific railway which sustained the town winds to its south side. [See Off the Beaten Path: BELLE PLAIN and FORT GRIFFIN] Past **Baird** the road enters Cretaceous limestone hills, climbing rapidly from an elevation of 1725 ft to 2000 ft (525 to 610 m). Some of these outcroppings are highly rich in fossils. In 1910, a runaway locomotive on the Texas & Pacific Railway, half a mile south of the freeway, was not able to brake going down the steep grade, and created a three-locomotive pileup at the depot in Baird. At the top near **Clyde**, the terrain is blanketed with reddish Permian soils, allowing for a lush agricultural production that earned Clyde a reputation for astounding fruit and vegetable production in the 1920s. The freeway then winds around the north side of **Abilene**.

■ Dallas - San Antonio TX

Interstate 35 (276 miles; 4.2 hours)

SPECIAL NOTE: Interstate 35 from Hillsboro to the Mexican border doubles as a backbone for NAFTA trucking between Mexico and U.S. markets, and is heavily congested. There is a heightened possibility of delays and accidents.

The freeway winds towards **Waxahachie**. For the entire route, fields are built entirely on vertisol soils, a gray clayey type common only in the western Gulf Coast region. Wheat, sorghum, cotton, and corn are grown in these fields south of Dallas. Very little roadside geology is seen, as there are few rock outcroppings. Eight miles south of Waxahachie is the small cotton-farming town of **Forreston** (Exit 391) which, dating back to 1843, is the oldest American settlement in the county. At Exit 374 is the legendary town of **Carl's Corner**, a truck stop built in 1982 and registered as a city in 1986 so that whiskey could be legally served. It is a longtime haunt of country singer Willie Nelson, who helped stage a fundraiser concert to rebuild after a 1992 fire. About three miles further is the junction of I-35W and I-35E. **Hillsboro** was built in the 1850s, becoming a railroad town and a major center of cotton production. The town of **West** has a hundred years of Czech culture, and a batch of kolaches at the Czech Stop are highly recommended. **Waco** is the site of Texas' deadliest tornado in modern history, which struck on 5/11/53, claiming 114 lives. Crossing the Brazos River one can see the reddish water color that originates from the iron-rich Permian soils north of Abilene. A stop at the Dr. Pepper Museum [N31.555 W97.130] (300 S. 5th St) is sure to amuse, and you can even get a hand-mixed soda here! **Hewitt**, **Lorena**, and **Bruceville** were all agricultural towns a century ago that grew into bedroom communities of Waco. Approaching **Lorena** is the KWTX tower, rising to 1080 ft. You then head through the manufacturing city of **Temple**, and the historic town of **Belton** which dates back to 1850 and had a large percentage of pro-Union residents! **Salado** is an equally old town, with a well-developed tourist trade and artistic roots which have made it a bedroom community for the wealthy. Further along, the town of **Jarrell** is legendary, being the site of two tornadoes that flattened the west side of town: one on 5/17/89 and another on 5/27/97. Chasers moved southward with this monstrous storm, which paralleled I-35 to the west. Along the banks of the San Gabriel River is the retirement city of **Georgetown**. Just south of town at **Exit 259** the limestone bedrock harbors vast caverns beneath the surface which were formed by undersea currents during the Cretaceous era when the region was underwater. The result: Inner Space Caverns, which is open to tourists. Interstate 35 actually crosses directly over these caverns at a point just south of the exit! **Round Rock** is becoming a large suburb of the **Austin** area, where there is a 20-mile stretch of heavy traffic. In spite of the heavy urban development, spectacular limestone bluffs and oak forest are common. **San Marcos**, with its thriving tourism, education, and manufacturing economy. Fifteen miles further is **New Braunfels**, founded by German colonists in 1845 and enjoys a thriving tourist economy (thanks in part to the Schlitterbahn water park on the Guadalupe River). Leaving **San Antonio**, the chaser can see the Hill Country lining the western horizon, framed by numerous quarries which carve out the limestone to manufacture cement.

■ Fort Worth - Santa Anna TX

U.S. 377 (149 miles; 2.4 hours)

The U.S. 377 route follows the old Fort Worth & Rio Grande (FW&RG) railroad, built from 1886-91 to connect Brownwood to Fort Worth. This is a delightful drive that begins near **Fort Worth** with broad grasslands and rolling terrain. The road descends into the Lake Benbrook basin, then through the isolated suburb of **Wheatland**, which got its start as a loose town surrounding a rural school during the 1890s, but has seen renewed growth into a bedroom Metroplex community a century later. The exposed terrain through this region is composed largely of Cretaceous limestone. At the top of a ridge is **Cresson**, which in the 1850s and 1860s was a key stagecoach stop linking Jacksboro to Waco and sported a hotel; the FW&RG railway arrived in 1887 to jump-start the agricultural economy. A few miles past Cresson, spectacular layers of Cretaceous limestone are exposed in the roadcuts. These rocks were laid down by the decay of marine organisms about 100 million years ago when a shallow sea once covered the southern Great Plains, and are teeming with fossils. Through hilly terrain and past the Brazos River crossing is **Granbury**, which has been a major producer of cotton, pecans, and peaches. [See Off The Beaten Path: DINOSAUR VALLEY PARK] Leaving Granbury, occasional patches of oak and mesquite appear. The small agricultural town of **Tolar** has a few buildings constructed of petrified wood from the local area. **Bluff Dale**, nestled against 200 ft hills to the south, grew from the arrival of the FW&RG railroad in 1889; an excursion on FM 3106 south from Bluff Dale will take you over the top of these hills and give you a great view of the sky! **Stephenville** is legendary as it was the site of a key weather radar that watched Dallas-Fort Worth for three decades until its decommission in 1995. **Dublin** was a town that moved a few miles to meet the Texas Central Railroad in 1881, which linked Cisco with Waco, and was linked to the FW&RG in 1892, forming a crossroad. The terrain changes to older Pennsylvanian limestones, and outcroppings often contain ancient fossils with snails, clams, and crinoids. The town of **Proctor** got its roots on the FW&RG line, initially farming cotton but switching to peanuts after a destructive boll weevil plague. **Comanche** was a frontier town in the 1860s, prospering in 1892 with the arrival of the FW&RG and becoming a major center for peanut and grain farming, as well as dairy and mohair. Just short of a pass through hills six miles west of Comanche, the road crosses through the ghost town of **Watson** [N31.870 W98.727] which tried to thrive on the FW&RG line; it had nearly 70 residents before the Great Depression but now almost nothing is left. In contrast, the town of **Blanket** prospered due to a modest ranching economy. Soon the chaser enters **Brownwood**, a boomtown during the 1880s which was a railroad hub and center of agricultural commerce. The road ascends a 150 ft hill, offering a vantage point southeastward. The town of **Bangs** grew along the GCSF railway, of little real importance until the 1910s. [See Off the Beaten Path: TRICKHAM] Approaching **Santa Anna**, a formidable chain of rocky hills looms north of the town: the Santa Anna Mountains. Sadly, these 200 ft (70 m) limestone hills are on private property, but in the 19th century they were used by Texas rangers as a lookout post.

The story of Carl's Corner

Chasers who find theirselves along Interstate 35E (Exit 374) between Waxahachie and Hillsboro will find Carl's Corner [N32.079 E97.055]. It was named after Carl Cornelius. In 1979 Carl bought cheap land on a remote stretch of I-35E and built a truck stop with a restaurant. But by the mid-1980s Carl wanted to create a trucker's oasis, with a bar, strip club, and drive-in theater. Liquor, however, could only be served under the jurisdiction of a city. So Carl bought 21 mobile homes, invited families in, and legally created the city. Willie Nelson, an "outlaw country music" legend who lived in the area and was a friend of Carl's, held a 1987 Fourth of July concert at the truck stop, drawing a crowd of 20,000.

Carl's philosophy was, "Everybody in the world should serve each other like brothers and sisters. Taking care of the people. Whatever they ask for, we try to help them." But the entrepreneur with the good heart ran into a stretch of bad luck. The truck stop burned down in 1990, uninsured. Willie Nelson staged a fundraising concert which allowed the truck stop to rebuild. But ten years later, Carl lost three of his four sons: two to hemophilia and one to suicide. Weary and disillusioned, Carl neglected the business, and it eventually closed in 2006.

Willie Nelson once again rescued the iconic city. He convinced Carl to re-open, with plans to create a new travel stop called "Willie's Place". It would sell a new bio-diesel fuel named BioWillie. Nelson also worked with several investors to plan an expansion, including a hotel and a golf course. Willie's Place finally opened in July 2008, kicked off by another legendary concert.

Storms in the I-35 region of Texas are often shrouded in haze due to close proximity to industrial sources of pollution in the eastern United States and the occasional advection of smoke from the "Mexican fire" phenomenon. This cumulonimbus cloud was photographed near Austin on 31 May 2004. *(Tim Vasquez)*

Off the beaten path

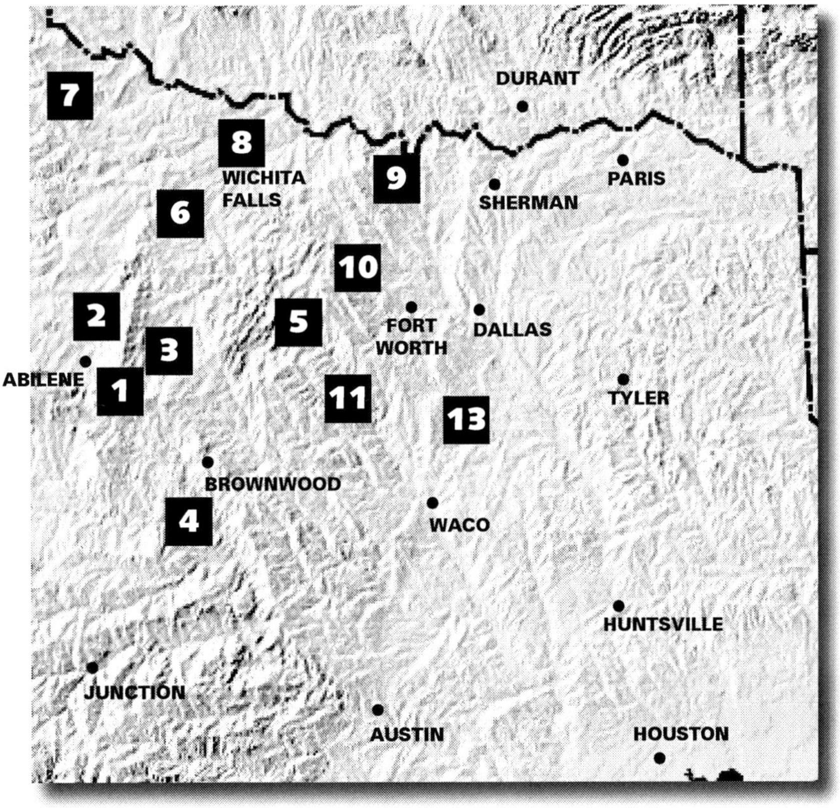

The Big Country

1 Atlas Missile Silos. Tour Atlas missile silos and a launch room southeast of Abilene with Atlas Missile Tours, available weekdays by appointment at 325-529-4949.

2 Fort Griffin [N32.925 W99.233] operated from 1867-81 as a stronghold against eastward Kiowa invasions into farmland west of Fort Worth. The fort occupied a 90 ft hilltop, however a town grew simultaneously along its northern foothills [N32.932 W99.230]. By the early 1870s, the town was known as the most lawless in Texas. Wyatt Earp, Doc Holiday, and Patrick Garrett made regular calls to sift through the sea of criminal characters who frequented Fort Griffin, including John Wesley Hardin and Mollie McCabe. Brawls and gunfights were commonplace. The situation became so extreme that in 1874 the Army post placed the town under martial law. By the 1880s, the community had grown to over 2,000 residents and visitors. The town vaporized over the next decade with the decline of the buffalo trade, the new railroad bypassing Fort Griffin through Albany, and the end of Indian raids. Fort Griffin is halfway between Albany and Throckmorton.

3 Belle Plain [N32.311 W99.361] is one of the most haunting ruins in north Texas, because it was a large settlement now lost to history, like the Texas coast town of Indianola. Belle Plain was a thriving, wealthy town with 300 residents and a college offering a full range of classic and artistic studies. A hotel persisted through much of the 1880s. After an 1886 drought, the town began declining, and it was mostly empty by the turn of the century. Nothing but ruins are left now.

4 Trickham ghost town. Explore the area between Brady and Brownwood to find the ghost town of Trickham [N31.588 W99.230]. The small town grew up in the 1870s around a saloon along a cattle trail, where legend goes that the owner got cowboys drunk and tricked them out of their money, thus the name Trick'Em. The US Post Office, with little sense of humor, rejected this name and selected Trickham in 1879. Some remains, as well as a few active buildings, are found. From U.S. 84 between Bangs and Santa Anna simply turn south onto FM 567, follow it for 3 miles until you see FM 1176, and go south for 8.5 miles.

5 Clark Gardens at Mineral Wells. If storms are expected to develop west of the Dallas-Fort Worth metroplex, a visit to Mineral Wells' Clark Gardens [N32.808 W98.023] on Maddux Road 5 miles east of Mineral Wells off Hwy 180, is a great way to pass time. The gardens comprise 83 acres of plants and flowers with the goal of becoming a model for landscaping and xeriscaping. Hours are Thu-Sat 10-6, Sun 1-5.

Northwest Texas

6 Archer City. The town of Archer City is home to the Royal Theater [N33.596 W98.626], located downtown and used in the 1971 coming-of-age film "The Last Picture Show".

7 Copper Breaks State Park [N34.112 W99.731] consists of 3 square miles of beautiful, rugged Permian terrain, with small mesas and vegetation consisting largely of mesquite and juniper. You can find many hiking trails through the park and tons of wildlife. Be sure to check out "off the beaten path" spot Medicine Mound, just 10 miles to the east. Head to Quanah

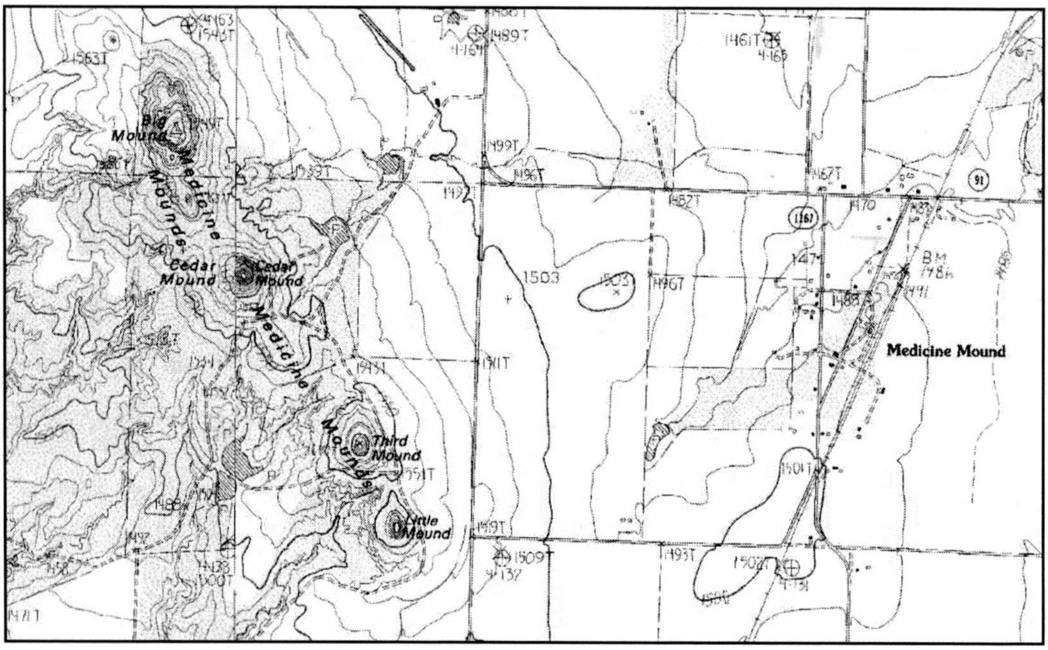

Topographic map of the scenic Medicine Mound region of Hardeman County, Texas. Keep in mind that like many Texas landmarks, the attraction is on private property and any posted signs should be respected. (USGS)

for a peculiar old town that offers a dose of tourism and history. Past Chillicothe is an 8-mile excursion to the ghost town of Medicine Mound [N34.188 W99.594]. It replaced an older townsite in 1908 when the railroad came through. The town eventually peaked at 500 residents, 23 businesses, and a newspaper. There are three 200 ft dolomite mounds to the west thought by Comanche tribes to have spiritual significance. Young braves would make solo trips to visit them, commune with nature, and receive spiritual guidance. It should be noted that these mounds are on private property.

8 Riverbend Nature Works at Wichita Falls. Within very easy reach of U.S. 277 just half a mile away is Riverbend Nature Works [N33.912 W98.512], at the entrance to Lucy Municipal Park. The one-mile interpretative nature trail is a must-see. There's a pond habitat, an automated weather station, and a butterfly garden, as well as spectacular seasonal exhibits. The town of Electra has a pumpjack festival each April.

North of the Metroplex

9 Frank Buck Zoo at Gainesville. A small zoo admittedly doesn't convey much flavor of the Great Plains, but it's an unusual attraction in a small Texas town. Chasers who always wanted to pass time at a zoo but didn't want to be buried in deep layers of urban traffic and congestion can do so in Gainesville, with immediate Interstate access. The Frank Buck Zoo [N33.623 W97.153] is located just west of I-35 at California St. Animals kept here are standard zoo fare including monkeys, zebras, bears, elephants, and flamingos. It's the sole survivor of the famous Frank Buck Zoo that operated from 1935-65 in Massapequa NY. Open daily 9-5.

10 Aurora Cemetery. A strange bit of Texas lore exists at Aurora Cemetery [N33.596 W98.626] which allegedly has an alien buried there. The cemetery is southeast of Aurora on Cemetery Rd off SH 114. The story goes that a UFO crashed in the area in 1897 and the pilot was buried. Hundreds of other cemetery victims fell to a meningitis outbreak that struck six years earlier; you'll recognize many of them by the ubiquity of headstones marked 1891.

South of the Metroplex

11 Dinosaur Valley State Park. What happens when large dinosaurs wade through mud flats, which are quickly filled in with soft sediment? You get some of the best preserved footprints of dinosaurs in the world. They can be found in the Paluxy River flats at Dinosaur Valley State Park [N32.247 W97.814], about three miles west of Glen Rose. You can't miss the outdoor life-size dinosaurs, nearly 30 ft tall. There are also many trails in the park that can be explored. Open 8 a.m. to 10 p.m. daily.

12 Corsicana Pioneer Village. While awaiting East Texas storm action, see recreations of 1860s Texas buildings: general store, a blacksmith, a trading post, slave quarters, and more. It's in the city park in Corsicana at the Pioneer Village [N32.095 W96.475] on the northwest side of downtown. This is no tourist trap; the recreations have been based on painstaking research, using exact materials and attention to detail. The society that operates the village even has a large archive of documents open to public and genealogical research. Visitors can either browse the village on their own or take a guided tour. Open 9-5 daily; Sunday 1-5; closed holidays; nominal admission fee.

GREAT PLAINS TRAVEL GUIDE

Panhandle Region

When it comes to springtime chase action, there's no finer chase country than the Texas and Oklahoma Panhandle. With dense gridded roads, sparse traffic, wide open fields, friendly folks, and possibly the highest rate of tornadic activity in the world, the region has established itself as a storm chaser's paradise.

The Oklahoma Panhandle had somewhat of a checkered history. From 1850 to 1890, it was literally in a state of anarchy, under the jurisdiction of no government. A *laissez-faire* economy blossomed, without benefit of any official postal service, land titling agencies, law enforcement, or government services. Although it is often remembered as a dangerous time in Oklahoma's history, old timers said that the memorable impact of vigilante justice and enraged mobs did more to prevent crime rate than any badge could.

The economy and relative wealth of the Texas and Oklahoma Panhandles comes largely from a mix of agriculture, including winter wheat and cotton, and cattle production. The border areas to the west extending into Colorado and New Mexico have scant and erratic rainfall patterns, as well as rocky terrain, so agriculture is given over to ranching activity or nothing at all.

A very important geological and meteorological feature bisects the Panhandle region: the Caprock Escarpment. This is a north-south area of steep terrain that separates the pancake-flat Llano Estacado, harboring Amarillo, Lubbock, and its farmland, from the lower rolling hills to the east. The Caprock Escarpment is often simply called the "Caprock". Any easterly component in low-level flow tends to produce terrain-following upward motion which is strongest at the Caprock. Therefore the Caprock is often an area where storms initially develop.

Wildflowers here are not as prominent as in central and north Texas, however late April can often be counted on for patches of striking color displays. These flower displays shift north over a period of several weeks.

Meteorology

The Texas Panhandle is truly a magical area. Not only does it share North Texas' proximity to Gulf moisture and favorable upper-level winds, but the higher terrain and

Sad Monkey Railroad

A place that has always held a special interest to me is the area at the bottom of the Palo Duro Canyon where the Sad Monkey rail line used to be. The big value of riding this miniature train was the enveloping feeling of being totally surrounded by nature.

Enjoying the various shaped and colored canyon walls, varied plant life, and solitude while on the ride always gave me a very peaceful feeling. Even though the Sad Monkey rail line was removed somewhere around 1996, I still make a special point of going there anyway, every year and walk the area where the old railbed used to be, as I once again soak in the sights, smells and feelings of nature, unspoiled.

RON THOMPSON
Woodland, CA chaser

Caprock haven

The area from the Caprock to Spur/Dickens, Texas is one of my favorite spots. Every year fate sends me an incredible visual feast in that corridor; I think a lot of that has to do with the dryline's effects on storms. Storms that form on the dryline—especially near sunset—have bolt blue backgrounds and incredible contrast.

JASON PERSOFF
Jacksonville, FL chaser

At the state line, quarterhorse peers over a fence from Oklahoma into Texas in May 1999, oblivious to a dryline storm in the distance. *(Tim Vasquez)*

Panhandle butterflies

While chasing, I am always on the lookout for new butterfly species. Roadside wildflowers are magnets for them, and are a nice diversion while waiting for storms to develop. While driving through near Turkey in May 2000 I found a large patch of thistle. On that patch were five butterfly species that I have never previously observed. I never saw a storm that day, but the new butterflies are still one of my most fond memories of that chase vacation.

BILL HARK
Richmond, VA chaser

increased incidence of boundaries, such as drylines, all combine to make this an unparalleled severe weather mecca. Some experienced chasers feel that the eastern Panhandle has the single highest probability of tornadoes in the world. Unfortunately, the data does not bear this out, due in part to the uneven nature of tornado reports across the Great Plains which still center around heavily-populated central Oklahoma.

The most active severe weather season for the Texas Panhandle is May and early June, when the dryline, polar fronts, and upper-level disturbances make regular appearances.

Early in the season, there is a strong tendency for thunderstorms to be associated with frontal systems punching eastward out of Colorado and New Mexico. Severe weather tends to be buried in the warm front soup where intense isentropic lift is occurring, or along rock-hard boundaries such as cold fronts, producing squall lines. It is only in April and May when boundaries and wind profiles are regularly weak enough to sustain slow-moving point convergence areas.

Some activity persists throughout much of the summer as the "monsoon", moisture, and dryline make their seasonal migration westward into the Rockies. During these months, storms develop over the central New Mexico mountains and foothills, and enter the western Panhandles after dark as they slowly die away.

On a hot June day, this cotton plant grows out of red Permian soils near Childress, Texas. Late spring hailstorms near vulnerable areas like Lubbock , Childress, and Altus can decimate the cotton harvest. *(Tim Vasquez)*

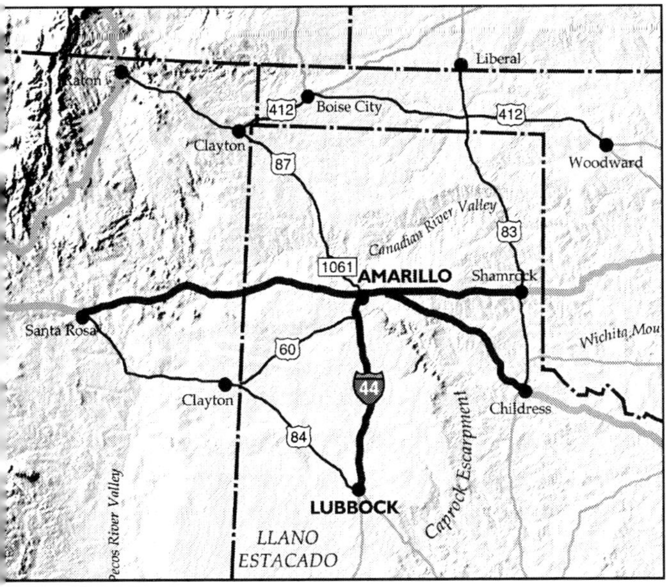

Road Guide

■ Childress - Amarillo TX

U.S. 287 (123 miles; 2.0 hours)

The second part of the "Highway To Heaven", from start to finish, takes the chaser on a fantastic ascent of 1700 ft (500 m), which is nearly the same as the climb from the Gulf of Mexico to Childress! This steep ascent makes the region a hotbed for upslope storm development. Leaving **Childress**, the chaser enters very rugged, eroded terrain, crossing through a mix of mesquite tracts and cotton fields. [See Off the Beaten Path: PARNELL] Winding into the Red River Valley past **Estelline**, the "Estelline S-curve" appears, which during the 1980's and 1990's was one of the Panhandle's most famous speed traps. Climbing through the Rolling Plains, then descending briefly into an eroded valley, the highway passes through **Memphis**, home of the Fighting Cyclones and a smattering of cyclonic billboards. The town had the only Carnegie library in the Texas Panhandle, unfortunately it was razed in 1985. The town of **Hedley** actually got its start a mile and a half northwest on the ghost townsite of Rowe [N34.875 W100.681]; the cemetery still exists on RM 1932 [N34.887 W100.673]. After over ten years of prosperity, Rowe was abandoned in 1907 essentially because of ridiculous zoning requirements and poor water quality; entire buildings were hauled to Hedley's current site. The railroad town of **Lelia Lake** was known for its watermelon production, now only a fraction of its 1920s-era population. **Clarendon** was built as a Christian colony, and its absence of saloons kept many cattle drivers away; in 1887 the entire town moved from its original location (now flooded by Greenbelt Reservoir) south to meet the new railroad. Nine miles further, the town of **Ashtola** was a small town that grew out of a stopping point on the FW&D railroad; it nearly became Poovieville in 1916 but postal authorities declined. **Goodnight**, the last town on the Caprock Escarpment, is a near ghost-town, sprouting up along the FW&D railroad with several stores, a school, and Goodnight College thriving by 1898; about five percent of the 1920s-era population still remain. About two miles south of Goodnight is an astounding 300 ft deep canyon carved by Spring Creek, part of the Palo Duro Canyon system; a few ranch roads will get you there. The highway continues winding through hilly country as it climbs toward the edge of the Caprock. For a dramatic excursion, take RM 2889 [N35.057 W101.239] south about four miles and you'll be led into Mulberry Canyon: a 400 ft deep chasm. Continuing the journey, the highway makes the final ascent onto the Caprock about five miles southeast of Claude. Rising to an elevation of 3300 ft (1000 m) MSL, you are suddenly emptied out onto an infinite expanse of flat wheat and sorghum fields [N35.074 W101.263]! The Caprock has been surmounted and you're now on the Llano Estacado, a flat blanket of very young erosional sands from the Rocky Mountains. The first town, **Claude**, was a bustling center of activity with the coming of the FW&D railroad in the 1890s, and after a lull after the Great Depression, it is now seeing growth as a bedroom community of Amarillo. Leaving town, you can look to the north and on a good day you'll see distant trucks floating on the horizon: Interstate 40, six miles away! **Washburn** had a brief sizzle of growth from 1888 to 1890, serving as a strategic junction between the FW&D line and the Santa Fe railroad (which ran from southern Kansas to the town of Panhandle). Dreams of further connections southward fizzled; its three hotels closed, andresidents moved to neighboring Claude and Amarillo. Finally the highway reaches **Amarillo**, an 1888 boomtown which has served as a cattle shipping hub ever since.

■ Shamrock - Amarillo TX

Interstate 40 (95 miles; 1.4 hours)

The town of **Shamrock** grew with the arrival of the Chicago, Rock Island & Gulf (CRI&G) railway in 1902. Rolling cotton and wheat fields mix with mesquite and sandsage. [See Off the Beaten Path: MAGIC CITY] **Lela** was established as a town on the CRI&G railroad, but by 1906 it was eclipsed by Shamrock and many businesses moved there. **McLean** was a railroad town that specialized in watermelons and hogs, but went through a slow decline since the Great Depression. **Alanreed** was a minor stagecoach stop between the large towns of Mobeetie and Clarendon, and grew with the arrival of the railroad in 1903. Past town, the terrain becomes very undulating, as the road climbs the Caprock Escarpment. Finally near **Exit 124** the chaser rises dramatically onto a flat expanse of wheat fields [N35.183 W100.907] as the freeway edges onto the Llano Estacado, a massive, flat blanket of young eroded sands from the Rocky Mountains. About 0.7 miles due south of this freeway exit is the ghost townsite of **Jericho** [N35.173 W100.907], which grew as a CRI&G railroad town, prospering in the 1930s, but withered away by the 1970s. Another ghost townsite is along the south I-40 service road near **Mile Marker 118**: the town of Boydston [N35.183 W101.014]; its history was almost identical to that of Jericho. Along the way is the railroad town of **Groom**, which prospered due to the 1970s oil boom. It is the home of the leaning watertower, said to be built that way on purpose. West of Groom the driver sees the 190 ft (58 m) Cross on the High Plains, designed by Catholic engineer Steve Thomas and built in 1997 to voice his disgust at a porn shop further down the freeway. Near **Mile Marker 107** the highway skirts the deep Salt Fork Red River canyon to the south, over 200 ft deep. The town of **Conway** grew along the CRI&G railroad, with an interdenominational church built in 1912. Once near **Amarillo**, watch for the billboards for the famous Big Texan Steak Ranch, where the 72 oz steak and fixings are free if you can eat it all in one sitting!

■ Amarillo TX - Santa Rosa NM

Interstate 40 (172 miles; 2.6 hours)

This remote stretch leaves **Amarillo**, passing mostly through wheat fields and grazing land. Northwest of **Exit 64** is the Chicago, Rock Island & Pacific (CRI&P) railroad ghost townsite of **Soncy** [N35.188 W101.940], which was given over to industrial uses: a grain elevator and helium production. **Bushland** and **Wildorado** are towns that sprung up along the CRI&P railroad in the late 1900s, the latter of which hosted a hotel, a bank, stores, and nearly 200 residnts during the 1920s. **Vega**, another railroad town, was a favorite stop along Route 66 in the 1930s and 1940s. At **Exit 28** is the tiny ghost town of **Landergin** [N35. 270 W102.557], headquarters for a ranch built by the Landergin brothers, who helped found the town of Vega. [See Off the Beaten Path: LA PLATA] Past the CRI&P railroad and Route 66 town of **Adrian**, founded in 1909, the ride on the Llano Estacado ends as the freeway suddenly drops off the western Caprock [N35.251 W102.777] into older Triassic terrain carved out by the Canadian River system. Soils from here on are predominantly aridisols, the exact type native to Arizona and Nevada. With this 350 ft (105 m) descent into rugged terrain, the farmland ends and a sea of splendid mesquite brush takes over. The CRI&P wanders south to make the descent smoothly, finally rejoining the freeway near **Mile Marker 4**. At **Glenrio** the **state line** [N35.182 W103.042] is reached. Travellers can take the exit into town; an incredible example of a ghost town that flourished along Route 66 but died during the 1960s as Interstate 40 became active. A border survey marker is found 60 ft (18 m) northwest of the old railroad depot. **San Jon**, dating back to 1902, was a ranching stop along the railroad. About nine nine miles west of San Jon the highway descends into **Revuelto Creek** [N35.168 W103.474], in which dinosaur bones have been found a few miles south of the freeway. **Tucumcari** got its start as the town of Liberty, serving the frontier fort of Fort Bascom, located 9 miles to the north along the Canadian River. When the fort closed, the town moved south to meet the new railroad in 1902. It was a tent city without any water supply; water had to be delivered each day for 50 cents per barrel, and it took years for its infrastructure to improve. About ten miles west of town, the highway crosses Jurassic rocks that yield a rich source of uranium. The town of **Newkirk** sits just south of a vast oil field, however its thickness and depth does not yet make it economical to extract. The road then reaches the 140-year old ranching center of **Santa Rosa**, dropping 200 ft during the last half mile into the Santa Rosa Sink, a circular valley formed by the collapse of limestone caverns. One of the town's main tourist attractions is its small but very deep sinkholes filled with crystal-clear water, found about a mile east of town, popular with scuba divers.

■ Amarillo - Lubbock TX

Interstate 27 (123 miles; 1.8 hours)

This corridor is a backbone route that has been traversed by every experienced chaser at one time or another. It crosses entirely on the Llano Estacado, a flat blanket of new Quaternary erosional sands originating from the Rocky Mountains. Leaving **Amarillo**, one soon passes over Palo Duro Creek and the town of **Canyon**. [See Off the Beaten Path: PALO DURO CANYON and CAPROCK COUNTRY] **Happy** was a town that initially developed two miles to the east until the railroad bypassed it in 1906, so the town moved to its present location; it was hit by a tornado on May 5, 2002. **Tulia** developed during the 1880s as a ranching center, initially serving as a wagon hub, then booming with the 1906 arrival of the Santa Fe line southward from Amarillo. **Kress** served as another agricultural center linking communities northward and southward. Continuing south towards the agricultural crossroads of **Plainview**, the chaser sees monotonous, pancake-flat cotton and sorghum fields. **Hale Center** was a farming and ranching community that remained fragmented until the railroad arrived from Amarillo in 1909; it was hit by a tornado on June 2, 1965. **Abernathy** moved southeast to meet the railroad in 1909, and profited from an oil discovery near town in the 1940s. Not surprisingly, the town of **New Deal** was named in 1949 after Franklin D. Roosevelt's public works programs, replacing the old name of Monroe. Near **Mile Marker 9**, the runways of Lubbock International Airport can be seen to the east. The freeway then leads into **Lubbock**, home of Texas Tech University and its famous tornado damage engineering research.

■ Amarillo TX - Clovis NM

U.S. 60 (106 miles; 1.6 hours)

The entire route follows the Pecos & Northern Texas (P&NT) railroad, constructed in 1898-99. Leaving **Canyon**, the highway reaches **Umbarger**, which developed in 1895 along the future P&NT route. Umbarger was settled by German Catholics in 1902 and by Swiss immigrants in the 1910s, adding European character; the town celebrates a sausage festival every November. **Dawn** also developed along the railroad, and by the 1910s it had a hotel that featured a band. [See Off the Beaten Path: LA PLATA] **Hereford** was a railroad boomtown, noted for its windmills and its naturally flouridated water (which made it a popular bottled-water source in the 1940s). Initially growing on sugar beets and wheat, Hereford's economy now thrives on cattle, wheat, cotton, and sorghum. Leaving town, the highway skirts several lakes. The road then enters XIT Ranch land, what was part of a huge ranch owned by a corporation during the 1890s and 1900s in return for constructing the Texas state capital building. **Friona** started as a XIT Ranch cattle shipping dock on the P&NT line, but grew into a town by the 1910s. It is home to several agricultural festivals each year. Rising onto a hill nearly 4200 ft above sea level, the road passes by the small ghost town of **Parmerton** [N34.580 W102.803], which developed in 1899 with the arrival of the P&NT railroad. It was the home of a XIT Ranch model farm that used non-irrigated methods to develop a wheat crop; there was a courthouse at the hilltop, a residence, and a cafe, but the town dissolved in 1908. **Bovina** was the site of an XIT Ranch railroad cottonseed shipment point in 1898; the spilled seed attracted large herds of cattle, which often had to be forced off the tracks. A town was established the next year, and the town name was obvious: Bull Town and later Bovina. The highway then reaches **Farwell**, the end of the original XIT Ranch property, merging onto U.S. 84 (q.v.)

■ Amarillo TX - Raton NM

U.S. 87 (211 miles; 3.4 hours)

Leaving **Amarillo** you opt for the scenic Boys Ranch route (FM 1061), which traverses rolling mesquite country carved out by the Canadian River. The route follows the old Fort Worth & Denver (FW&D) line just to the north. Several miles outside of Amarillo near the FM 2381 junction, take a look south and you'll see a mesa that appears to float in mid-air, an illusion created by an artist named Stanley Marsh III. After brushing the **Canadian River** and beginning its turn west is the ghost town of **Ady** [N35.485 W102.132], which served as a stop along the old railroad until the 1930s; a gravel pit is now based here. After turning north onto U.S. 385 junction you'll reach the FW&D railroad grade. Half a mile east down this rail line was the ghost town of **Tascosa** [N35.511 W102.251], which can be reached via a dirt road a block further; it was a Dodge City of its own during the 1870s, serving as a stagecoach destination. It died by the 1900s. Cal Farley's **Boys Ranch** is just to the north on the other side of the Canadian River; it is still a thriving operation to this day (*www.calfarleysboys-ranch.org*). Ascending out of the Canadian River valley, the road reaches **Channing**, which replaced Tascosa as the region's trade center; it was center of the sprawling XIT Ranch operation. Winter wheat fields begin appearing. **Hartley** was another FW&D railroad town, losing out in 1903 in a heated rivalry to Channing as the county seat. Approaching **Dalhart**, Rita Blanca Lake appears to the west. Dalhart was a thriving town at railroad crossroads. Past town, farming activity ceases, replaced by sand-sage and grazing land. Cattle becomes the primary economic activity. Only 25 miles out of Dalhart is the ghost town of **Perico** [N36.276 W102.864], which flourished as a farm town during the 1900s but gradually vaporized during the mid 20th century as people chose to settle in Dalhart and Clayton. A mile past **Texline** is the **state line** [N36.388 W103.041], and just past that is the town of **Clayton**. [See Off the Beaten Path: OKLAHOMA MESAS] Here, the sandy, loamy soil of the Great Plains ends, and from here on the geology consists mostly of igneous rocks from northeastern New Mexico's dormant volcanoes. From Clayton to **Des Moines**, the highway ascends a tongue of volcanic rocks, now grown over with native grasses, and passes within ten miles of over 30 volcanic cinder cones and intrusions. Ten miles past Des Moines is **Capulin**, a prominent dormant volcano can be seen just two miles to the north. [See Off the Beaten Path: CAPULIN VOLCANO] The Rocky Mountains finally come into view. About ten miles past Capulin the volcanic zone ends, and rocks are replaced with Cretaceous shales, formed from hardened mud when a shallow sea covered the Central U.S. about 100 million years ago. Driving into **Raton**, the chaser is now at an elevation of 6700 ft (2040 m) MSL, almost double that at the start of the trip!

■ Woodward - Boise City OK

U.S. 412 (187 miles; 2.9 hours)

Leaving **Woodward**, built along the Santa Fe Railway and the North Canadian River, one drives across red Permian soils which turn to newer Tertiary soils near **Fort Supply**. This town grew as Camp Supply in the late 1860s, being used by Generals Custer and Sheridan to launch campaigns against hostile Indian tribes in northwest Oklahoma. Crop fields consist almost completely of wheat and sorghum. Around 8 miles past the railroad town of **May**, the U.S. 283 junction is reached, which connects Dodge City and western Oklahoma. Just past a long bend in the road, you cross into **Beaver County** [N36.620 W100.00] and officially enter the Oklahoma Panhandle: the lawless no-man's land of the 1880s. The town of **Slapout** started as a roadside store in 1933, eventually taking its name because of owner Joe Johnston's knack for describing how an item was out of stock. A major natural gas plant [N36.616 W100.424] appears about 17 miles further, drawing its products through pipelines radiating more than 50 miles northeast and southwest. The tiny farming community of **Elmwood**, lying just north of the highway, connects to Beaver to the north. About twenty miles further [N36.616 W101.077] the highway climbs the Caprock Escarpment. **Hardesty** is one of the oldest towns in the Panhandle, dating back to 1885, but was moved to its current location in 1901 to meet the railroad tracks. The road descends 120 ft to cross **Optima Lake**, dammed in 1978. The road then ascends the Caprock again, heading west and rising about 10 ft per mile. It crosses some of the thickest beds of Ogallala Formation found anywhere on the Great Plains, well over 700 ft deep. The small city of **Guymon**, nestled on the north side of the sandy, eroded Beaver River basin, developed in 1901 along the Chicago, Rock Island & Pacific railroad, becoming a major cattle shipping point and a petroleum boomtown in the 1920s. About ten miles northwest of Guymon, the road reaches the northern edge of the Beaver River erosion and ascends back onto the Caprock. [See Off The Beaten Path: MOUSER] The highway crosses very desolate terrain, with few features or history for the remaining fifty miles. Crop fields slowly disappear due to the lack of groundwater, and the terrain becomes rugged, consisting of very young Quaternary-era rocks and soil washed off the face of the Rocky Mountains. At the U.S. 56 junction [N36.762 W102.385], you turn southwest for the remaining six miles to **Boise City**, a ranching town that did not grow until the coming of the Santa Fe railroad in 1925; the old railroad depot can be found intact at the Cimarron County Museum.

■ Abilene - Childress TX - Liberal KS

U.S. 83 (353 miles; 5.8 hours)

Starting out near **Abilene**, the chaser enters a vast belt of wheat and cotton farmland. Undeveloped lots are populated with oak and mesquite. Farmland begins disappearing around **Hamlin** and is replaced by low-topped mesquite and lotebush forests and extensive grazing land. [See Off The Beaten Path (Southwest Texas): RAYNER] **Aspermont** is nestled between the two forks of the Brazos River, which ultimately lead southeast to Waco. The chaser enters **Guthrie**, a sleepy ranching town sitting on one of the most remote spots in northwest Texas and in the state's black hole of surface weather data. Call your forecasting friends and haggle a good price for your weather observation. Approaching **Paducah**, wheat and sorghum farmland begins reappearing. Near **Childress** it consists mostly of mesquite and farmland. North of town is the descent into the Red River Valley. On the other side, a long expanse of mesquite sets in, followed by flat wheat fields near **Wellington**. Mesquite sandsage mixes with farmland through the town of **Shamrock** near Interstate 40. [See Off The Beaten Path: MOBEETIE and MAGIC CITY] Approaching **Canadian**, and after passing a brontosaurus guarding a hilltop, the road crosses the Washita River [N35.717 W100.379] which feeds the heart of central Oklahoma, then descends into the broad Canadian River valley. Vegetation consists mostly of mesquite shrubs. Wheat fields begin reappearing near the Oklahoma border near **Perryton**. The chaser crosses the state line at [N36.500 W100.806] just 100 feet south of a dirt road. The chaser crosses the Kansas-Oklahoma border at [N36.999 W100.891] directly at the intersection of a dirt road that leads south.

■ Lubbock TX - Santa Rosa NM

U.S. 84 (205 miles; 3.4 hours)

Northwest of **Lubbock**, the road leads into farmland. [See Off The Beaten Path: LUBBOCK LAKE]. U.S. 84 roughly follows the Pecos & Northern Texas (PN&T) railroad, completed in 1914. Its construction was responsible for the appearance of most of the towns along the route, and it led to a lively abundance of trains taking the shortcut between the Gulf Coast and California and prosperity for this corridor. Just south of **Muleshoe** is a broad outcropping of sand-sage and oak. Muleshoe paid homage to the mule's contributions to the WWI effort, and features a statue downtown. **Progress** was a railroad town with a sad history: it was intended to be a regional fruit production center, but the lack of economical water sources led it back into a cotton-based economy. At the ranching town of **Farwell**, the state line is crossed exactly at the railroad track [N34.389 W103.043]. Just eight miles further is **Clovis**. The town is heavily dependent on Cannon Air Force Base, about six miles further, home to dozens of F-16 fighter jets. About six west of **Melrose** [N34.425 W103.750] the road slowly descends the Mescalero, the west bank of the Llano Estacado and enters a vast, rugged area carved out by the Pecos River system during the past several million years. The railroad town of **Tolar** [N34.451 W103.931] was flattened by a munitions train which exploded in 1944 and has been a ghost town ever since. Located on the Pecos River, **Fort Sumner** is an old railroad town, now a tourist town built on the legend of Billy The Kid [the cemetery where he's buried is three miles south of town at N34.404 W104.193]. The town of **Santa Rosa** is nestled among natural spring lakes, and evolved from scattered cattle ranches in the 1860s.

The Oklahoma - New Mexico border near Kenton on S.H. 325 / 456, looking west into New Mexico. This road serves as as one possible route for the 148-mile haul between Boise City, Oklahoma and Trinidad, Colorado. It's an astonishingly scenic excursion but the highway gradually falls apart in New Mexico into a 30-mile long dirt road which should never be used after rainstorms or in an unreliable car. In spite of how it looks on maps, the standard route through Clayton and Raton is actually one mile shorter. New Mexico's volcanic hills loom in the distance. Note the old road bed to the left, evidence of life in the remote reaches of the Panhandle in another era. *(Tim Vasquez)*

Off the beaten path

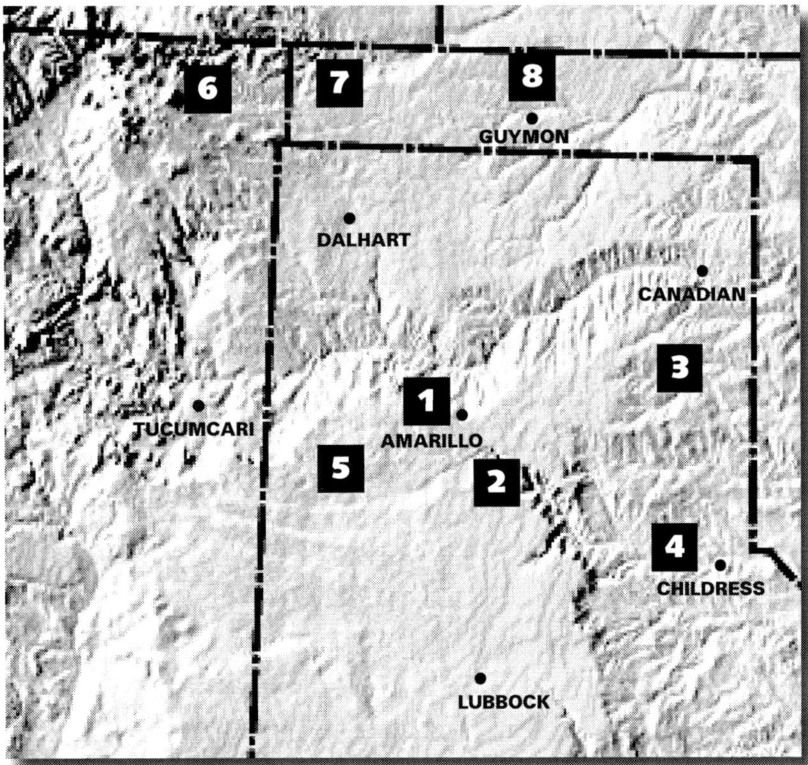

Along the Caprock

1 Cadillac Ranch. Several miles west of Amarillo just south of I-40 is Cadillac Ranch [N35.187 W101.987], an open-air art exhibit made of cars sunk into the ground. It's not to be confused with Nebraska's Car-henge. Near the Big Texan Steak Ranch east of Amarillo on I-40 [N35.193 W101.755] which offers the 72-ounce steak challenge, chasers used to be able to walk next door to the Texas Tornado Museum, which rode the coattails of the Twister craze but closed in late 2004.

2 Palo Duro Canyon. An eight-mile excursion from Canyon to Palo Duro Canyon [N34.986 W101.703] is an essential pilgrimage. It offers a spectacular glimpse of the steepest part of the Caprock Escarpment, revealing where erosion has carved into the flatland, revealing the older Permian limestone and sandstone, as well as fossils and bones from another era. The road drops nearly seven hundred feet from 3460 ft MSL at the top of the Caprock to 2775 ft MSL at the lowest part of the park drive. During the late 19th century, these canyons were favorite hiding places for outlaws, both American and Native American. Nowadays they make a great spot for picnicking and hiking. Palo Duro Canyon State Park is in a class of its own and has been listed separately.

Rolling Lowlands

3 Old Mobeetie. Northwest of Shamrock, see the granddaddy of ghost towns: Old

Mobeetie [N35.513 W100.441]. It developed in the 1870s as a trading post, also serving Fort Elliott [N35.518 W100.457] (1875-90) a mile to the west. By the 1890s, Mobeetie was the dominant city in the Texas Panhandle. Stage lines across much of the Southern Plains ran to this destination. A tornado hit Mobeetie in 1897, coinciding with a slow spiral into recession. In 1929, the Clinton-Pampa rail line bypassed the town a mile to the north, while nearby Shamrock became a oil production center. This spelled the end for Mobeetie. Most of what remained of the town moved to the tracks, resulting in New Mobeetie. For those with a GPS, take a side tour on FM 1046 to just west of Allison, where you can stand within the core of F4 damage from the June 8, 1995 tornado [N35.605 W100.129], extending north and south along the crossroad from here.

Just past Shamrock, leave I-40 to see the ghost town of Magic City [N35.358 W100.378]. Though this name might have special meaning to a storm chaser, its name was derived from its oil boom history in 1926. The population numbered in the hundreds. A railway serviced the area in 1932, however oil dried up in 1935 and a slow decline began. By 1954 the post office was closed, and the railroad was gone in 1970. To get there from I-40, take Exit 152 and go north 9 miles, then go east on FM 2473 for 3 miles.

4 Parnell ghost town. Head west from Estelline to see the ghost town of Parnell [N34.523 W100.603]. It grew in 1888 as the controversial seat of Roberts County, unleashing a rivalry with Miami that often got the Texas Rangers involved to quell feuds. Parnell lost the title in a 1898 election, owing to Miami's railroad presence. The post office was closed that year and the residents scattered. Go west 9 miles from Estelline on TX 86 to get there.

Northwest Panhandle

5 La Plata ghost town. An hour-long excursion south from Adrian takes the chaser to the ghost town of La Plata [N34.970 W102.598]. It was a lively town in the 1880s with a hotel, blacksmith, post office, and more. A drought, blizzard, and railroad bypass scattered the residents. Only a few abandoned buildings are left. To get there, drive 3 miles east of Simms then 4 miles south.

New Mexico

6 Capulin Volcano. A real geologic treat is Capulin Volcano, a 5-mile excursion located about halfway between Clayton and Raton. This volcano looms 1350 ft (410 m) above the surrounding terrain, with the ring road itself reaching two-thirds of this height. It's a great place to look for distant convection, and to contemplate life on this land millions of years ago. To get there, simply head north from the town of Capulin, following the posted signs.

Oklahoma Panhandle

7 Kenton area. When wandering through this area, it's strange to think that you're closer to Albuquerque, Durango, and Aspen than you are to Oklahoma City. And it certainly shows. These incredible moonscapes are missed by most travellers sticking to the main roads. The town of Kenton is nearly a ghost town itself and is worthy of exploration. If you have three hours to kill and plenty of water, head five miles north from Kenton to a parking lot and take the trail to reach the highest point in Oklahoma, Black Mesa [N36.932 W102.997] at 4973 ft MSL, marked by a granite obelisk.

8 Mouser ghost town. Take a trip north from Guymon to see the ghost town of

Mouser [N36.871 W101.415]. Initially developed in the late 1920s, it peaked at 100 residents in the 1930s, with two stores and two gas stations, but with no post office, school, or church. The north-south streets of Mouser were named, not surprisingly, after cat breeds. The town slowly disappeared over the next few decades. Sharp spotters will find the abandoned railroad grade. To get to Mouser, after going a few miles out of Guymon, take the split for OK 136 and continue for 8 miles. Turn east onto EW10 Road, go 4 miles, then turn north onto NS89 Road, go half a mile.

The carved topography of Palo Duro Canyon. The highway approaches from the top left side. *(USGS)*

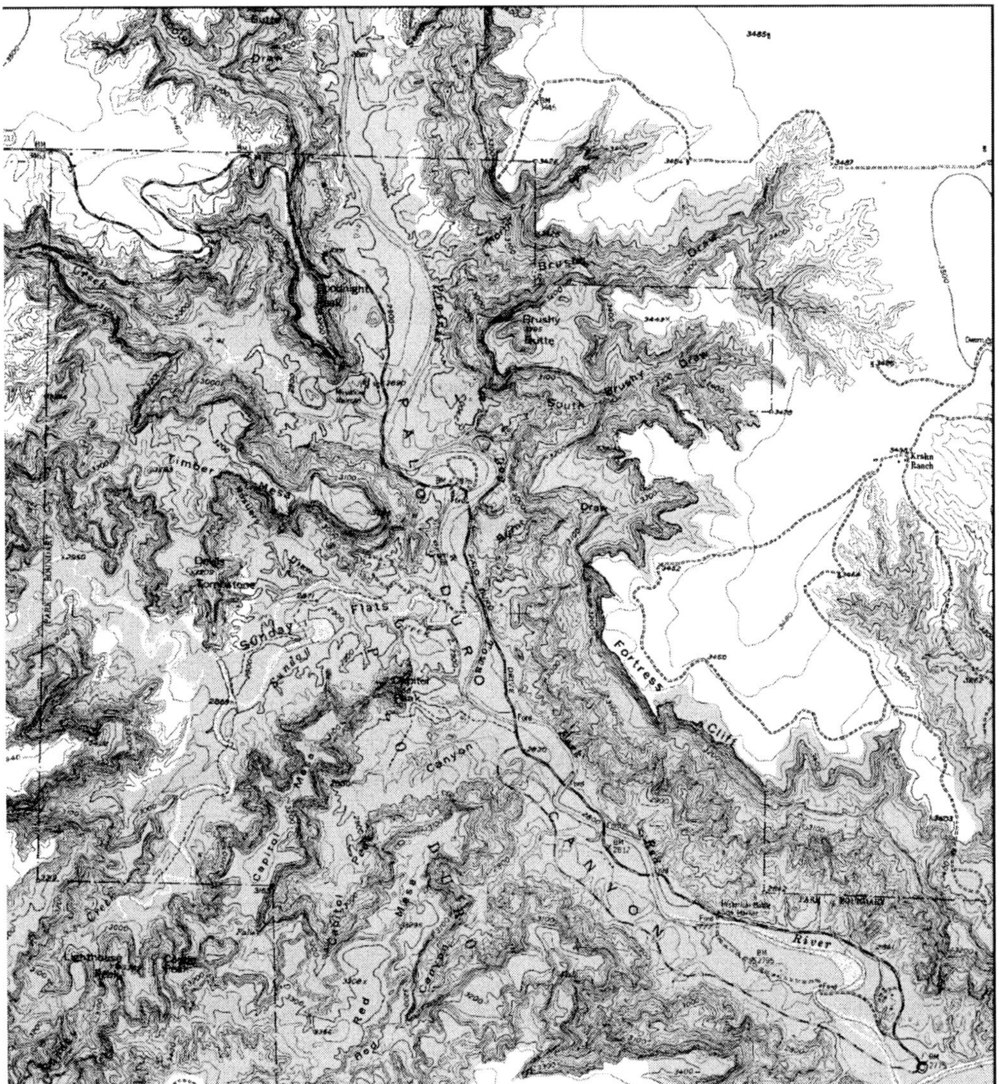

GREAT PLAINS TRAVEL GUIDE

Oklahoma

The Panhandles may be the tornado capital of the Plains, but all storm chase roads lead to Oklahoma. The state, and more specifically the city of Norman, is the center of United States severe weather research and a mecca for the hundreds of chasers who prefer to live as close to Tornado Alley as possible while still keeping all the conveniences of a large city. It is here where the National Weather Center (NWC), the University of Oklahoma School of Meteorology, the National Severe Storms Laboratory (NSSL), the Storm Prediction Center (SPC), and the Cooperative Institute for Mesoscale Meteorological Studies (CIMMS) are located. It is also home to Oklahoma City and Tulsa, which have one of the most competitive weathercasting markets in the country with every dangerous storm tracked by helicopters, media storm chasers, and radar.

Needless to say, Oklahoma's history is quite unique. During much of the 19th century, displaced Indian tribes nationwide were sent here by the Federal government. The entire region was made up of dozens of Indian reservations, and was titled on world atlases and national maps as "Indian Territory". White settlers could not be kept out, and many began to settle illegally. Finally the Federal government bought out two million acres of land in central Oklahoma and scheduled the Oklahoma Land Rush of April 1889, a large-scale land grab. This was the beginning of the end for tribal land. In 1897 oil was discovered in Oklahoma, and this quickly built one of the mainstays of the state's economy.

In spite of the state's complex and somewhat tarnished history, it is a beautiful land. One of the sights enjoyed by all travellers are wildflowers, which peak in early to mid May. Bluebonnets and their reddish counterpart, Indian paintbrush, are often found together in fields and along highways, especially along the Interstate 35 corridor.

Meteorology

Any severe weather book is quick to point out that Oklahoma is one of the world's hotbeds for severe weather. Such claims are not exaggerated. Incidence maps for hail, high winds, and tornadoes published over the past 50 years show that North America's (and probably the world's) severe weather peak is concentrated in central and southwest Oklahoma, though there is probably some element of population bias involved. After all, hailfalls and tornadoes in western Oklahoma and eastern Texas Panhandle might go unob-

Oklahoma chasing

Like all Tornado Alley states, Oklahoma has its share of both great and terrible chase terrain. It's well-known among chasers that you want to avoid the area generally east of the Interstate 35 corridor, although good areas do exist in the eastern portions of the state. The western half of Oklahoma (west of I-35), provides the state's most lucrative viewing.

The best areas are northern Oklahoma (which probably accounts for the largest single area of consistent flatlands) and the southwestern corner of the state, along the U.S. Highway 62 corridor and points south. These two areas can compete with any place on earth for storm observing. The road networks aren't top-notch, but they're good enough to keep most storms in sight for several hours.

Though several Plains states offer great chasing, Oklahoma will always be my favorite, for a few reasons. First, regardless of whatever state is popular among the newbies that week, I still believe Oklahoma has as high (if not the highest) a frequency of tornadic supercell days as any place in Tornado Alley. Secondly, it's home.

SHANE ADAMS
Norman, Oklahoma chaser

Storms come to life near Asher, Oklahoma in 2002. *(Tim Vasquez)*

The many paths of Moore

One area with a bad track record for tornadoes has been Moore, Oklahoma. After dark on October 4, 1998 the city was hit by an F2 tornado that moved south-to-north along Santa Fe Avenue. Seven months later, significant destruction occurred with the May 3, 1999 F5 tornado that moved into the Moore and Oklahoma City area. The tornado killed 36 and overall was the most costly tornado on record in terms of adjusted dollars. Four years later, another twister closely followed the same path on May 8, 2003, producing F3 damage within Moore. Fortunately there were no deaths.

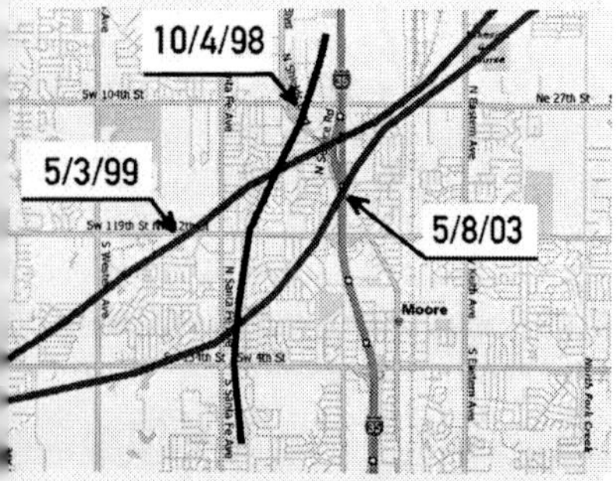

served over the sparsely-populated rangelands, especially at night, while most areas of central Oklahoma have population densities often exceeding 50 people per square mile.

Early in the season, strong frontal systems sweeping out of New Mexico and Colorado, producing linear storms and squall lines, tend to be responsible for most March and April storms. Tornado activity is relatively scarce partly because of significant cell competition and seeding, and partly because of marginal instability. Strong winds and hail are the main severe weather problems.

The state's favored severe weather season comes in May. The majority of damaging weather events at this time of the year are associated with dryline activity or old slow-moving boundaries. Significant modern tornado outbreaks affecting Oklahoma have occurred on May 24, 1998, May 3, 1999, and May 5, 2007.

A second season may occur in late September and early October. One noteworthy tornado outbreak hit on October 4, 1998 with slow-moving, picturesque tornadoes near Watonga.

From a chasing perspective, Oklahoma can be divided into two key areas: the favorable prairie of west and central Oklahoma, comprising most of the north and west part of the state, and the unfavorable woodland and hills of east Oklahoma, found along and east of the U.S. 75 corridor. This area is a navigational and strategic nightmare that was dubbed in the 1970s by NSSL chase teams as Oklahoma's jungles, where a chaser must "break out the chainsaw" to get good photos.

Similar to the situation in Texas, there is often a diurnal bias for severe thunderstorms in western Oklahoma and a nocturnal bias in eastern Oklahoma. This is because the dryline's usual position during the afternoon is western Oklahoma, and here it serves as a late-afternoon focus for development. In a classic situation, storms propagate eastward on their own, reaching the Interstate 35 corridor around midnight, and arrive in eastern Oklahoma before dawn. Therefore unless a particularly strong weather system is moving through the area, chasers will often find theirselves on the western fringes of Oklahoma and the Red River Valley, with most lightning opportunities close to Interstate 35.

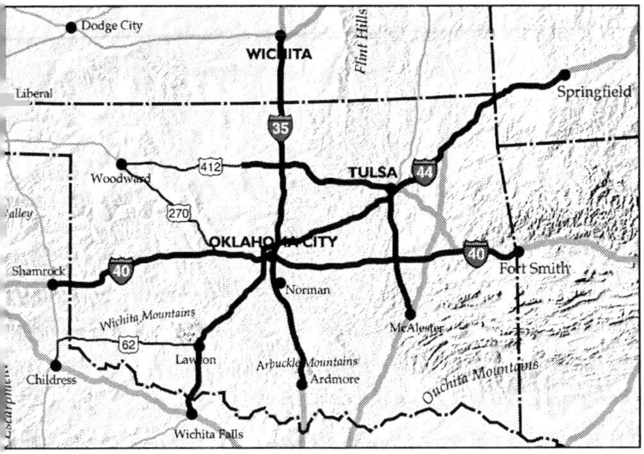

Road Guide

■ Fort Worth TX - Oklahoma City OK

Interstate 35 (200 miles; 3.0 hours)

Leaving **Fort Worth**, the drive consists mostly of grassland and farmland, interspersed with the large metroplex town of **Denton**. Keep your speed legal in heavily-patrolled **Valley View**. North of **Gainesville** [See Off the Beaten Path (North Texas): FRANK BUCK ZOO] the chaser reaches the **Red River**, aptly named as its roots are in the heart of iron-rich, reddish Permian soils (one of its main forks comes from Palo Duro Canyon!) Don't let the granite state line marker on the north side fool you: the state boundary actually follows the southern bank of this river rather than bisecting the waters. Once in Oklahoma, the chaser enters what was Indian Territory before 1907! The road ascends into rolling limestone terrain deposited from a shallow ocean that covered Texas and Oklahoma during Cretaceous times. North of **Ardmore**, the chaser ascends dramatically into the 500 ft **Arbuckle Mountains**, an ancient mountain range that dates back to Precambrian times (1.3 billion years ago). It can be thought of as a giant uplift of billion year-old rock that forms the geologic basement of much of North America. The Arbuckles contain one of the largest exposures of Paleozoic sediment in the United States. Interstate 35 cuts well over 100 ft into the rock, providing ample opportunities for roadside amateur geologists. For an alternate parallel route, take **Exit 42** to U.S. 77 north for the scenic bypass; it gets you to Exit 51 by winding along the ridges flanking the freeway and passing near the 77-foot Turner Falls waterfalls. It's well worth the detour! Leaving the Arbuckles, the road bottoms out in the flat, alluvial plain of the Washita River, whose waters are rooted in the Caprock Escarpment south of Canadian, TX. Outcroppings of extremely red soil begin appear; these are alfisols which are steeped in iron and aluminum oxides. Alluvial plains and rolling limestone/sandstone Permian hills are found. The trademark of **Pauls Valley** is its brick streets: the town claims it has more miles of them than any other town in the nation. Near **Purcell**, the chaser reaches an outlying bedroom community of the Oklahoma City metro area. The chaser then reaches **Norman**, the heart of the Great Plains storm research community. Only 20 miles further is **Oklahoma City**.

■ Dallas TX - Tulsa OK

U.S. 75 (258 miles; 4.1 hours)

Leaving Dallas, the chaser negotiates urban sprawl through the high-tech bedroom communities of **Plano, Allen, and McKinney**. Suddenly the man-made developments end, giving way to open wheat and sorghum fields and natural grasslands. Towns such as **Melissa**, **Anna**, and **Van Alstyne** had benign, sheltered histories, slowly growing during the 1860s and 1870s with the frontier about a hundred miles west, then reaped the rewards of the Texas Central Railway in 1873 that connected Dallas and Denison. **Howe** was a major stop on the rather advanced, electrified Interurban line that connected these two cities from 1914 to 1948. The traveller then reaches **Sherman**, a prosperous city that began in the 1850s and wielded a huge influence over the region by the 1880s. Surprisingly, it was **Denison** that got the first major railroad connection in 1872 and for decades it remained the transportation hub of the region. Crossing the Red River, the traveller can look west and see the mammoth Denison Dam, which holds up Lake Texoma with a waterline 87 ft (27 m) above the flood plain. Near the blue-collar boating and casino playground of **Calera** (currently the site of major road construction), post oak and blackjack oak forest emerges, interspersed with grassland. **Durant** is the next major city, which served as a key relay station on the first cross-country mail route west of the Mississippi: the Butterfield Overland route. The road then passes through southeast Oklahoma, known as "Little Dixie". Northeast of **Caddo** is where the Texas Astronomical Society maintains an outstanding observing site always open to its members (*www.texasastro.org*). The terrain becomes quite hilly, and north of **Atoka** the road passes through the Missisippian-era Ouchita Mountains, which tower 550 ft (170 m) above the surrounding terrain. Erosion in the valleys has uncovered Pennsylvanian rocks, among the oldest exposures on the Plains. Finally near **Kiowa**, the hills open up into wide plains. The town of **McAlester** houses the state's maximum security prison, as well as an ammunition plant. Recreational signs and vehicles towing boats hint at the presence of **Eufaula Lake** to the west, the 15th largest lake in the United States. The rugged terrain and numerous lake inlets impose difficulties on anyone chasing this region. **Henryetta**, straddling major railway lines, was the center of smelting for the mines to the south. **Okmulgee** grew uneventfully in 1868 as the center for the relocated Creek Indians. After the town of **Preston**, the sky opens up as the terrain flattens, finally bringing the traveller to **Tulsa**, a corruption of the name Tallahassee as the town was originally a Creek Indian community.

■ Oklahoma City OK - Shamrock TX

Interstate 40 (165 miles; 2.5 hours)

Near **Oklahoma City**, the drive starts with broad prairie land and a smattering of post oak forests on red Permian soil. The Czech-rooted bedroom community of **Yukon** proclaims itself as the home of country singer Garth Brooks. **El Reno**'s Army presence at Fort Reno, five miles northwest of town, dates back to the Indian relocations of the 19th century and the housing of German and Italian prisoners of war during WWII. Oklahoma's strongest earthquake occurred in El Reno on April 9, 1952, measuring magnitude 5.5; the area is part of a seismic zone that extends south to the Arbuckle Mountains. About eight miles west of El Reno the freeway descends into the highly eroded, rugged Canadian River valley. **Exit 108** offers an interesting detour along Route 66. [See Off the Beaten Path: ROUTE 66 DETOUR] Near **Mile Marker 99**, the faded town of Bridgeport can be seen to the north, thriving in the 1900s as it received bridges across the Canadian River, including Route 66. The region becomes a major producer of winter wheat, with substantial harvesting operations in May and June. **Hydro** was another major stopping point on Route 66; some old gas stations in town are still standing. The terrain finally begins flattening past **Weatherford**.

Clinton, lying on the Washita River, was the hub for several railroads near the turn of the 20th century. South of **Exit 53** is Clinton-Sherman municipal airport, which has the longest runway on the Great Plains. Don't be surprised if you see large military freighter jets flying around. They come from Altus Air Force Base, 47 miles to the south, to practice landings. Just south of the runway is the second deepest drillhole in the world, drilled in 1974 and reaching 6 miles below the earth's surface. The wheat fields are gradually replaced with cotton near **Elk City**, home of an actual working Carnegie library, one of eight in Oklahoma, and some of the nation's deepest gas wells. Further along is **Sayre**, the self-proclaimed Quarter Horse capital of the world. Exit at **Erick** and head west from downtown to drive alongside original sections of Route 66; the route rejoins the Interstate at **Texola**. The **state line** is just past town; for those with GPS units, it's at 100 deg W exactly. A mile into Texas is the ghost town of **Benonine** [N35.228 W100.014]; it prospered during the 1910s as a town on the Chicago, Rock Island & Gulf railroad, replete with a bank and post office, but dissolved late in the decade when neighboring Shamrock outpaced Benonine in terms of growth. The freeway crosses these historical railroad tracks four miles further [N35.226 W100.105]. **Shamrock** was named by an Irish shepherd in 1890 and became a bustling railroad town by the 1910s.

■ Oklahoma City OK - Wichita KS

Interstate 35 (161 miles; 2.5 hours)

Leaving **Oklahoma City**, the road passes the bedroom community of **Edmond**. It then begins over a hundred miles of travel which are largely devoid of scenery and cultural sights. Red Permian landscapes are the mainstay, these soils being quite young, the result of millions of years of erosion from the Rocky Mountains. **Guthrie**, located in the fertile Cimarron River valley, was the official state capital from 1890 to 1910, until forced into Oklahoma City in a partisan political move. [See Off the Beaten Path: PLEASANT VALLEY] From **Perry** northward, fields are heavily dedicated to wheat production. The Interstate loosely follows the Chisholm Trail northward. Terrain is highly eroded, alluvial in the riverbeds and Permian in the hills, making for an endless succession of rolling hills that don't relax until near **Tonkawa**. Much of the land in this area was impacted by the oil boom of the 1920s. Four miles north of the **Braman** exit, a bridge that crosses over the freeway [N37.000 W97.342] marks the state line. Just west of this spot is the ghost town of Hunnewell, which being on the state line was a major gathering point for the last big Oklahoma land rush in 1893. **Wellington** was a boom town in the mid-19th century with the growth of the Chisholm Trail leading in from Texas. It also marks the start of a toll road; here you only take your ticket. Two towns to the east, Oxford and Udall, suffered Kansas' worst tornado disaster ever, where 82 died and 270 were injured on May 25, 1955.

■ Springfield MO - Tulsa - Oklahoma City OK

Interstate 44 / 285 miles; 4.3 hours

Along the freeway hillsides near **Joplin** are outcroppings of 350-million year old Mississippian shales. Crossing into Oklahoma, the traveller is unknowingly within 745 feet of Kansas but never enters it! However you can take a convenient exit to go stand at the tri-state marker. Like night changing into day, the freeway quickly enters flat, open land just eight miles into Oklahoma and the sky becomes big. The freeway loosely follows the old Route 66 highway that led travellers from Chicago to Los Angeles in the 1920s, and near **Miami** (pronounced my-AM-uh) there is actually a preserved section you can drive on. **Vinita** holds a tied record for Oklahoma's coldest temperature, -27 deg F, set in 1905. Just past town is the first tollbooth: have $3.50 ready! About ten miles past Vinita the road re-enters the hills again, but the geological hands of time are set forward, with outcroppings revealing Pennsylvanian-era shales, laid through sedimentation when a sea covered this area 300 million years ago. Near **Catoosa**, Oklahoma's largest shipping port, is a bridge spanning the McClellan-Kerr waterway over the Verdigris River; a barge loaded with grain can make it from here to New Orleans in just ten days! The bustling metropolis of **Tulsa** is then travelled through, and the freeway then ascends back into hilly, eroded terrain. This stretch of freeway was built in 1953, however the remarkable lack of character is partly due to the limited entrance-exit options. Just past **Bristow** is the second tollbooth: have $3.50 ready. The geologic hands of time keep advancing forward, and near **Stroud** outcroppings consist largely of 250-million year old Permian sandstones and shales, the result of sand and mud that washed down from the eastern Oklahoma mountains at that time. Around **Chandler**, pecan orchards can be seen throughout the area's flat alluvial river plains. The town itself still has the gravesite of famous lawman Bill Tilghman, Dodge City marshal killed in 1926 while trying to serve as chief of police in the lawless town of Cromwell (q.v.) to the south. The terrain, part of the carving of the Canadian River system into the red sandy clay, is highly eroded and takes the freeway on a monotonous up-down roller-coaster ride as it nears **Oklahoma City**.

■ Oklahoma City OK - Wichita Falls TX

I-44 to U.S. 277 / 139 miles; 2.0 hours)

Nearly the entire drive bounds southwest across red Permian soils steeped with iron oxides. Leaving south from **Oklahoma City** on the H. E. Bailey Turnpike and passing **Tuttle**, the chaser parallels the track of the violent 5/3/99 tornado, just a few miles northwest of I-44. The first tollbooth of the route will charge $1.25. The desolate nature of this route rapidly becomes apparent; although the road was opened in 1964, the limited freeway access has made development of roadside points of interest impractical. Many drivers plying the H. E. Bailey seem to go insane from sheer boredom and will simply put the pedal to the metal. In the countryside along the freeway, many of the fields are used for hay production, winter feed, and peanuts. Just past **Chickasha** is the second tollbooth: $1.50. On a good day, the Wichita Mountains loom into view straight ahead, towering 1200 ft above the surrounding prairie and often visible for 50 miles. [See Off the Beaten Path: WICHITA MOUNTAINS] On the north side of **Lawton**, the freeway skirts Fort Sill. The freeway crosses a broad, flat plain, where agriculture is primarily cotton and winter wheat. Past **Walters** is the third tollbooth: $1.25. Crossing the **state line** is **Burkburnett**, an oil boomtown that peaked in 1918, with an area population of 20,000 and twenty trains a day coming and going. The chaser soon enters **Wichita Falls**, the site of a devastating tornado on 4/10/79. The terrain consists mostly of rolling mesquite land with some oil production evident.

■ Oklahoma City - Woodward

U.S. 270 / 141 miles; 2.5 hours)

NOTE: *See Oklahoma City - Shamrock (Interstate 40) for the first 40 miles of this route.*

Leaving **Oklahoma City**, broad prairie extends in all directions, topped with red Permian soils. Taking the less-travelled Exit **115** route, the traveller passes through **Calumet**, which was once a thriving town in the 1920s on Route 66. **Watonga** is the home of Oklahoma's only local cheese producer: Watonga Cheese Factory (314 E 2nd). [See Off the Beaten Path: EAGLE CITY] The chaser crosses through a very dense belt of hard red winter wheat production, a region that spans from Altus to Wichita. This wheat is a major cash crop, sown in the fall and harvested in June, and is mostly used for producing breads. In the 1900s, **Seiling** was the home of hatchet-wielding prohibitionist Carrie Nation. For decades developers kept promising that the railroad would come to Seiling and it never did; the town's salvation came only through paved highways in the 1920s. The highway then leads across desolate rolling hills, finally winding into **Woodward**. This was the site of Oklahoma's deadliest tornado, April 9, 1947, with 117 fatalities.

■ Fort Smith AR - Oklahoma City OK

Interstate 40 / 181 miles; 2.7 hours

Fort Smith is the center of the nation's poultry economy. The first Indian relocations in Oklahoma occurred at **Sallisaw** as Cherokee arrived from the Georgia hills. West of **Vian** the highway leads through some spectacular 150 ft hills which flank the highway. The **Arkansas River** crossing [N35.486 W95.097] was the site of an Interstate 40 bridge collapse on May 26, 2002; the impact from a barge resulted in 14 deaths, however, the span was reconstructed and open to traffic two months later. Just past **Checotah**, I-40 crosses the largest lake in Oklahoma: Lake Eufaula, then skirts by its southern shore before ascending 280 ft up onto Tiger Mountain. **Henryetta** has been a mining and smelting center for over 100 years, while **Okemah** is in the heart of Oklahoma's pecan belt. [See Off the Beaten Path: STRUGGLEVILLE & CROMWELL]. The highway enters the Permian red soils of the Oklahoma City area, crossing into older Pennsylvanian geology near **Shawnee**, which once vied for the state capital and even built a governor's mansion. From this point on, traffic thickens, and the thirty-mile stretch from here to the eastern suburbs of **Oklahoma City** is said to have one of the highest rates of road rage and speeding incidents in the region. If you take the I-240 split, you will pass by the massive GM Plant [N35.388 W97.395] which produces the GM Envoy and Chevy Trailblazer line.

■ Tulsa - Woodward OK

U.S. 64 to U.S. 412 (203 miles; 3.1 hours)

Leaving **Tulsa**, the road follows the Arkansas River westward. Nestled on a hilly slope, **Sand Springs** (insert history). The highway negotiates its way through 250 ft bluffs lining the river via a series of roadcuts and bridges, before crossing the center of Keystone Lake, a man-made lake constructed in 1962 and rich with bass, crappie, and catfish. This was the site of an Army camp in the 1830s which allowed negotiators to mediate tribal disputes in western Oklahoma. The highway crosses heavily rolling terrain: the Osage Hills, which are actually the southward extent of the Kansas Flint Hills. **Hallett** was the site of a fireworks factory explosion in 1985 which killed 21. Near **Morrison**, the road descends into a valley and crosses over the old St. Louis - San Francisco railway line. About ten miles past the **Interstate 35 junction**, the terrain begins flattening out.

The highway reaches **Enid,** hometown and alma mater of the late veteran weathercaster Harold Taft, who did television weather in Dallas-Fort Worth from 1948 to 1991. Further is **Lahoma**, home to Oklahoma's Pakwash-type storm of August 1994. Several miles south of **Meno** is Ames [see Off the Beaten Path: AMES ASTROBLEME]. The highway ends at **Cleo Springs**, and a left turn is needed. The road immediately crosses the Cimarron River, then reaches **Orienta**, home to a well-known NSSL tornado intercept in 1979. Turning right at Orienta, the road passes through a gap in the Glass Mountains, 200 ft mesa-like peaks which stretch north to south. Some oil production is found in the valleys past this ridge. Reaching **Mooreland**, the road begins paralleling the Santa Fe railway, which was the key southern route from Kansas to the Pacific Coast. It becomes quite obvious what railroad presence does to the countryside. Finally the town of **Woodward** is reached.

■ Lawton OK - Childress TX

U.S. 62 (123 miles; 2.2 hours)

Leaving **Lawton** [see margin: LAWTON: Traffic] the road empties onto red Permian soils and open farmland. Just to the north of town are the igneous granite Wichita Mountains, which rise 1200 ft (370 m) above the surrounding terrain. The exposures are Cambrian-era, about 500 million years old. The range is part of a rift that formed when southern Oklahoma unsuccessfully tried to split away. This resulted in volcanoes during the Pennsylvanian era which are now extinct. Most of the southern foothills belong to the U.S. Army at Fort Sill, and helicopters and low-flying jets such as A-10 "tank killers" might be spotted. The Oklahoma granite capital of **Snyder** was a railroad town that sat on a Frisco Railroad crossroad connecting Vernon to Enid and Lawton to Quanah; a May 10, 1905 tornado levelled the town and killed 97, making it the second deadliest on record in the state. Past Snyder the road skirts the 500 ft Long Mountain, occasionally visited by hang gliders. The land flattens and cotton, peanut, and winter wheat fields spring into view. Soon, travellers pass by the sprawling **Altus Air Force Base**, which is the training base for America's largest freighter jet: the C-5 Galaxy. You'll see a lot of these behemoths flying around on weekdays. The town of **Altus** is built on agriculture and the military base. The old railroad town of **Duke** is followed by the town of **Gould** (occasionally dubbed Ghoul'd by chasers due to the ghost-town atmosphere), then the farming center of **Hollis**. Cotton becomes the dominant crop as one reaches the progressively-deserted western edge of this route. [See Off the Beaten Path: RON] Five miles west of Hollis is the **state line** [N34.681 W100.00], marked by the Gannet Survey in 1929 with concrete cones, and thought to be one of the most accurate placements in United States surveying history. Be prepared for the abrupt highway ending ten miles inside Texas [N34.668 W100.188], requiring the 17-mile journey south to **Childress**.

THE OFFICIAL
STORM CHASING HANDBOOK MAP
Norman, Oklahoma

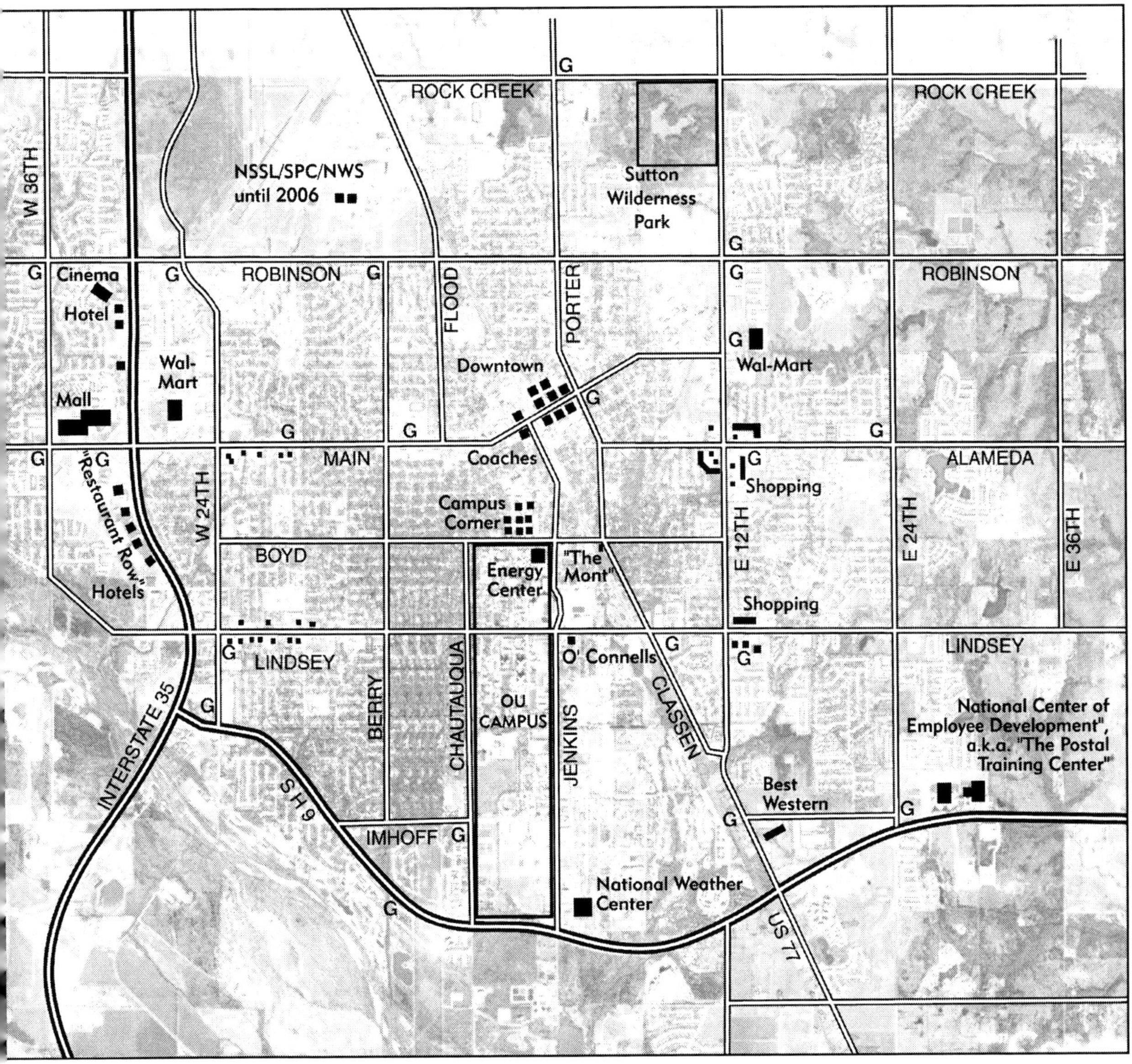

Chaser's map to Chase Mecca: Norman, Oklahoma. Sarkeys Energy Center, at 180-ft the tallest building in Norman, used to host all of OU's meteorology classes until 2006. Now all except the basic undergraduate courses have moved to the National Weather Center (NWC) location. The NWC hosts the National Severe Storms Laboratory, the Norman forecast office, the Storm Prediction Center, and the NOAA Warning Decision Training Branch. The NWC is a confederation of federal, state, and academic organizations that work together in partnership to improve understanding of severe weather forecasting. Access is restricted. Tours for the general public are offered on Mondays, Wednesdays and Fridays at 1 p.m.; contact tours@nwc.ou.edu or call 405-325-1147. Spots marked "G" indicate major fuel stations. When visiting, it's advisable to be aware of major OU game days, which can result in bottlenecks of the entire south campus and Highway 9 area for hours at a time.

The National Weather Center was built in 2006, consolidating a number of Oklahoma weather institutions including the Storm Prediction Center, the Norman forecast office of the National Weather Service, the National Severe Storms Laboratory, the Cooperative Institute for Mesoscale Meteorology Studies, and the University of Oklahoma. The facility provides 5.6 acres of office space, has a top floor observation deck, and has a cafeteria named The Flying Cow with brick oven pizza and Chik-Fil-A. It's located on the south side of Norman near State Highway 9 at Jenkins Ave, but interior access is only by employment, appointment, or escort. The building is seen here on 31 October 2008. *(Tim Vasquez)*

The lead forecaster at the Storm Prediction Center works on a forecast in October 2008, monitoring a cluster of strong storms in northern Arkansas. The Storm Prediction Center can be viewed as part of the National Weather Center tour. *(Tim Vasquez)*

Off the beaten path

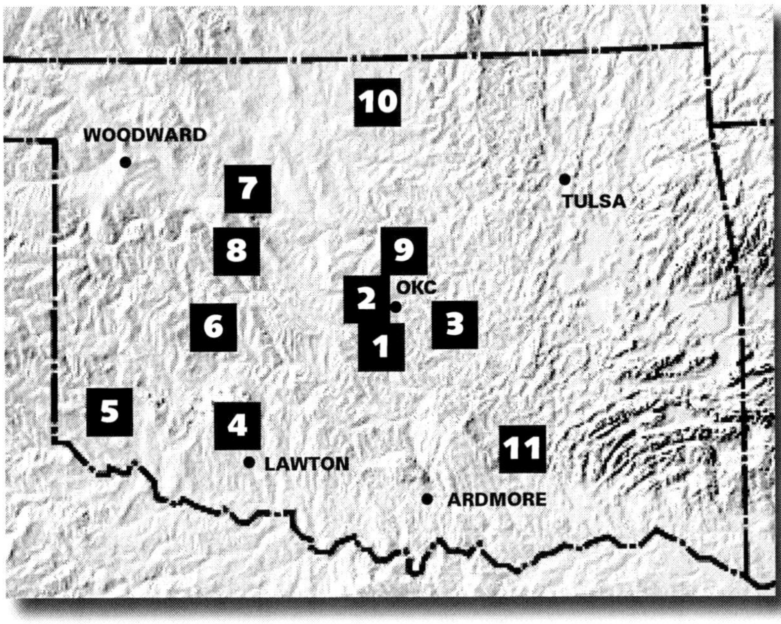

Central Oklahoma

1 Norman, Oklahoma. Norman, Oklahoma is the worldwide mecca of severe weather. You can find the older National Severe Storm Laboratory and Storm Prediction Center buildings [N35.237 W97.462] near the airport on Halley Circle, but it's all moved to the National Weather Center [N35.181 W97.439] near Jenkins Dr and Hwy 9. Tours of the National Weather Center are Monday, Wednesday, and Friday at 1 pm; call 405-325-1147 for more information. Sarkey Energy Center [N35.210 W97.440] is on the northeast side of OU and up until 2006 it held the OU weather school. Don't miss the non-weather points of interest, too. The Sam Noble Museum of Natural History [N35.195 W97.449] is southeast of campus at Chautauqua & Timberdell (405-325-4712). See Norman's only zoo: the Little River Zoo [N35.177 W97.264] about 11 miles east of town on SE 120th St (405-366-7229); 7 days a week and guided tours only. For those interested in tornado damage, the city of Moore has had bad luck with Oklahoma twisters. About 500 ft east of Pennsylvania & SW 134th is a concrete bridge over a creek [N35.334 W97.546] that withstood the May 3, 1999 tornado, which was producing F4 damage at the time. The tornado moved east-northeast into neighborhoods. The neighborhood about a half mile north-northeast of Santa Fe at NW 12th St was ravaged twice, once by the October 4, 1998 tornado (producing F2 damage) and again by the May 3, 1999 tornado (producing F4 damage).

2 Omniplex Science Museum in Oklahoma City [N35.524 W97.475] at MLK & NE 52nd St is the largest museum in the region and has a fantastic aerospace exhibit. The Oklahoma City National Memorial [N35.472 W97.517] is just north of downtown, built on the site of the 1995 Federal Building explosion.

3 Cromwell and Struggleville ghost towns. If you take Exit 212 and drive south, history unfolds. Less than 3/4 mile south of the freeway is the former ghost town of Struggleville [N35.375 W96.459], and two miles further, the aging town of Cromwell [N35.340 W96.459]. They were both 1920s oil boomtowns. Struggleville was named after the nearly impassable hill it was built on, while Cromwell was a violent town without any law enforcement for many years. Both towns fizzled by the 1930s when oil dried up.

Southwest Oklahoma

4 Wichita Mountains. The Great Plains of Oklahoma is not quite where you would expect to find mountains, but this is indeed the case. A range of very small mountains, or large hills, depending on your point of view, measures approximately 20 miles long and 10 miles wide northwest of Lawton. This is part of a geologic uplift, where granites and older Pennsylvanian rocks are exposed. GPS coordinates are not given here since there are several ways into the park. Northern areas of the park are set aside as nature preserves and are off-limits, while southern areas are open to hiking and climbing. When looking for signs of convection, drive to the top of Mount Scott [N34.744 W98.532]: it's free and in five minutes you can ascend 1000 ft with a visibility of over 100 miles on a good day.

5 Ron ghost town. Just an 8 mile excursion from U.S. 62 is the ghost town of Ron [N34.792 W99.859]. At its peak in the 1920s it contained a school, a store, a church, eight houses, and a cotton gin. After the Depression it contained only a consolidated regional school until its closure in 1964. To get there, head north on NS174 Road (3 miles east of Hollis) for 7.5 miles.

6 Original Route 66. When along Interstate 40 west of Oklahoma City, the chaser can opt for an interesting detour on the old U.S. Route 66 by taking Exit 108 for U.S. 281 [N35.532 W98.233]. This rejoins with I-40 at exit 101 [N35.529 W98.354].

Northwest Oklahoma

7 Ames underground crater. West of Enid, is the town of Ames, home to one of only a handful of underground meteor craters detected on Earth. Over 500 million years ago, a mile-wide meteor slammed into Earth at this spot [centered on the west edge of town at N36.254 W98.194], producing a crater that was 10 miles wide and 3,000 ft deep! Unfortunately, years of sedimentation and erosional deposits have buried this fantastic structure to a depth of 9000 ft beneath the surface. No trace of it remains except through unusual magnetometer and gravitometer readings. Still, it's awesome to stand here and think that one of the largest craters on Earth is here under your feet, and that it is still there.

8 Eagle City ghost town. Just past Watonga is a great ghost town worth visiting: Eagle City [N35.933 W98.591]. Sprouting up in the 1900s were banks, drugstores, churches, and a large office building, and a population of at least 300. The town began declining in the 1920s with the routing of a railway 10 miles to the west, and most residents were gone by the 1970s. Many buildings still stand. To get there from US 281, take OK 58 north for 6.5 miles and it will be a quarter mile west of the road.

North Central Oklahoma

9 Pleasant Valley ghost town. Near I-35 head to the ghost town of Pleasant Valley [N35.989 W97.300]. This community was a meeting point for cattle drivers and outlaws, and it thrived through the 1900s. A slow decline ensued over the second half of the 20th century. To get there from I-35, take Exit 157, go east, and take the split for OK 33 northeast towards Langston. After several miles, head north on NS320 Road for 3.2 miles.

10 Wakita Twister Museum. Featured in the 1996 movie *Twister*, Wakita has a tornado museum (101 W. Main) [N36.883 W97.922]. It's an especially reflective stop for chasers now that the movie has faded into the past. The published hours are 1 to 5 pm daily April through October, but call first (580-594-2312) as the hours can be erratic. The museum also offers use of a furnished guest house, "Twister Country Guesthouse", on 102 W. Pawnee St, with kitchen and washer and dryer. It's available by reservation; call the number above.

Southeast Oklahoma

11 Lehigh ghost town. Only 8 miles north on U.S. 75 from Atoka is Lehigh [N34.469 W96.216]. It exists now only as a scattered shell of a community. Its glory days were in the 1900s, when the town was known as the cultural capital of Oklahoma, complete with the Bijou Opera House and a solid economy based on coal mining. The boom in oil production in the 1920s sounded its death toll.

Mount Scott is a favorite stop for chasers refining their position in southwest Oklahoma. With a summit at 2464 ft MSL, compared to the surrounding 1340 ft MSL valley floor, Mount Scott offers a great view of any distant convection. *(USGS)*

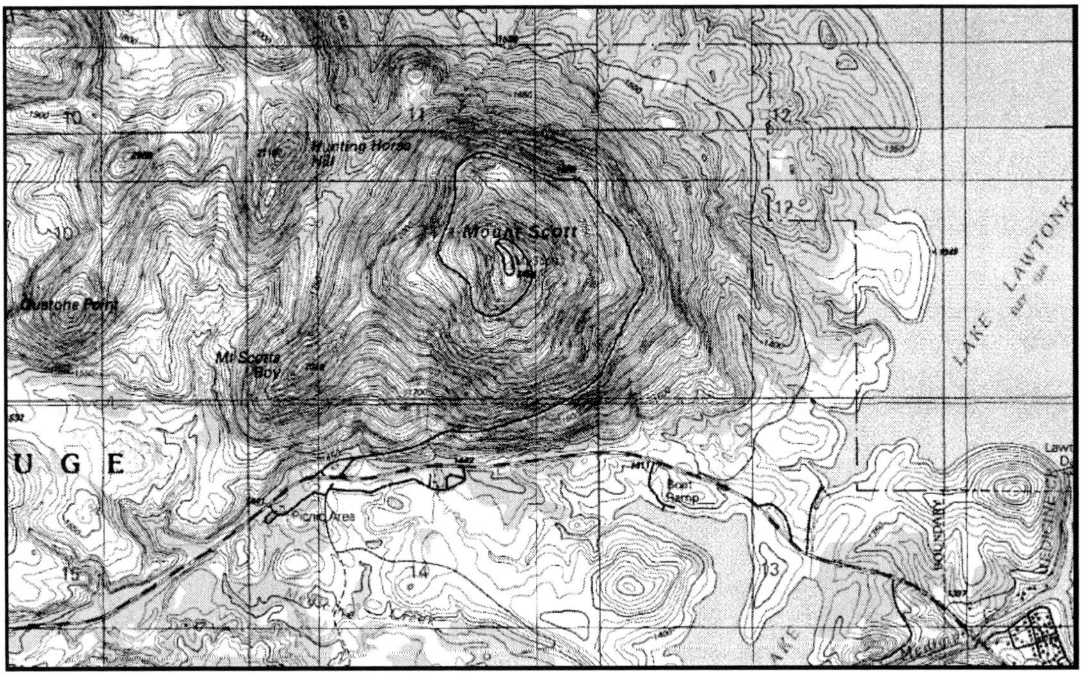

GREAT PLAINS TRAVEL GUIDE

Eastern Kansas

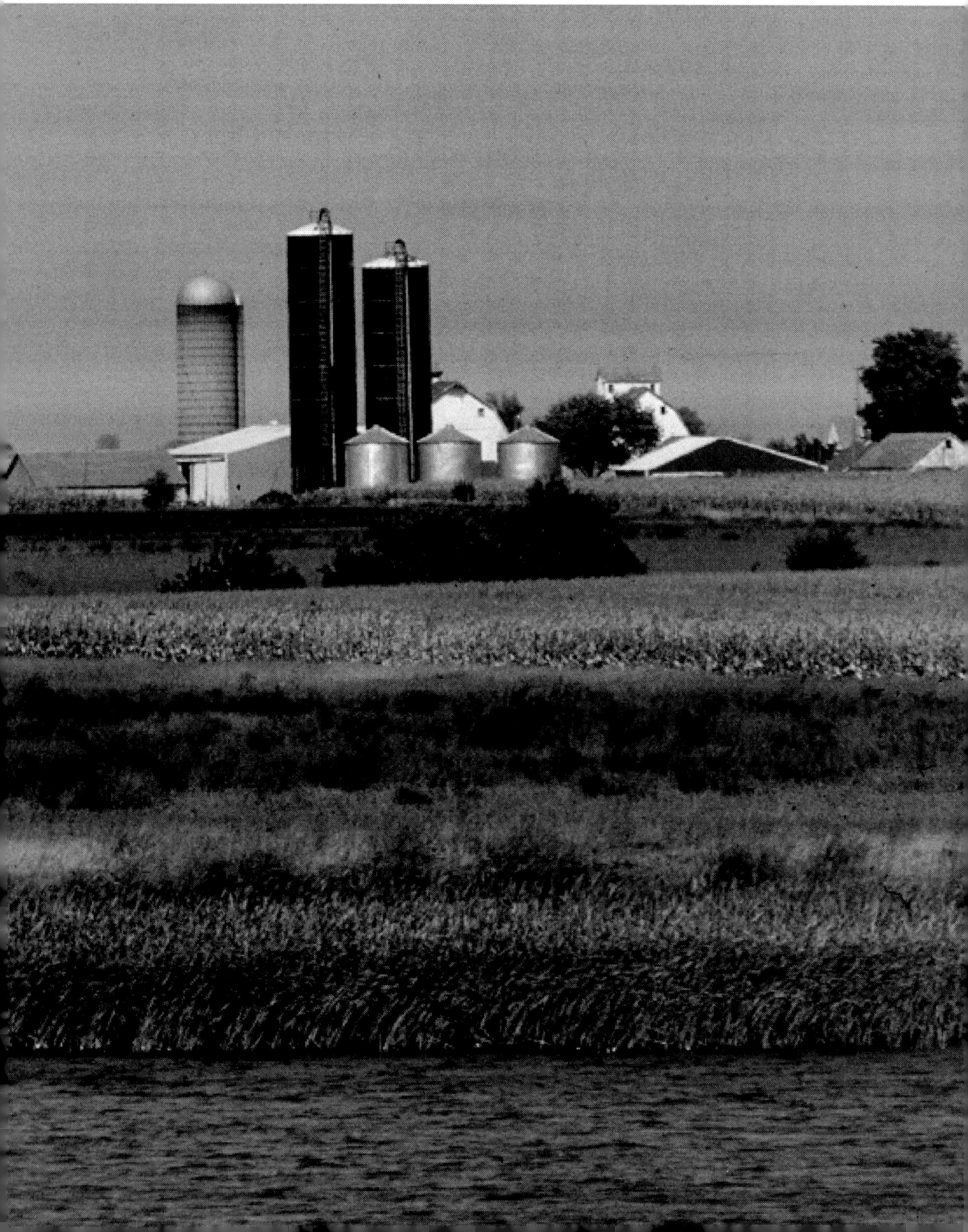

During the middle of the 19th century, Eastern Kansas formed the front porch of the Wild West. In close proximity to bustling Kansas City, it enjoyed some of the most civilized and comfortable living anywhere on the American prairies. However, to the west was the specter of the unfathomable Great Plains, roamed by the feared Cheyenne Indians. The newborn towns of north central Kansas, such as Lincoln and Mankato, were nearly decimated in attempts by the tribe to retake their traditional bison hunting ground. Cornfields, of course, won out in the end, and eastern Kansas settled on an economy of agriculture. This was punctuated some decades later by the discovery of oil.

Eastern Kansas has long enjoyed the limelight of the romantic pioneer spirit. For two years it was the home of Laura Ingalls Wilder's *Little House on the Prairie*, where the family resided before moving onward to South Dakota. More significantly, Eastern Kansas was the setting for L. Frank Baum's *The Wizard of Oz*, written in 1900, and the MGM theatrical release a few decades later. The tornado's appearance as a plot device was no accident: early scientific analysis had showed that this region had the highest incidence of tornadoes in the United States. In the public conscience, Kansas tornadoes were about as American as apple pie. It was only in the early 20th century when reliable tornado reports began filtering out of Indian Territory, later Oklahoma, and the southwestward march of apparent tornado incidence began.

The agricultural nature of eastern Kansas makes for excellent chase territory due to the familiar system of north-south/east-west gridded roads every square mile. The only exceptions are in the rocky expanses of the Flint Hills. With dense data coverage and easily-available National Weather Service Radio and cellular phone availability, this is prime territory for new chasers to learn the ropes.

Meteorology

Eastern Kansas enjoys a rich reputation for severe weather. Unfortunately most of this distinction lies in an abundance of severe squall lines. This occurs when thunderstorms in the central and western part of the state consolidate into large lines, moving into Eastern Kansas region after dark and bringing large hail and strong winds. The

Kansas meteor crater

East of Dodge City in Kiowa County is the tiny Haviland Crater, formed by the impact of a large meteor that dumped 2000 lbs of olivine across a square mile of land. It's located just south of Brenham, but sources disagree widely on the exact coordinates and it may be known only to locals. The downside is that the crater resembles a shallow mud hole, and the site is locked away on private property. However it's fascinating to know that Kansas has a miniature Meteor Crater of its own!

Like a stratified geological layer, we see elements of lush farmland and prairie in central Kansas near McPherson. (Tim Vasquez)

Largest hailstone

The largest officially-accepted hailstone on record of the 20th century occurred in southeastern Kansas in the month of September.

Kansas birds of prey

I have always been interested in birds of prey, and nowhere have I seen more variety and numbers than in western Kansas. I could drive for hours and never get over the wonder of these beautiful birds. In particular, prairie falcons seem to be everywhere, diving, swooping, rising on thermals. Their flight seems an exercise in pure joy--I wish I could join them in that azure sky. To be a citizen of the heavens, companion to the clouds; what a life that must be!

PEGGY WILLENBERG
Minneapolis, MN chaser

best opportunities for isolated daytime supercells in eastern Kansas come with warm fronts slowly lifting north.

The terrain is rather flat, with some weak orographic contributions coming from the Flint Hills stretching from Manhattan to Sedan. Strong easterly flow tends to put the entire region under upslope flow, however this synoptic-scale lift is so broad that it favors multiple cells: multicells and squall lines. Therefore, as in most prairie land on the Great Plains, point convergence responsible for isolated supercells must come from small-scale weather disturbances embedded in the larger-scale pattern.

Early in the season, severe weather is rare in eastern Kansas. The low terrain and close proximity to the path of plunging polar airmasses usually keeps the region stuck in the icebox, even when most of the Great Plains is warming up. The best potential for severe weather is found in the higher terrain to the west and southwest, where polar air is more easily mixed out and dispersed and lapse rates can steepen. Severe weather potential ramps up gradually in April and May with the loss of deep polar air surges, which allows for boundaries to stall in this area. The region reaches its severe weather peak in June.

During the summer months, Eastern Kansas is sometimes lucky enough to catch brief intrusions of polar air or outflow boundaries working southward from Minnesota, Iowa, and Nebraska. This can serve as a focus for surface convergence, making it active with thunderstorms late in the season while Texas and Oklahoma simmer under a subtropical ridge.

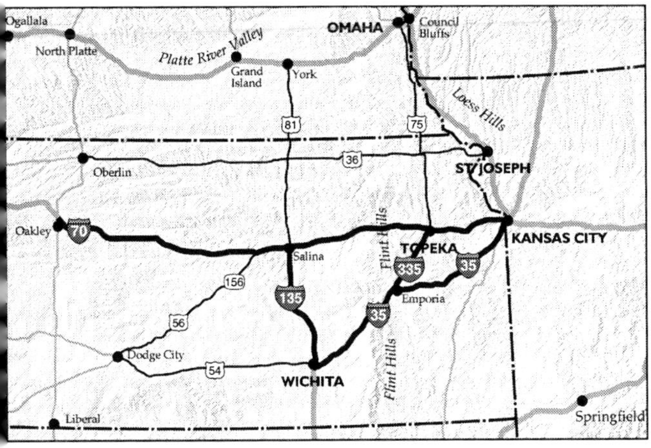

Road Guide

■ Wichita - Dodge City KS

U.S. 400 (155 miles; 2.5 hours)

Heading west from **Wichita**, the chaser embarks on a exciting journey toward the High Plains, passing the bedroom community of **Garden Plain**. Past this town, the road descends into a river valley where the very new, dusty loess has been eroded to reveal 250-million year old Permian shale outcroppings, one of the few such exposures on the route where fossils can be found. **Kingman** was settled in the 1870s as an agricultural center. Here the road reaches the Ogallala Formation, the broad blanket of sands and clays eroded from the Rocky Mountains 5-10 million years ago, largely covered with several feet of newer, sandy loess. The loess fields are dedicated heavily to winter wheat all the way to **Pratt**. The town was settled on Kiowa hunting territory in 1884, and anxiety about the possibility of 1870's-style Indian raids persisted for the town's first few years. Rich loess soils become commonplace that allow a variety of winter wheat, sorghum, and alfalfa. Near **Cullison** the road skirts the Great Bend Sand Plains, a region of real dune sand. In **Greensburg**, the world's largest hand-dug well, 109 ft deep and 32 ft wide, as well as an authentic half-ton pallasite meteorite discovered in the county, are on display. Chasers anxious for geologic diversity can head to southeastern Kiowa County, where erosion along the Medicine Lodge River reveals 100-250 million year old Cretaceous and Permian fossil-bearing rocks. Near **Mullinville** one can find roadside kinetic art, as well as the massive Fromme-Birney Round Barn, built in 1912 according to the winds of an architectural fad. It originally housed a team of horses. Then the legendary town of **Dodge City** looms in sight.

■ Wichita KS - York NE

I-135/U.S. 81 (232 miles; 3.8 hours)

Wichita is on a sandy alluvial plain, with the fields largely winter wheat and sorghum producers. Oil is also an important resource. The years 1871 to 1873 were a booming time for **Newton**; here, the railroad met the Chisholm Trail which brought cattle up from Texas. After 1873 the railroad reached further south. Here the soil becomes a rich black loess. The region was a Mennonite farming center as early as 1874, whose people brought a legendary strain of wheat known as Turkey Red to the region. **Moundridge** is home to one of the deepest portions of the Equus Beds, a geological depression formed when underground salt beds dissolved (see illustration in Off the Beaten Path). About 7 miles north of **McPherson**, the flat, rolling terrain stops [N38.465 W97.620] and enters the rugged Smoky Hills region. The geology changes from new alluvial sands and gravel captured by the central lowlands during the past one million years to sandstones and shales of Cretaceous age, about 100 million years old, exposed when a large sea covering this area slowly retreated, and a system of new rivers carved the weathered the terrain down to uncover these older rocks. **Lindsborg**, a town founded by Swedish immigrants in 1868, is located in the young alluvial flats of the Smoky Hill River. The paintings of Lindsborg artist Birger Sandzen (1871-1954) portray much of the beauty of the Smoky Hills and central Kansas and can be found in his estate's gallery in town (1-5 pm except Monday). Approaching **Bridgeport**, the Smoky Hill Buttes loom about 4 miles to the west; the southernmost one, Coronado Heights, is over 250 ft high and is said to have been scaled by Francisco Vásquez de Coronado in 1541 while searching Kansas for gold. A public park and a bizarre stone castle are atop this hill. **Salina** thrived in the 1850s and 1860s as a trading post between the Kansas City region and the Plains Indians, then became a railroad town in the 1870s. North of Salina, the road leaves the flat alluvial plains and re-enters the Smoky Hills, then after about 6 miles it drops back onto another alluvial plain. Here the road brushes by **Minneapolis**. [See Off The Beaten Path: ROCK CITY] Three miles north of the junction with U.S. 24, the road climbs onto a bluff capped with Greenhorn limestone, traditionally formed into blocks and used as local building material. **Concordia** grew just after the Civil War, and is home to the Brown Grand Theatre, a large opera house financed by a local millionaire in 1907. Leaving town, the highway skirts within a mile of an old WWII POW camp [N39.617 W97.640] that housed 5,000 Germans; it ruins can be visited. **Hebron** lays claim to the world's largest porch swing, located in the municipal park. It holds 25 adults! Past town, the road reaches flat terrain. The road reaches **I-80** at **York**.

■ Kansas City - Wichita KS

Interstate 35 (196 miles; 2.9 hours)

The chaser begins in heavily-populated **Kansas City**. It is on the edge of an area that was covered during the Ice Age and now harbors soy and some wheat and corn. Near **Gardner**, the chaser exits the southernmost glacial region and arrives in the Pennsylvanian-era Osage Cuestas, a unique landform that consists of shallow north-south hills that have steep eastern faces. This is caused by beds of limestone and shale tilted upward and eastward, weathered at their edges. [See Off the Beaten Path: MINNEOLA] After leaving **Emporia**, the chaser enters the newer Permian-era Flint Hills, which have a high composition of flint and have resisted natural erosion. The hills are strewn with limestones and shales, making them far too rocky for agriculture, therefore it survives as some of the only unmolested tallgrass prairie in the United States. In early April, these hills are usually covered with fires and smoke, a process ranchers use to burn off invading tress and weeds to restore the native grasses for their cattle. If it weren't for this burning, the tallgrass prairie would not exist, being invaded by trees from eastern regions. The prairie extends to **Cassoday**, which dedicates itself to the prairie chicken. Leaving the Flint Hills, the chaser enters the Arkansas River Lowlands which consist mostly of alluvial, sandy erosion from rivers. The economy of **El Dorado** has been built on petroleum since 1915, and sits on Kansas' single most productive oil field. Further along is **Andover**, known for the devastating tornado and haunting media footage of 4/26/91. Arriving in **Wichita**, the road skirts Boeing and Cessna facilities just south of the freeway, where legendary aircraft like the B-52 and Cessna 172 were constructed.

TRAFFIC NOTE: Chasers should plan on delays from Wellsville to Ottawa, and from

Lebo to Emporia, which have had lane closures since late 2000. The route from Emporia to Wichita costs $3.20; those continuing to Oklahoma will pay $4.75 total.

■ Kansas City - Hays KS

Interstate 70 (266 miles; 4.0 hours)

In densely populated **Kansas City**, it is hard to believe that this spot was once under 500 feet (150 m) of ice during the last Ice Age! This new Holocene-era geology alternates with outcroppings of Pennsylvanian shale and limestone on hillsides. Travelling west, suburbs give way to soy fields, along with some wheat and corn. [See Off the Beaten Path: STULL] **Topeka**'s darkest day was brought about by a tornado, which struck on June 8, 1966; 16 dead and 406 injured. Near **Alma** the driver reaches the limits of Ice Age glacial coverage, and the fields in this region (especially a few miles to the north) are littered with thousands of boulders which were carried southwestward and left behind. The road then enters the northern Flint Hills. **Manhattan** is the site of Kansas' strongest earthquake: 5.1 on the Richter Scale on April 24, 1867. [See Off the Beaten Path: PARKERVILLE] A heavy belt of wheat production begins around **Junction City**. In 1867, **Abilene** was where the railroad met the Chisholm Trail, originating from central Texas, and it was a lively, festive boomtown. However by 1872 the railroad had been extended to Ellsworth, 60 miles southwest. A few miles west of Abilene, the freeway passes through three miles of sand dune topography, now grown over with native grasses. Near **Exit 260**, there is a gradual transition from younger Permian rocks to newer Cretaceous. Near **Salina** one enters the geology-rich Smoky Hills region. Ascending west out of Salina the highway climbs through outcroppings of Dakota Formation sandstone. The road descends into an alluvial plain near **Wilson**. [See Off The Beaten Path: GARDEN OF EDEN] Past Wilson, the chaser enters the third major belt within the Smoky Hills. Approaching **Russell**, the traveller crosses outcroppings of Niobrara Chalk. Look for stubbly limestone fenceposts near **Dorrance**. About five miles west of **Russell** near **Mile Marker 179**, a series of sinkholes extends for a mile, marked by sharp dips in the freeway. They form from dissolved salt beds about 1500 ft below the ground. The tiny town of **Victoria** is actually home to a marvel of architecture: the Cathedral of the Plains, constructed in 1908-11 with 8500 tons of Greenhorn limestone. The remainder of the drive to **Hays** consists of monotonous flat farmland with outcroppings of thin chalky shale on slopes. Stop in at Hays to see the Sternberg Museum of Natural History on the east edge of town next to the Interstate.

■ Emporia - Topeka KS - Omaha NE

I-335 / U.S. 75 (221 miles; 3.5 hours)

Leaving the northwest outskirts of **Emporia**, the freeway drops into the Neosho River valley. For the next 50 miles, there are very few points of interest. A mile short of the **Topeka** U.S. 75 interchange is an area of orange and pink quartzite rocks and boulders, dropped here at the furthest advance of Ice Age glaciers. Topeka itself was a major railroad center in the 1880s, but most of the railyards are found northeast of town. U.S. 75 leads northward across the Kansas River and across rolling hills. After two forced relocations, this area was home to the Potawatomi tribe, later the Prairie Band after the Citizen Band moved to Oklahoma. A Harrah's casino along U.S. 75 near **Hoyt** is owned by the Prairie, and the town of **Mayetta** is headquarters of the tribe, which owns a giant expanse of rangeland to the west. At the town of **Fairview**, the road comes to a stop. Turning west, you drive three miles then continue north. The highway reaches **Bellevue**, one of the southern suburbs of **Omaha**, and neighboring Offutt AFB, longtime headquarters of the Strategic Air Command.

■ St Joseph MO - Oberlin KS

U.S. 36 (313 miles; 5.4 hours)

Leaving **St. Joseph**, you cross into Kansas on the Missouri River. After heading west over alluvial river flats, the highway enters a gap between 200 ft hills, joining the apple-production town of **Wathena** and the Chicago, Rock Island & Pacific (CRI&P) railroad. The hills here are rolling 100 ft loess hills, composed of soil particles which were accumulated into large deposits by high winds during the Ice Age. Near **Hiawatha** a ten-mile stretch of glacial deposits, boulders and rocks unloaded by the furthest glacial advances tens of thousands of years ago, are found in the fields, much of it consisting of quartzite. [See Off the Beaten Path: BAKER] Near **Fairview** a sixty-mile stretch of glacial deposits begins. Rockhounds will be interested in a side trip to Pony Creek, eight miles due north of Fairview [N39.956 W95.712], which yields a few hidden outcrops of rare orange celestine, crystals of strontium sulphate. **Marysville** was the crossroads for numerous pioneer trails, including the Pony Express in 1860. [See Off the Beaten Path: IRVING] Just nine miles west of Marysville is the county line, where the highway crosses the mid-continent rift, an abyssal subterranean crack extending from here to Minnesota. Over a stretch of several miles the gravity drops by about 0.01% because of a change in composition through this rift! Near the railroad town of **Washington**, the highway reaches the furthest advance of Ice Age glaciers. Exposures of Dakota sandstone are found for several miles. Cuba is found at a railroad junction, and the terrain begins flattening somewhat. In the alluvial Republican River plain is **Scandia**. The **Republican River**, just past town, does not have political affiliation but rather takes the name of the Republican Pawnee, named by explorers who noted the tribe's form of government. A mile past **Montrose** you'll see limestone roadcuts; the northeastern-most roadcut shows a fault line, where the layers slipped a few feet and probably produced an earthquake. **Mankato**, known initially as Jewell, was a stronghold against Cheyenne raids in the early 1870s as it settled into its agricultural roots; a memorial is found in the city park. Eighteen miles further, you can drive a few miles north to **Lebanon**: home to Kansas' coldest temperature (-40 deg F in February 1905) and site of the geographical center of the conterminous U.S. [N39.828 W97.579] posted a couple of miles northwest of town. **Smith Center** has a dutch windmill in its city park. The terrain here was the inspiration for Higley's *Home on the Range*, written in 1872. About 25 miles south of **Athol**, Alton holds Kansas' hottest temperature record, 121 deg F in 1936. In **Agra**, look for the watertower and its paint mark covering a space before the word "AGRA"; it covers the letters "VI" added by a local prankster in the late 1990s. **Gretna** is a name that graces the collection of many meteorite fanciers; 12 miles north of town, a large specimen was found in a field in 1912. Sources, however, conflict whether it weighed 80 kg or 80 lbs. At the CRI&P railroad town of **Stuttgart**, the road reaches 2000 ft elevation for the first time, passing some oil fields that tap the Stuttgart-Huffstutter Anticline. It climbs through a rugged valley past the town of **Prairie View**. The hills between the highway and **Calvert** to the north are mined for volcanic ash, a site that was in the path of volcanic plumes from Northeast New Mexico, Yellowstone, California, and Mt. St. Helens during the past million years, and whose terrain has collected it and kept it from being eroded. A large part of it was deposited by Mount St. Helens in 1980! **Norton** is a popular center for pheasant hunting in the fall. Just past Norton are a series of north-south rolling hills at one-mile intervals. Norcatur. The terrain almost exclusively consists of a bed of very young Quaternary erosion from the Rocky Mountains. The road then reaches **Oberlin**, site of the last Plains Indian raid in Kansas; in this 1878 incident 40 settlers died at the hands of a Cheyenne band.

■ Salina - Dodge City KS

S.H. 156 / U.S. 56 (160 miles; 2.7 hours)

NOTE: *See Interstate 70 Salina - Hays for first portion of route.*

At **Exit 225** is the junction for S.H. 156 southwest. The road winds along the East Elkhorn Creek, ascending onto rolling prairie. **Ellsworth** was the end of the trail for many cattle drives between 1867 and 1885, complete with saloons, gambling houses, gunfights, and even a buffalo stampede through town square. The limestone jail on Court Street is the oldest building in town, having been constructed in 1872. [See Off The Beaten Path: KANOPOLIS] Holyrood. About eight miles past **Claflin** is Cheyenne Bottoms, home of a wildlife refuge and a favorite birdwatching spot. Leading into a flat alluvial plain of the Arkansas River, the highway links up with U.S. 56 and the historic Santa Fe Trail leading to New Mexico, and enters **Great Bend**. The town was slowly settled in the 1860s, suffering through a series of Cheyenne raids, and in 1872 the Santa Fe railroad reached town, allowing an agricultural economy to survive. The road follows the Santa Fe railroad along the Arkansas River across flat terrain. At **Pawnee Rock**, documented by early explorers, a public park is located on a 60 ft bluff, giving a wide view of the sky. **Larned** began as a key Cavalry fort (1860-78) that protected Santa Fe Trail travellers and railroad workers from Plains Indian raids. A townsite rapidly grew six miles east of the fort, and is what the highway passes through. [See Off the Beaten Path: HARMONY] **Kinsley** bills itself as the halfway point between New York and San Francisco, and the roadside park southwest of town has a steam locomotive and sod house on display. Offerlee. Spearville. The road descends shallow hills into the Arkansas River town of **Dodge City**; southeast of these bluffs is the Cavalry town of Fort Dodge (1864-82), which protected Santa Fe Trail travellers from Indian threats.

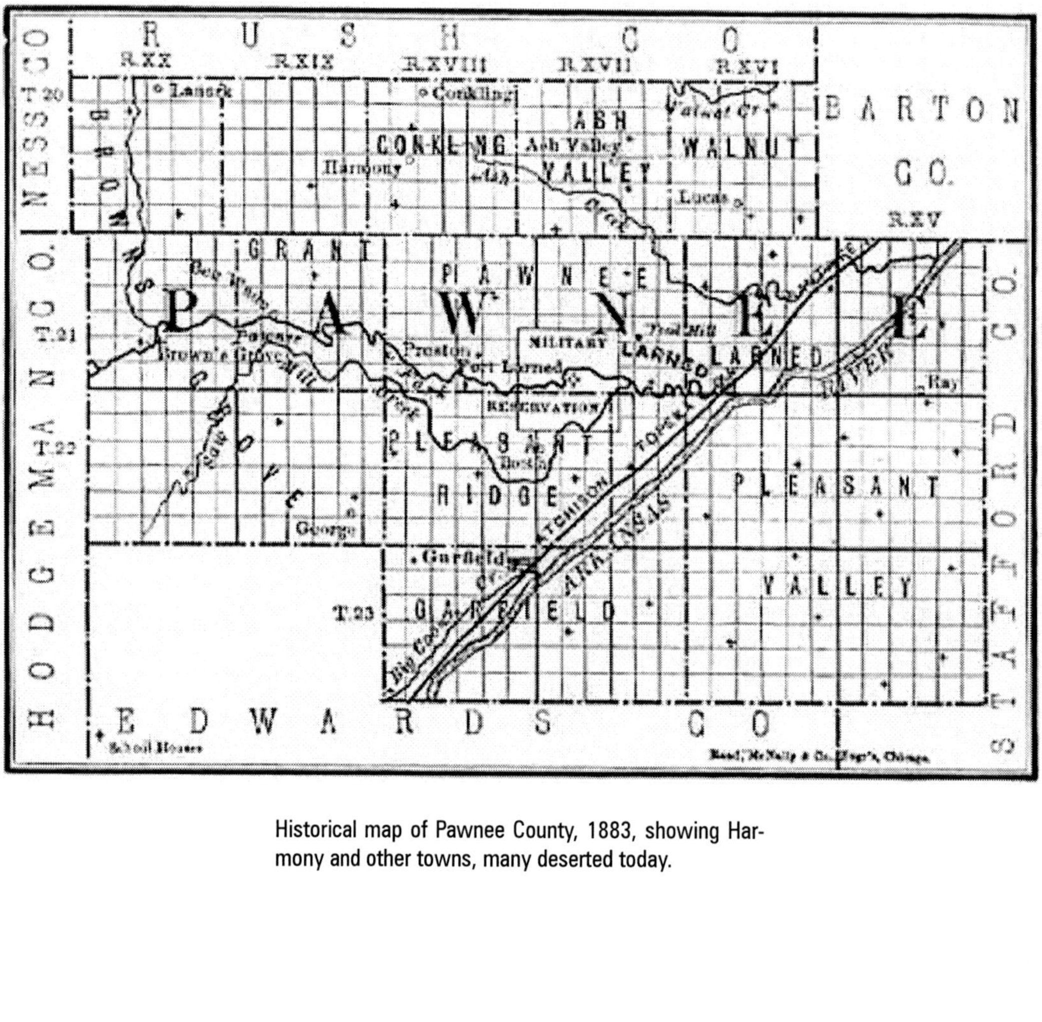

Historical map of Pawnee County, 1883, showing Harmony and other towns, many deserted today.

Off the beaten path

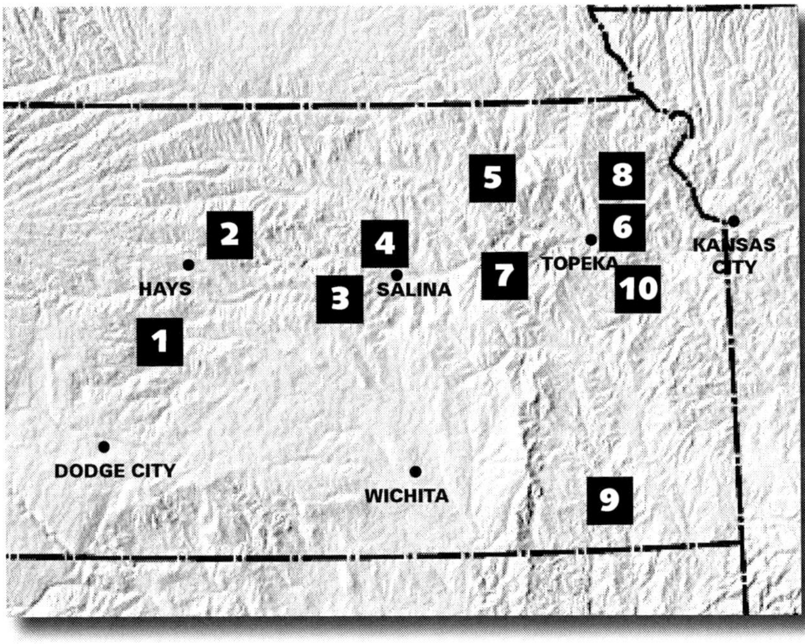

West Central Kansas

1 Harmony ghost town. Here we have chosen a random ghost town in western Kansas, one which shows no trace on maps anymore. Harmony [N38.305 W99.331] appears on old maps dating back to the 1880s, however very little is known about its history. Some ruins are said to be still intact. The location is 18 miles northwest of Larned. From the U.S. 183 / K-156 junction the ghost town is 8 miles north, then 1.5 miles west. About 12 miles southwest is the thriving town of Burdett, which was the childhood home of Dr. Clyde Tombaugh, discoverer of the planet Pluto.

North Central Kansas

2 Garden of Eden. In the town of Lucas, about 20 miles northeast of Russell, is the century-old Garden of Eden. It is actually not a garden, but a large assemblage of eccentric Populist Samuel Dinsmoor's bizarre political and biblical art [N39.058 W98.535], fashioned between 1907 and 1930. Check out the All-Seeing Eye, the Adam and Eve sculptures, and Sam Dinsmoor himself in a glass-shrouded coffin

Central Kansas

3 Kanapolis. Head 4 miles east-southeast of Ellsworth to the small town of Kanopolis [N38.710 W98.156], which in 1893 was being seriously considered as the capital of Kansas; it has survived since then as a salt mining town and, on weekends, it hosts one of the few drive-in theaters in Kansas still operating! A jaunt a little further east brings you to Mushroom Rocks State Park [N38.726 W98.030], a 5-acre site that contains bizarre toadstool-shaped sandstone formations.

4 Rock City. Just a couple of miles southwest of Minneapolis, which is 20 miles north of Salina, is Rock City [N39.090 W97.734], a public park harboring 5 acres of massive spherical sandstones nearly 20 feet high. You'll get a great view of the sky and easy access to chase routes in all directions. To get there, take K-106 south out of Minneapolis for 2.5 miles, then head west for half a mile. Nominal admission 9-5 daily; you can also view them from the road.

Northeast Kansas

5 Irving ghost town. Well south of Marysville and located exactly 4.3 miles southeast of Blue Rapids, the ghost town of Irving [N39.638 W96.596], founded in the 1860s. One of the earliest Irving tales tells about a pioneer family that dealt with snakes constantly entering their sod home. Irving succumbed to Kansas' first major tornado disaster on May 30, 1879, with 66 dead. The residents pressed on, and by the turn of the century there were nearly 500 residents, banks, telegraph offices, schools, a public library, churches, and a watertower. Urbanization and the depression took its toll, and what little was left became a flood stage area for the Tuttle Creek Dam. Some buildings were moved to Blue Rapids. All structures are long gone, but many streets, sidewalks, foundations, and a flagpole still remain. This is a true ghost town.

6 Stull Cemetery. The ghost stories of Stull Cemetery [N38.971 W95.454] snowballed during the 1970s, with one claim that it was one of the seven portals to hell. Over the next decade it became overrun by visitors on Halloween and the spring equinox, forcing the county sheriff to begin issuing trespassing citations. Whether it's just urban legend or not, the scenic town makes a great stop to await convection, with easy access to I-70. Oh, did we mention that part of the stone church collapsed in March 2002 under mysterious circumstances? Located halfway between Lawrence and Topeka on U.S. 40.

7 Baker ghost town. Located 6 miles south-southwest of Hiawatha, the town of Baker [N39.754 W95.562] is mostly crumbling ruins on a limestone ridge. It was founded in 1882 as an agricultural center along the Missouri Pacific railroad. At least 25 residences and businesses were built here by 1883, including a grain elevator, and old maps show a grid of ten streets in each direction. The town slowly decayed due to urbanization and the Great Depression, and now ruins are all that remains.

8 Parkerville park. When waiting for East Kansas convection, park at the municipal park at Parkerville [N38.764 W96.662], located about 10 miles northwest of Council Grove. It's nestled in an alluvial plain of the Neosho River among the Flint Hills. This is unlike many municipal parks, though: there's very little here, and the town is falling headlong into the upper echelons of ghost town status. By the 1880s, the town had a newspaper, and by some accounts, 40 buildings and 500 residents. Parkerville anticipated becoming the county seat, with the courthouse at the park location. It lost the vote, and a slow downward spiral began. Railroad service ended here in 1950, and the tracks were removed in the 1960s.

Southeast Kansas

9 LeHunt ghost town. A few miles northwest of Independence is the ghost town of LeHunt [N37.269 W95.751]. The Missouri Pacific railroad brushes by just a few hundred feet to the east. There is an old concrete plant half a mile east near the railroad tracks, said to have a pickaxe in the wall as a monument to a Mexican worker who was killed when he fell into a vat of concrete. The area is said to be haunted. Table Mountain, 150 ft high, is to the west.

East Kansas

10 Centropolis ghost town. It is hard to believe that a ghost town was on the edge of becoming the state capital of Kansas, but that is exactly what happened in Minneola [N38.713 W95.333] located north of Ottawa a mile east of Centropolis. The vision was to eliminate the feud between legislative factions based in Lawrence and Lecompton. Both sides reached a compromise, buying land at the future Minneola as a new capital site, and built a meeting hall and $8000 hotel. In 1858 a bill was passed by the acting state legislature that established the capital at Minneola. This was vetoed by the acting governor, and the appeals process failed. At this time, a town of 500 residents had come together at Minneola, but the failure quickly scattered the population and almost nothing was left at the turn of the century except several farms, which exist to this day. And to think that in an alternate reality, by just a narrow margin, these hills would today be filled with endless miles of administrative buildings, skyscrapers, malls, and suburbs!

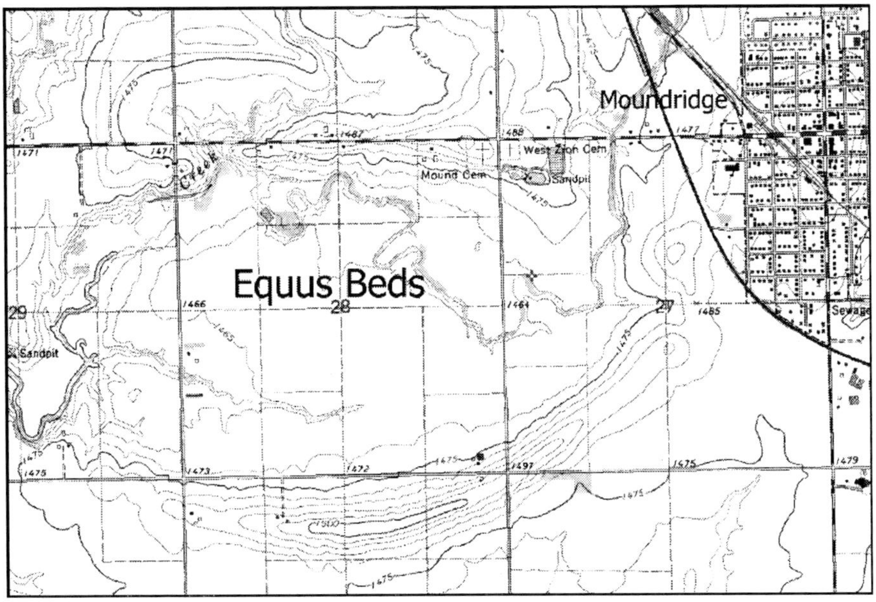

A circular pattern of contours southwest of Moundridge delineates a striking extension of the Equus Beds, part of a geological depression that extends from Wichita to McPherson. The Equus Beds are thought to be formed by an underground salt bed that was gradually dissolved by ground water millions of years ago, causing the ground to sink. Ice Age horse fossils have been found among the alluvial deposits here.

GREAT PLAINS TRAVEL GUIDE

Colorado & West Kansas

East Colorado and West Kansas forms the heart of the Great Plains. This region shares the same rugged, individualistic identity, economy, and culture, differing from that of their parent states. In these remote regions of the Great Plains, powerful weather systems emerge from the Rocky Mountains, escaping the chaos of rugged terrain, and their eastward destinies are finally pinned down by numerical models. It is this initial uncertainty that makes chasing here a challenge. This is compounded by the wide gaps that exist between surface and upper air stations.

Nearly the entire area consists of flat rangeland, with some irrigated land in western Kansas atop the Ogallala Aquifer. Here, the lonely towns are as weathered as the surrounding topography, eroded by springtime windstorms, harsh summer heat, relentless northerly winter winds, and frequent drought. So what is it that attracted people to these flat towns, rather than towards the western mountains which beckon against the setting sun, which call out to the fabric of American pioneer spirit, where the common man can strike it rich panning in the cold river streams, smell the rich scent of pine and aspen, and simply commune with nature?

These are questions which are posed and contemplated every time chasers travel the remote eastern realms of Colorado. It's the only part of the state in which organized storms can regularly develop, except of course for those storms that occur near the Front Range. The empty roads and forgotten towns here are part of the region's mystique. And eastern Colorado is commonly overlooked in travel guides. *Colorado Scenic Guide*, for example, lists only 3 destinations east of Interstate 25 out of a possible 100. Is this a good thing? Perhaps it is. Here, the towns are unacquainted with tourists, devoid of the Main Street facades of Texas and Oklahoma, and their rich pioneer history is exposed eloquently among the quietly decaying structures and dusty lots.

Meteorology

During the spring, the eastern border area of Colorado and western Kansas is the preferred daytime stomping grounds for the dryline. When the upper-level flow is fast and moisture is shallow, such as in the early spring, the

Colorado forecasting

I've chased Colorado for three years, which is rather limited experience, but I'll share what I've found:

1) On days when there is not a lot of forcing, boundaries and topography are very important. On the plains, the east-west oriented topographical maxes of the Cheyenne Ridge (North), Palmer Divide (Central), and Raton Mesa (South) are places to watch very closely, especially when old outflow or existing convergence boundaries exist. On capped afternoons, these may be the first places that go.

2) The Denver-metro area is a hot spot for non-supercell tornadoes on days when the Denver Cyclone is present, especially those with a strong convergence line which usually stretches from close to Denver International Airport to the Palmer Divide.

3) At night, storms rarely make it off the mountains without upper level support. Usually it takes a strong shortwave moving through to maintain the strength of the storms. This is mostly important if you're chasing lightning.

4) Chasing in the metro area is pretty much futile and will frustrate you to no end. Unless you want to get flooding video. In that case, hang out along I-25 near Alameda or 6th Avenue.

DANN CIANCA
Denver, Colorado

A field in southwest Kansas makes an excellent ambassador for the rest of western Kansas and eastern Colorado. *(Tim Vasquez)*

Colorado magic

In Colorado, we don't get the high dewpoints like the midwest, but with our higher terrain, we really don't need them for great storms. Dewpoints in the low to mid 50s are great for Colorado and Wyoming!

TIM SAMARAS
Denver, CO chaser

Destinations from Denver

Living in Denver, I often leave in the morning for even a local chase. I like to get into position for initiation early because the last thing you ever want to do is be late. But this presents the opportunity to take in some local color while waiting for storms to fire.

One of my favorite spots is the area between Sterling, Colorado and Sidney, Nebraska. The Cheyenne Ridge extends eastward into southwest Nebraska from the Rocky Mountains near Cheyenne, Wyoming and provides for some fascinating rock formations to explore. The countryside is hilly with many buttes providing scenic vistas. Further, the Cheyenne Ridge is one of my favorites for storm initiation, providing for majestic views of developing supercells over the colorful countryside.

ROGER HILL
Denver, CO chaser

dryline often moves quickly into western Kansas, shifting the best moisture and convergence east. Therefore storms tend to affect central Kansas proper. On the other hand, when the upper-level flow is slow and moisture is deep, such as during the summer months, the dryline stays in eastern Colorado or the border area.

Upslope flow is another big severe weather ingredient. It is important to bear in mind that elevation of the Colorado and western Kansas high plains spans a wide range: between 2500 ft (750 m) MSL at its eastern periphery and 5500 ft (1650 m) just short of the Rocky Mountain foothills. Sustained flow with a pronounced east-to-west component into these higher elevations helps force parcels upward, and there they may reach their level of free convection regardless of heating or available moisture. So while Wichita and Oklahoma City remain capped, a flurry of upslope storms can fire in the Dodge City and Goodland areas. This advantage is offset by the fact that such strong easterly components are not that common. The area is also quite far north and west of the Gulf of Mexico and escapes the best moist trajectories. So more often than not, Wichita and Oklahoma City will indeed remain capped, while the high plains lacks the moisture to generate storms. The net result is a boring chase week, with the dryline sloshing east towards central Kansas and back into Colorado at night.

While Texas has its own sharp lifting mechanism, the Caprock Escarpment, the high plains has its own version: the Palmer Divide. This ridge is located between Denver and Colorado Springs. It will often serve as a location for initiation when moisture is plentiful and there is no clear focusing mechanism.

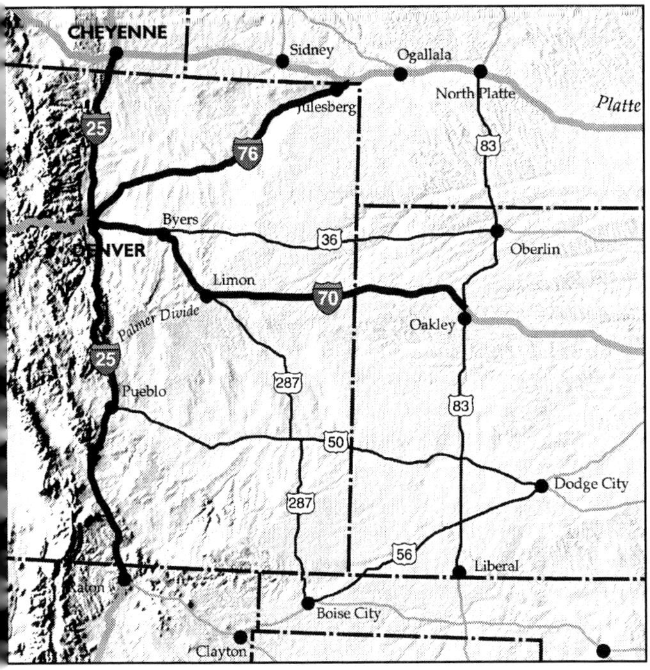

Road Guide

■ Hays KS - Denver CO

I-70 (334 miles; 4.9 hours)

Hays sits amidst a mixture of windblown loess and alluvial sands, and its fields are primarily dedicated to wheat. Some oil production occurs here. Near **Ogallah** the outcroppings of Cretaceous chalks and limestones disappear, slowly giving way to very young Ogallala Formation (named after the Nebraska location, not the nearby Kansas town). Ogallala Formation consists of sands and clays blown off the Rocky Mountains during Miocene times (10 million years ago), deposited on top of much older layers and forming a large bed on much of the High Plains. In the Ogallala Formation, bare patches of ground have a sandy, dusty appearance with very few rocks. **WaKeeney**'s strange name is derived from 1870s landowners Albert Warren and James Keeney. Onward geology becomes dull with soils almost entirely loess. At **Exit 99** is **Park**, once a haven for paleontologists in the 1870s who braved Indian raids to accomplish their field work in outcroppings of Cretaceous chalk. In fact, **Oakley** begs for a stop at the Fick Fossil and History Museum, which has many of these specimens on display (daily 9-5; Sun 2-4). [See Off the Beaten Path: CHALK PYRAMIDS] Around **Colby**, the chaser enters a major beef producing center. The contents of most of the fields are actually corn to be milled into feed and consumed by cattle. Wheat and some sorghum are also grown, and fields become heavily irrigated. About five miles past **Ruleton** the highway elevation is 120 ft short of the highest in Kansas, but for that you can drive 22 miles south to Mount Sunflower. [See Off The Beaten Path: MOUNT SUNFLOWER] The road then descends and crosses the **Kansas-Colorado state line** [N39.330 W102.048]. The road continues riding on the Ogalalla Formation, with a few older Cretaceous shales exposed in deep gullies approaching **Flagler**. At **Genoa** is a curious roadside attraction, the 60 ft Genoa Tower, built in the 1920s as a tourist trap along U.S. 24 but currently seeing hard times. Past Genoa the highway permanently leaves the Ogallala Formation, dropping off the western Caprock and beginning a 250 ft descent to the town of **Limon**. In these lower elevations, the Ogallala has been eroded away, exposing older Cretaceous shales that were once below a vast sea and are rich with fossils. Limon itself was a key weather radar site for three decades until its decommission in 1995. Wheat is mixed with barley, a chief ingredient in beer production. [See Off the Beaten Path: CALHAN PAINT MINES] Bending northwest out of town, the shales give way to rough sandstones, which makes harsher growing soils and favors ranchland rather than crops. These Cretaceous sandstones continue for about 30 miles to northwest of **Deer Creek**, replaced by young sand and conglomerates. The mountains usually come into view by the time you reach **Byers**. The town of **Bennett** holds Colorado's hottest temperature record: 118 deg F set in 1888.

■ Dodge City KS - Pueblo CO

U.S. 50 (276 miles; 4.3 hours)

From **Dodge City** to the state line, the road remains almost entirely on a young alluvial plain, flanked by 100 ft Ogallala Formation bluffs. These bluffs are actually the Kansas prairie itself, representing the deep carpet of sands deposited here 5-10 million years ago from Rocky Mountain erosion, while the river valley has carved itself into the prairie. However it has not carved deep enough to reveal the much older bedrocks that cover all of the central United States. A large percentage of the region's fields are used for sorghum, wheat, and corn production. The corn is a major source of feed for the many cattle feedlots in the area. Twice, at **Ingalls** and past **Pierceville**, the road ascends onto the Ogallala Formation. It then passes the airport and descends back into the alluvial plain into **Garden City**. Just past Dodge City is the tiny, dusty town of **Holcomb**, the site of a 1959 home robbery ending in grisly tragedy that was sensationalized by the press, in a Truman Capote novel, and in film. The road continues following the alluvial plain, hugging the Arkansas River valley, the Santa Fe Trail, and the AT&SF railway. From **Lakin** to **Kendall**, the road rides atop the Ogallala Formation. Past Kendall, it descends back into the alluvial plains, however there is now an important geological highlight: the lowest 10 to 20 feet of the bluffs contain outcroppings of 100-million year old Cretaceous Greenhorn limestone, the first bearers of fossils on this trip. As you go west for the next 30 miles, the Ogallala Formation thins out at the top, and the ancient limestone rises from below to replace it, no longer covered by the young sands and soils of the High Plains. The **Kansas-Colorado State Line** [N38.048 W102.044] is a great stopping point. Continuing westward, the Ogallala Formation bluffs have almost completely been replaced by Cretaceous limestone and sandstone bluffs, yielding a myriad of canyons, rock faces, and ledges reminiscent of southwest Texas. **Lamar** has a bizarre history of its own: in 1886 the Blackwell depot, run by an uncooperative landowner who was not keen on any town developing near his spot, was secretly dismantled and moved three miles west overnight while he was in Pueblo to an already-developing townsite. Lamar proper was the result. There is some sorghum and wheat production in the fields. [See Off the Beaten Path: BENT'S OLD FORT] **La Junta**, surprisingly, is a cantaloupe farming district, and the remote valleys south of town contain an outcrop of Jurassic rocks impressed with dinosaur footprints. The remainder of the route continues following the alluvial plain, occasionally contacting the Cretaceous limestone outcrops on either side of the river. **Pueblo** is then reached.

■ Dodge City KS - Clayton NM

U.S. 56 (205 miles; 3.1 hours)

This path loosely follows the Cimarron Cutoff, a risky southern route of the Santa Fe Trail; cattle coming from New Mexico to Kansas on this trail sometimes did not make it during the dry season. Crossing the **Arkansas River** and leaving **Dodge City**, the road rides the Ogallala Formation all the way to New Mexico, a broad table of sands and clays deposited during the last 5-10 million years due to erosion from the Rockies. Just south of town it crosses through a belt of loose sands, deposited only on the river's south slopes from bitter prevailing northerly winds winds during the Ice Age. You then ascend the Ogallala Formation, topped with windblown loess which comprises the majority of Kansas' soils. Interesting geological formations are not too common on the Ogallala. **Sublette** is mainly a grain production town for feed-lots, which in turn are the second biggest industry. The public Cimarron Valley Golf Course at **Satanta** is one of North America's few golf courses devoid of trees! Past here, some outcrops of dune sand mingle with the loess flatland, a landscape that continues for the next hundred miles. The dune hills are often stabilized by native grasses, but can grow out of hand if the vegetation is disturbed. **Hugoton** became the county seat of Stevens County after it was wiped off the maps from 1881-86 due to an early lack of population. Near **Wilburton** the road is close to the Cimarron Grasslands, rescued in the 1930s from overcultivation and Dust Bowl erosion. The ranching and petroleum center of **Elkhart** is an oasis in these remote areas. A startling transition from flat prairie to eroded terrain is found approaching the **Beaver River** crossing [N36.630 W102.681], which has cut a 150 ft gorge. Once the **Oklahoma-New Mexico state line** is reached [N35.522 W103.002], another three miles will bring you to **Clark's Monument** [N36.5000 W103.0416], a two-foot high marker 30 feet south of the highway and 40 feet west of a gravel driveway. It marks the exact northwest corner of Texas! The 1870's-era cattle-driving town of **Clayton**, as well as a landscape of igneous rocks and a volcanic history, are reached.

■ Liberal KS - North Platte NE

U.S. 83 (305 miles; 4.9 hours)

This route rides entirely on a bed of very young Ogallala Formation sands and clays, eroded from the Rocky Mountains 5-10 million years ago. Only in a few eroded outcroppings in very steep terrain does interesting geology stand out. Leaving **Liberal**, the road heads north across terrain rich in natural gas and oil. About fifteen miles north of Liberal, the road descends into a 3-mile wide, 200 ft deep gorge carved out by the **Cimarron River**, crosses it, then rejoins the prairie on the other side. The road brushes by **Sublette**. About 5.5 miles north is the long-gone ghost town of Ivanhoe [N37.555 W100.870] marked by a cemetery. About two miles north of **Plymell** the road enters a region of sand hills caused by Ice Age windward deposition across the Arkansas River; since there is no corresponding deposition north of the river, it suggests cold north winds prevailed. The road crosses the **Arkansas River** and enters the town of **Garden City**. Past town, natural gas wells are once again in abundance. [See Off the Beaten Path: RAVENNA] Ten miles north of **Scott City** the highway brushes by the 100 ft deep **Ladder Creek** valley and by **Lake Scott**. Several miles later the flat prairie ends as the road plunges back into the valley, crossing an landscape where the Ogallala Formation was carved down by the **Smoky Hill River** system. [See Off the Beaten Path: CHALK PYRAMIDS] The Union Pacific railway station of **Oakley** is home to the Fick Fossil and History Museum. The road crosses over Interstate 70 north of town. The town of **Gem** is named after a ranch, not any valuable stones. Crossing through rugged terrain, **Oberlin**, site of Kansas' last Indian raid in the 1870s, is reached. Beginning an ascent out of the Beaver Creek valley, the state line is reached at [N40.002 W100.567]. The road then passes along the ridges of highly symmetrical north-northwest to south-southeast erosions. Nestled at the base of 150 ft hills along the Republican River is the town of **McCook**. Crossing Willow Creek, you can look northwest and see the Rutler Lake dam. The road eventually descends 200 ft into the South Platte River valley and into North **Platte**.

■ Denver CO - Raton NM

Interstate 25 (217 miles; 3.1 hours)

The road slowly ascends the Palmer Divide, topping out at 7300 ft MSL [N39.123 W104.864]. At these elevations there are a few outcroppings of volcanic rock. Just north of **Colorado Springs** the terrain becomes much older, composed of Cretaceous sandstones. Continuing south on I-25, the road follows an alluvial plain. **Pueblo.** South of Pueblo the road climbs through Niobrara limestones and shales. About 10 miles north of **Walsenberg** near Exit 59 is the conical Huerfano Butte [N37.754 W104.826], a volcanic plug; it is visible east of the freeway and rises 210 ft above the surrounding terrain. Near **Aguilar** the Interstate runs perpendicular to the Spanish Peaks, located about 20 miles to the west. These mountains, which tower to 13,625 ft MSL, are actually eroded volcanoes whose cores are now exposed. South of Trinidad, the road ascends through Tertiary sandstones.

■ Denver CO - Cheyenne WY

Interstate 25 (102 miles; 1.5 hours)

The freeway passes parallel to the Rocky Mountain Front Range, only 20 miles to the west, with many peaks approaching 14,000 ft MSL. The roadbed crosses Tertiary shales and sandstone as it enters a bustling agricultural region. Hay and corn are major crops. Past the **Boulder exit,** outcroppings are much older Cretaceous rocks. [See Off the Beaten Path: PAWNEE BUTTES] North of **Wellington** near **Exit 281** the freeway suddenly leaves the shale plains and enters the sandstone hills. The rugged, sandy terrain makes it suitable only for grazing. The freeway begins a gradual ascent from 5300 to 6300 ft MSL over the next 20 miles. The **Wyoming state line** [N40.998 W104.906] is crossed. The road peaks at 6300 ft as it nears **Cheyenne**. This higher terrain is often a focus for upslope thunderstorms.

■ Boise City OK - Limon CO

U.S. 287 (214 miles; 3.5 hours)

The road leaves **Boise City**, which grew as a rairoad town in the 1920s and a petroleum town after the 1940s. The highway gradually leaves young Quarternary sands and enters a region of older Ogallala sand. At the **Colorado state line**, we enter the Comanche National Grassland which extends for the next 29 miles. [See Off the Beaten Path: PICTURE CANYON] Past **Springfield**, some dryland and irrigation farming is done, including corn, wheat, and milo. About 20 miles north of Springfield the sandstones change from Ogallala sandstone to older Cretaceous Dakota sandstone. The town of **Lamar** was a major stopping point along the Santa Fe Trail, eventually becoming a railroad town. From **Wiley** to **Eads** the road crosses through exposures of Niobrara limestone that were laid down when a sea covered the region in Cretaceous times. [See Off the Beaten Path: CHIVINGTON] The town of **Kit Carson** was a major trading post and in the 1870s became a Union

Pacific railway town that connected Denver and Kansas City. West of town, the sands become older Cretaceous shales.

■ Julesburg CO - Denver CO

Interstate 76 (181 miles; 2.6 hours)

Leaving **Julesburg**, the road closely follows the South Platte River, riding on a bedrock of Ogallala Formation, a layer of dust and sand originating from Rocky Mountain erosion 5-10 million years ago. Past **Crook** (Exit 149) the Ogallala Formation thins out and disappears, allowing Cretaceous rocks to become exposed in the rare locations where the loess and grass-stabilized sand dunes don't cover them. The South Platte River was a source of life and activity for Plains Indians, and this led to many skirmishes with the U.S. Cavalry during the 1860s around **Sterling**. [See Off The Beaten Path: SUMMIT SPRINGS BATTLEFIELD and PAWNEE BUTTES] From **Wiggins** to **Keenesburg** the freeway crosses Cretaceous sandstones largely covered with new sands; past this point the bedrock is new Tertiary sands covered with the same newer sands. Near **Hudson**, one can see a string of aircraft in the sky from south to north: this is the flight path from the new Denver International Airport to the south.

■ Oberlin KS - Byers CO

U.S. 36 (208 miles; 3.3 hours)

Nearly all of the route crosses over very young Ogallala Formation soil, blown off the Rocky Mountains 5-10 million years ago, in turn covered with a blanket of loess sands. Leaving **Oberlin** at an elevation of only 2600 ft, the road heads west across rolling hills sculpted by deep eroded gullies. Ogallala rocks occasionally crop out. **Atwood** was settled by Irish Catholics and is a popular pheasant hunting center in the fall. Past Atwood, the road ascends onto the backbone of a ridge, leading west to the town of **McDonald** on the Burlington Northern railroad. At this point, it is like climbing the Texas Caprock: the eroded terrain is left behind and the road rides upon flat Ogallala with corn, milo, and wheat fields, and occasional playas. **Bird City**, named after an local elite, was a frequent stop-in for pilot Charles Lindbergh. Just past the junction with K-17, the road descends through eroded outcroppings of Ogallala sandstones and into the town of **St. Francis**. For thirteen miles it struggles back up onto the flat plain, reaching the state line [N39.751 W102.050]. Idalia. Joes. Cope. Anton. About three miles east of **Linden** the road departs the Ogallala Formation [N39.739 W103.337], entering rugged, eroded terrain consisting of Cretaceous shales and limestones. This presents one of the first opportunities for fossil hunting. This region lacks the smooth Ogallala soils to the east, and the railroad infrastructure to the west, and is perhaps one of Colorado's most unproductive, desolate areas. **Last Chance** floats in storm chase circles as the site of the July 21, 1993 tornado east-northeast of town. **Byers** is then reached at the junction with Interstate 70.

The town of Bust, Colorado west of Colorado Springs just might be the place to grab a refreshment when you have to throw in the towel. *(Tim Vasquez)*

Off the beaten path

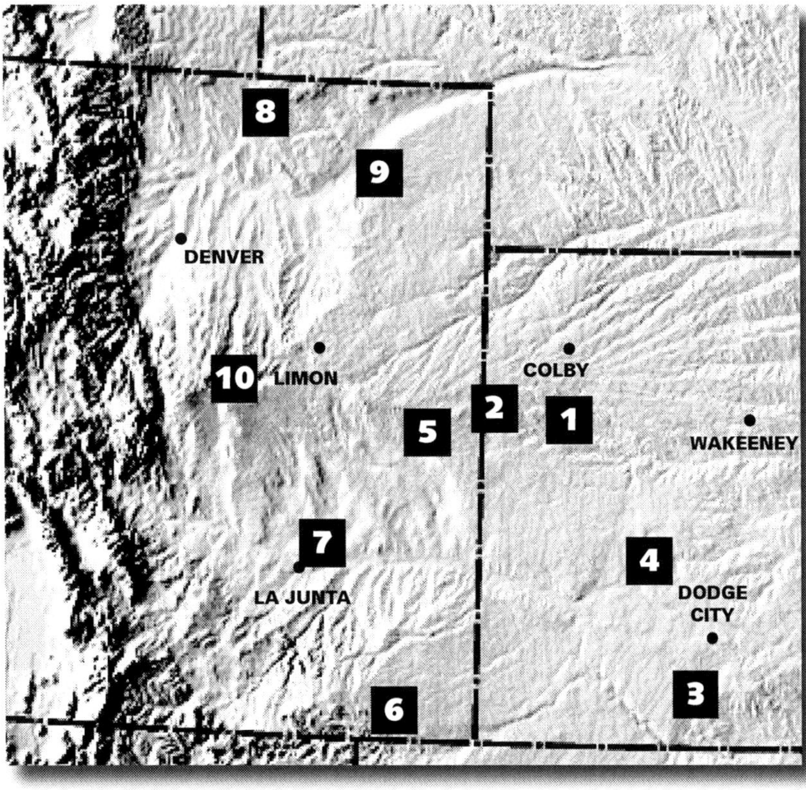

Northwest Kansas

1 Chalk Pyramids. About halfway between Oakley and Scott City on U.S. 83, you can head several miles east to the Chalk Pyramids, also known as Monument Rocks and Kansas Pyramids [N38.794 W100.763]. These breathtaking 70 ft tall outcroppings of chalk are reminiscent of sandstone arches found in Utah and make for fantastic photo opportunities. They are one of the most well-known scenic stops in western Kansas, so expect to find other visitors and perhaps a few chasers!

2 Mount Sunflower [N39.022 W102.037] is the highest point in Kansas at 4039 ft MSL. Just drive right up to it! From Weskan, head 11 miles north, then 3 miles west, 1 mile south, then 1 mile west; the flat hill is a few hundred feet northwest.

Southwest Kansas

3 Dalton Gang Hideout. hat's there to do when you're awaiting convection in southwest Kansas? The Dalton Gang Hideout [N37.281 W100.337] is a curious attraction in the town of Meade, a microscopic tourist trap with great significance in Kansas folklore. In 1887, the outlaw gang lived in Meade with sister Eva Whipple and her husband, a prominent Meade merchant. For five years the gang remained here, entirely out of reach of the law thanks to a legendary 95 ft escape tunnel connecting the Whipple house with a barn. The Dalton Gang remained at large until being gunned town in 1892 while robbing a Southeast Kansas bank; four of the five brothers died and the other went to prison. The Whipples quickly moved away and the tunnel was found some years later. The tunnel is open for visitors to walk through, and there is a small museum to browse through. Open 9-5 (Sun 1-5), an hour later after Memorial Day; nominal admission.

4 Ravenna ghost town. A true ghost town is located about 20 miles northeast of Garden City: Ravenna [N38.161 W100.381] was initially known in 1878 as Bulltown, then Cowtown in 1880. In spite of the name, it didn't start as a rip-roaring boomtown; rather, the town grew very slowly as a ranching center under the hand of founder and merchant John Bull. By the early 1880s, a hotel became the nucleus of the town, and farmers began arriving. They insisted on a name change, and the town became Ravenna in 1885. The lively Fourth of July festival held here in 1886 made the news across many counties, and the town enjoyed its glory days. A two-story limestone courthouse was built in 1889, but Ravenna lost the county seat election the same year. After a series of tough winter, farms began to fail, and the town finally dissolved during in 1893. The post office closed in 1922. Some foundations, including that of the courthouse, still remain. From K-156 / K-23 intersection go 7 miles north then 4.5 miles east. After looking at Ravenna, head three miles east to the Finney State Game Management Area for a scenic stop [N38.178 W100.328].

Southeast Colorado

5 Chivington ghost town [N38.437 W102.540] is halfway between Eads and Sheridan Lake, and is still marked on some road maps. It began as a lively railroad town in 1887, intended to become a trade center halfway between the Kansas border and Pueblo. The town featured 13 saloons, 18 restaurants, pharmacies, general stores, and a three-story hotel with sixty rooms, a town truly the size of La Junta. The downward spiral began in 1895 when railroad workers moved onward to other projects. Since then, the town has withered slowly, hanging onto an economy of ranching. It was hit hard during the Great Depression and the Dust Bowl era. The post office closed in 1982, beginning the empty era of ghost town status. Ruins as recent as a 1960s-era cafe and school can be found.

6 Picture Canyon. A beautiful diversion is at Campo, Colorado, where one can drive 15 miles west into Picture Canyon [N37.037 W102.749], the site of spectacular sandstone cliffs. If you are not prone to getting lost, explore the roads leading southward to see deeper and more extensive canyon regions. Archaeologists have found evidence that prehistoric hunter-gatherers, perhaps during the era of Roman Civilization, lived within Picture Canyon's rock overhangs. Rock art uncovered in Picture Canyon has been ascribed to later periods, perhaps several hundred years ago. Some writing has been found that strongly resembles Old World Celtic (Irish) characters; the circumstances of these inscriptions remains mysterious. Most human settlement attempts were abandoned in 1930s during the Dust Bowl.

7 Bent's Old Fort [N38.040 W103.429], just northeast of La Junta on U.S. 50, is not just some Calvary outpost: rather, it was a huge trading post, and is of very old age. Constructed in 1833, it predates the railroad era by a wide margin. Located on the Santa Fe cattle trail, the fort's importance was its central location. It was here where the fort owners negotiated with Mexican

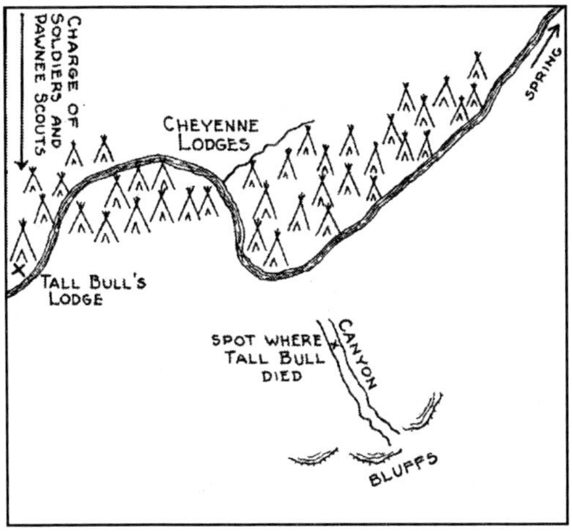

Old historic map of the Summit Springs battle. North is up, and the map measures about half a mile square. The access road ends at the top left.

traders from the west, American traders from the east, and Plains Indian traders throughout the Great Plains. Mexican and Indian uprisings in the mid-1840s led to its rapid decline, and it was abandoned in 1849. Since the 1970s it has been restored as a historic side. Open daily; nominal admission.

Northeast Colorado

8 Pawnee Buttes. For something really off the beaten path, head to Pawnee Buttes [N40.822 W103.974] between Fort Collins and Sterling. These bulky spires are nearly 250 ft high, composed of young shales and sandstones that resisted millions of years of weathering. Skeletons and fossils dating back to the past ten or twenty million years have been preserved in the rocks here. The hills were important to the Pawnee tribe, who frequently camped and hunted in their shadow. Starting at Keota, go 2.7 miles north, 3 miles east, 4 miles north, then follow the curve west and find the first road leading northeast; the buttes are only about 2 miles away.

9 Summit Springs Battlefield. One of the most significant events in Colorado history occurred south of Sterling and is an easy drive for a roaming chaser: Summit Springs Battlefield [N40.433 W103.139]. During the 1860s a faction of Cheyenne and Sioux warriors, led by Tall Bull, led a series of brutal raids and massacres against white settlements in outrage of the tribe's persecution and to assert sovereignty over their hunting grounds. It was here on July 11, 1869 where General Orr, led by Pawnee scouts, confronted a camp of over 500 Cheyenne. At least 52 Cheyenne were killed in the battle, while the rest fled or were captured. Later in the day after the battle, a large hailstorm ravaged the site. Today there actually is very little to see: those without imagination or historical interest. It is located on the Washington-Logan county line four miles east of S.H. 63.

Front Range area

10 Paint Mines. Located along the Palmer Divide between Limon and Colorado Springs, the Calhan Paint Mines [N39.011 W104.268] are neither a mine nor a source of paint. These are knobby, smooth cliffs made of spectacular, colorful rock formations. Reddish and yellowish clays hued by iron oxides alternate with layers of whitish gypsum. There's also a great view of the sky and of the distant horizon. To get there, start at Calhan and drive 0.6 mile south on Calhan Road; turn east onto Paint Mine Road; follow it for about 2 miles.

GREAT PLAINS TRAVEL GUIDE

High Plains

Tucked away in the northwest corner of the central United States are the High Plains, vying with Southwest Texas as the last frontier east of the Rockies. It is remote even for modern technology. Standing in Broadus, Montana, you're 150 miles from the nearest NEXRAD radar. Any beams that reach here are over 20,000 ft above the ground, much too high to detect tornadic circulation. And if your car breaks down? Well, it's 75 miles to the nearest auto parts dealer.

For those that who can deal with the severed technological links and the remoteness of the territory, the High Plains is an exciting place to chase. It escapes the hordes of chasers plying the southern Plains. Although the limited amounts of moisture caps the number of tornadoes that occur here, access to a smorgasbord of forcing mechanisms in the presence of steep lapse rates allows for exquisitely sculptured storm structure.

The downside is that the region is covered by a sparse road network, since very little agriculture is found here. It's a territory where your intercept may involve positioning yourself at an optimal point along a north-south road, and waiting for the quarry to arrive. Considering the remoteness of the region, successful chasing here requires the sharpest of chase skills and extreme attention to detail when the morning analysis is done. Fortunately you'll have good visibility on your side, as Eastern American haze and obscuration from aerosols rarely makes the rounds here.

The High Plains are punctuated by three main features: the Nebraska Sand Hills and the South Dakota Badlands and Black Hills. The rugged terrain through these regions will make chasing difficult or impossible in these regions. The rest of the High Plains consists mostly of rangeland, and navigation will be much the same as what you'd encounter chasing in southeastern Colorado.

Meteorology

Forecasting for the High Plains is characteristically quite difficult for several reasons. First, the area is remote and does not have an abundance of surface stations. Only a handful of sites were put down here by the ASOS upgrades of the past decade, so surface analysis here is still a relic of

The Nebraska plains

I felt something different in the air in North Platte, I didn't know what it was. In five minutes I did. We got back on the truck and roared off. It got dark quickly. We all had a shot, and suddenly I looked, and the verdant farmfields of the Platte began to disappear and in their stead, so far you couldn't see to the end, appeared long flat wastelands of sand and sagebrush. I was astounded.

"What in the hell is this?" I cried out to Slim.

"This is the beginning of the rangeland, boy. Hand me another drink" . . .

We zoomed through another crossroads town, passed another line of tall lanky men in jeans clustered in the dim light like moths on the desert, and returned to the tremendous darkness, and the stars overhead were pure and bright because of the increasingly thin air as we mounted the high hill of the western plateau, about a foot a mile, so they say, and no trees obstructing any low-leveled stars anywhere. And once I saw a moody whitefaced cow in the sage by the road as we flitted by. It was like riding a railroad train, just as steady and just as straight.

JACK KEROUAC
On The Road, 1955

A roadcut on this monotonous stretch of Interstate 80 near Cheyenne, Wyoming begs for a dose of geological trivia. *(Tim Vasquez)*

Northwest of the Plains

In southwest Montana, rotating storms are possible! On days when an approaching trough is moving through Idaho and surface winds are out of the south, this is the best scenario for rotating storms. Often, Pacific moisture will mix with upslope moisture being advected in from Eastern Montana (sources usually Hudson Bay or the Gulf of Mexico). The Dillon area, though distant from NEXRAD sites, can have some surprising storms. Also the area between Three Forks and Bozeman is a hot spot. Top this off with stunningly beautiful topography, and it can be a very enjoyable place to chase. The road networks are not awful either, with some decent highways available.

I have not personally chased the so-called Milk River Supercell, but I see a couple of them every year. The storm usually fires off of the Rocky Mountain front near Browning and rides an arc, almost following the path of the Milk River along the highline in Montana. This storm will often right-move down through Glasgow and eventually end up forming a mesoscale complex as it moves into North Dakota late at night, already having traveled hundreds of miles. U.S. Highway 2 is a great road to follow.

DANN CIANCA
Denver, Colorado

the 1950s. Second, it is at these northerly latitudes where the dryline tends to become more diffuse. The region is 900 to 1100 miles from the Gulf of Mexico and the character of the moisture field becomes much more mottled and inconsistent. This, coupled with the poor surface network, makes it quite difficult to estimate exactly where the highest dewpoint values are lurking. Third, areas of the High Plains are hilly, and it takes considerable experience to anticipate the magnitude of orographic effects. Fourth, the area is in a rawinsonde hole: North Platte is too far east, while the lower levels of the Denver and Rapid City soundings are heavily affected by orographic interactions. It is never quite clear just how strong the cap is. This calls for educated, refined imagination on the part of the chaser! It should be clear that in the High Plains, the chaser's skills are put to the ultimate test, not just in terms of navigation, but in forecasting, too!

The higher terrain means that dewpoints need not be as high to produce severe weather. Generally, a reading in the 40s is sufficient for thunderstorms, and 50s suggests the possibility of chaseable weather. Readings in the 50s combined with upslope flow are associated with most chase events here. Dewpoints reach the 60s during the summer, but this is compensated by warmer upper-level temperatures.

The dryline as a convergence mechanism is not quite as important at these northern latitudes. Most often it serves merely to define the limits of the surface moisture. Storm initiation tends to concentrate heavily along stalled fronts, outflow boundaries, pressure troughs, and orographic forcing mechanisms.

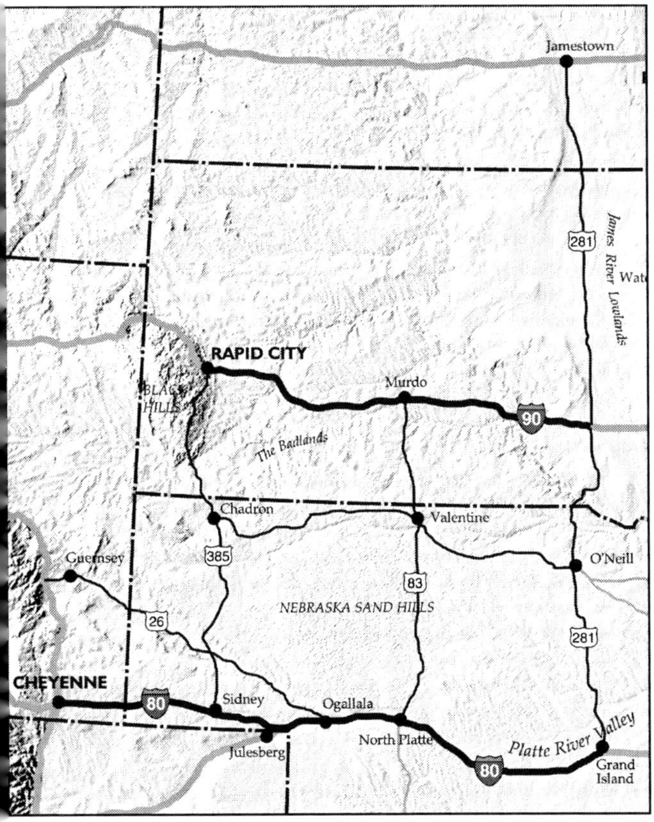

Road Guide

■ North Platte NE - Julesburg CO

Interstate 80 (75 miles; 1.1 hours)

Leaving **North Platte**, wheat and corn is grown along much of the route, much of which lies in the ten-mile wide flat, fertile alluvial plain of the Platte Rivers. On either side of the freeway is the plateau of the Ogallala Formation, a huge layer of fine sands and silts deposited 5-10 million years ago that covers most of the western Great Plains from Texas to Nebraska. The lowest elevations, away from the river plains, contain outcroppings of older, whitish White River Formation sands and clays. Approaching **Southerland**, a ridgeline appears north of the freeway, essentially forming the fork of the North Platte and South Platte Rivers. At **Ogallala**, you reach the hallowed town that gives the Great Plains' Ogallala Formation its name, coined by N. H. Darton in 1898. From Texas to Nebraska, the Ogallala Formation is often a key part of underground water stores called aquifers, since the loose sandstones hold rainwater like a sponge until it is tapped by a well or discharged via springwater. The road follows the alluvial plains westward, reaching the **Interstate 76 junction**. Continuing west on Interstate 80 near **Julesburg**, the road departs from the river and climbs 200 ft onto the Ogallala formation.

■ Julesburg CO - Cheyenne WY

Interstate 80 (170 miles; 2.5 hours)

Leaving Julesburg, Interstate 80 travels west on the plateau of the Ogallala Formation, the deep blanket of tough sands deposited here about 5-10 million years ago. Formed from erosion of the Rocky Mountains, it covers much of the western Great Plains. Near **Chappell** it is carved out by Lodgepole Creek, revealing near the bottom a layer of older, whitish White River Formation sands and clays, colored white because of deposits from West Coast volcanic ash about 30 million years ago. Near **Sidney** the road travels parallel to Lodgepole Creek, riding along the older White River Formation lodged between the river's alluvial gravels and the Ogallala Formation making up the bluffs and hills. Near Kimball the freeway climbs back onto the Ogallala Formation. Near the Wyoming town of **Pine Bluffs** is the **Nebraska-Wyoming state line** [N41.186 W104.053], located just north of a ridge among 300 ft Ogallala sandstone hills, tall pieces of the Ogallala Formation that refuse to weather down. At the top of one of them is a statue of the Virgin Mary! It is possible to take a side trip 12 miles south of Pine Bluffs to the highest point in Nebraska, Panorama Point [N41.011 W104.029], on ranchland and open to the public. Near **Egbert** the road leaves the alluvial plains and ascends slowly onto a plateau of Ogallala and Arikaree sandstone. The freeway then reaches the town of **Cheyenne**.

■ North Platte NE - Murdo SD

U.S. 83 (209 miles; 3.3 hours)

The first three-quarters of the route crosses young Ogallala Formation sandstones, deposited here 5-10 million years ago due to erosion from the Rocky Mountains. There are no outcroppings of any older rocks. Leaving **North Platte**, the road climbs out of the alluvial plain into Ogallala Formation hills, and immediately into the Sand Hills region. Stapleton. A small park is at the **Dismal River** crossing [N41.779 W100.530]. At the Middle Loup River is the town of **Thedford**. Settlers trickled here in 1887 to grab free land, but there were few takers, and dry, rough ground forced many of the new arrivals to take up ranching. [See Off the Beaten Path: NEBRASKA NATIONAL FOREST] The road leads through the Valentine National Wildlife Refuge, with numerous marshy lakes. The road then meets with the Chicago & Northwestern railroad as it crosses the **Niobrara River** and arrives in the town of **Valentine**. At the **Nebraska-South Dakota state line** [N42.998 W100.573] the Rosebud Indian Reservation is entered. [See Off the Beaten Path: LAKEVIEW] Finally, near **Mission**, the terrain becomes unusually flat. You must travel 3 miles west before continuing north. The terrain becomes hilly once again, and the road dips briefly into the Little White River valley, arriving at the town of White River. The road passes through very rugged terrain, riding along a major ridge line. The road then arrives in Murdo along Interstate 90.

■ Ogallala NE - Scottsbluff NE - Guernsey WY

U.S. 26 (186 miles; 3.0 hours)

This route closely follows the Oregon Trail; in 1850 following the California gold strike one settler recorded nearly 100 wagons and 350 people per hour making the journey! Leaving **Ogallala**, the road ascends out of the Platte River valley onto a caprock of 200 ft Ogallala Formation bluffs overlooking the town. The Ogallala Formation is about 5-10 million years old, essentially a thick layer of sands deposited here through weathering of the Rocky Mountains, and which makes up most of the western Great Plains. The road rides on the highest plateaus of this Ogallala Formation rock, a close analogy to riding on the flat Ogallala Formation of Lubbock, Amarillo, and Midland. Looking north you can get glimpses of **Lake McConaughy** about 3 miles north. The road then reaches the caprock edge, descending rugged, eroded terrain. The Oregon Trail also descended here through the same valley, but had to follow a tortuous routing with switchbacks. The road then reaches the town of **Lewellen**, after crossing north of the North Platte River. The Oregon Trail, however, remains on the south side of the river. Just north of the road is the North Brier Canal. **Oshkosh** holds the record for Nebraska's coldest temperature: -47 deg F in 1989, being in a low river basin where cold air pooled under clear skies and snow cover. Near **Broadwater** the Ogallala Formation hills are largely replaced by older Arikaree and White River Formation sands. Just past **Bridgeport** before ascending into sandstone hills, the road crosses the Oregon Trail [N41.670 W103.147]; if you look closely you might be able to find the wagon ruts. The striking pinnacle of Chimney Rock comes into view, a 325 ft erosional remnant that was actually buried under the Ogallala Formation and was exposed, eroded only to what it is now. The road then reaches the town of **Gering** and **Scottsbluff**. **Mitchell**. **Morrill**. Just past the town of **Henry**, you cross the **Nebraska-Wyoming state line** [N42.003 W104.052]. The highway continues to follow the alluvial sands and clays, flanked by whitish 30-million year old Oligocene sandstones, especially past **Torrington** and **Lingle**. **Fort Laramie** was a massive Army post (1849-90) which protected settlers on the Oregon Trail. Continues to follow the Emigrant Trail. Near **Guernsey** are very soft sandstones which expose the ruts of the thousands of wagons that plied the Oregon Trail. The hills extending west through north of town consist of ancient Paleozoic rocks, an uplifted area that connects the Rocky Mountains with the Black Hills. The hills are rich with hematite, a mineral used by Plains Indians for war paint and now mined for iron. The road then rides on a bed of new Pliocene sands. The road meets **Interstate 25**, at a modest elevation of only 4920 ft.

■ Sidney NE - Rapid City SD

S.H. 113 and U.S. 385 (201 miles; 3.2 hours)

Near **Sidney**, the road crosses Lodgepole Creek, and ascends back onto the Ogalalla Formation. Past **Dalton**, the road descends terrain carved by the Platte River system into the Ogallala Formation, and reaches the fertile alluvial plain near **Bridgeport**. It then crosses the **North Platte River**. Crossing the river, the spire of Chimney Rock, 325 ft high, can be seen far to the west. and the soils become predominantly alluvial. Ascending north of **Northport** the road leaves the alluvial plains, briefly crossing some reddish 20-million year old Arikaree sandstone outcrops. This rock is then rapidly covered by sands and dunes comprising the extremely young Sand Hills, an enormous sea of grass-stabilized sand that formed only in the past 8,000 years. Look for telephone poles and fenceposts that have been buried or uncovered by the shifting sands. The sands dunes are usually stable unless their native grass cover is eroded or disturbed. **Alliance** is built on Arikaree sandstones. [See Off the Beaten Path: ANTIOCH, SALLOWS ARBORETUM, and BELMONT] The highway winds over the Pine Ridge, a surprisingly heavily-forested area with tremendous hiking opportunities. There are roadcuts into bright white 30-million year old Oligocene siltstones and sandstones. The bright color in the rock comes from Western U.S. volcanic ash that fell on this area during that era. Past **Chadron** the road approaches the touristy Black Hills region, and arrives at **Rapid City**. [See Off the Beaten Path: MUSEUM OF GEOLOGY]

■ Cheyenne WY - Spearfish SD

U.S. 85 (282 miles; 5.0 hours)

Leaving **Cheyenne**, the route follows the Interstate for about four miles, then branches northeast. It mainly rides upon the young, plateau-like Arikaree and Ogallala Formations, only 5-10 million years old. As geologically-minded chasers in Texas know, the Ogallala often has a caprock at its edges, and here is no exception, occurring about 22 miles after leaving the Interstate. At this location [N41.442 W104.345] the road reaches the edge of an eroded basin and descends nearly 600 ft in several miles. Reaching the valley bottom, older 30-million year old Oligocene sandstones and whitish clays of the White River Formation appear. White River formation is unique in that its whitish clays are of volcanic origin, from a time when West Coast volcanoes dropped their ash on these soils. The road descends into the eroded basin of Little Horse Creek, then passes around the east side of 700 ft Bear Mountain: essentially a pillar of uneroded Arikaree sandstone. At **Hawk Springs**, the road crosses the Union Pacific railroad tracks, and the terrain becomes flatter. Approaching **Silver Tip** and **Yoder**, the Cretaceous rocks become covered up by young White River Formation sands and clays. At **Torrington** the **North Platte River** is crossed. Approaching **Lusk**, the hills to the west are ancient Paleozoic rocks, part of an uplift that connects the Rocky Mountains with the Black Hills. About 9 miles north of Lusk, the highway descends the Hat Creek Breaks [N42.886 W104.407], descending about 700 ft in only a few miles. At **Riverview**, the Cheyenne River is crossed at an elevation of only 3640 ft MSL. The Burlington Northern railroad and its ghost towns can be seen in the distance to the west, and eventually the railroad comes to a confluence with the highway at the town of **Newcastle**, nestled against a low mountain range. The road then ascends from 4400 ft to 5200 ft on Jumbo Table, leading north along its ridgeline. The rock forms become older Jurassic formations, becoming even older as you travel into Black Hills, since they represent a giant uplift of older rocks. About ten miles of hilly terrain follows, then the Spring Prairie is reached. The road then winds tightly through the deep valleys of the Black Hills, eventually reaching **Spearfish** at **Interstate 90**.

■ Valentine NE - Lusk WY

U.S. 275 (219 miles; 3.5 hours)

Leaving **Valentine**, U.S. 275 follows Minnechaduza Creek west-northwestward. About ten miles further is the ghost town of **Crookston**, full of fascinating architecture in dilapidated condition. The town had a promising agricultural future in the 1890s, but was hurt by a combination of 20th century urbanization and the routing of U.S. 83 through Valentine, and fizzled as residents moved away. Past town, the highway turns west into the Sand Hills. Kilgore. Cody. The town of **Merriman** is an oasis, but is also home to a small seismic region extending from here to **Gordon**; Nebraska's strongest earthquake was recorded here south of Merriman on 3/28/64, registering magnitude 5.1, just seven hours after Alaska's devastating 1964 earthquake. By Gordon, the road is on relatively flat terrain and a loose system of grid roads appears. After **Hay Springs**, the road once again traverses rugged terrain; the Ogallala Formation is replaced by older, whitish White River Formation sands and clays. The road emerges at **Chadron**. The **Nebraska-Wyoming state line** [N42.661 W104.051]. The road continues following the Chicago & Northwestern railroad across a vast plain of Arikaree and Ogallala sands and very little interesting geology. The town of **Lusk** is reached.

■ Grand Island NE - Jamestown ND

U.S. 281 (450 miles; 7.4 hours)

Leaving Grand Island, U.S. 281 follows the Union Pacific line northward. At the confluence of the Middle and North Loup Rivers near St. Paul, the highway crosses both rivers. It then traverses eroded terrain feeding the Loup River basin. Near Greeley the terrain flattens, and the Sand Hills are entered. Cummins. Very flat. O'Neill. Spencer. Near the **Nebraska - South Dakota state line** [N42.998 W98.725] you cross a few last bits of Ogallala Formation, leaving it and crossing into Cretaceous Pierre shales. The road then diverts east around the spectacular Lake Francis Case, crossing its dam, where the shales have worn down to expose Niobrara chalks, then ascends into glacial drift: soil hundreds of feet thick and boulders, all deposited here by retreating Ice Age glaciers. This glacial drift soil extends north for the rest of the route, resulting in generally flat moraine. The road marches ten miles east from **Lake Andes** then north into the Yankton Indian Reservation across very flat terrain. Armour. At Plankinton the road reaches Interstate 90. **Wolsey** was the site of a 160 lb meteor that was found in 1981; it is displayed at the Museum of Geology in Rapid City. Redfield is the first major town. Flat terrain. Past small town of Mellette to the east. [See Off the Beaten Path: STORYBOOK LAND and WINSHIP]

■ Sioux Falls - Rapid City SD

I-90 (343 miles; 5.0 hours)

Leaving the Minnesota border, the highway rides on a soil of sediment deposited by Ice Age glaciers. This glacial drift is in turn underlain by a bedrock of incredibly ancient billion-year old Precambrian quartzite. Outcroppings of this pinkish quartzite can be found wherever significant erosion has uncovered the sediments, such as in Palisades State Park north of **Exit 406** where it forms tall spires that are a magnet for rock climbers. Corn, soil, and hay farming is abundant. The highway brushes past **Sioux Falls**, settled in the 1850s. The quartzite bedrock stops near **Hartford**, replaced with vastly newer 100-million year old Cretaceous shales, but the topsoil is still composed of hundreds of feet of glacial drift. Near **Mitchell**, oat production is among the highest in North America. North of Kimball by 20 miles is Gannvalley, which holds South Dakota's hottest temperature record: 120 deg F in 1936. All farming tends to tapers off near **Chamberlain**. Near here is the furthest extent of the Ice Age glaciers and their cargo of sediment, glacial drift, and boulders. The 100-million year old Cretaceous shales break out here. They contain a large proportion of bentonite, which swells when wet, and this produces an unstable foundation that causes a large number of road problems throughout much of the road here westward, ranging from gentle bumps to the rare landslide. During the pioneer days, the deep, wide Missouri River created a natural impediment that could not be forded until winter when frozen; the first bridge was finally built here in 1893. The rock becomes cretaceous shale and chalk, and the fields are replaced with wheat. [See Off the Beaten Path: OKOBOJO] **Murdo** was a legendary northern cattle drive town. [See Off the Beaten Path: OKATON] From **Kadoka** to **Wall**, the road temporarily crosses newer Tertiary silt and sandstones. The town of **Wall**, home to popular tourist trap *Wall Drug*, is named after the 100 ft north-south cliffs that guard its approach. [See Off the Beaten Path: CONATA] The route soon arrives in Rapid City. [See Off the Beaten Path: MUSEUM OF GEOLOGY]

Contrary to urban legend, Montana does not have unrestricted speed limits anymore. In December 1995, Montana repealed the 65 mph speed limit and signposted its highways "reasonable and prudent". A convicted motorist who appealed his case resulted in the state supreme court striking down the ambiguous limit in 1998. The state reverted to a 75 mph limit on May 28, 1999. *(Tim Vasquez)*

Off the beaten path

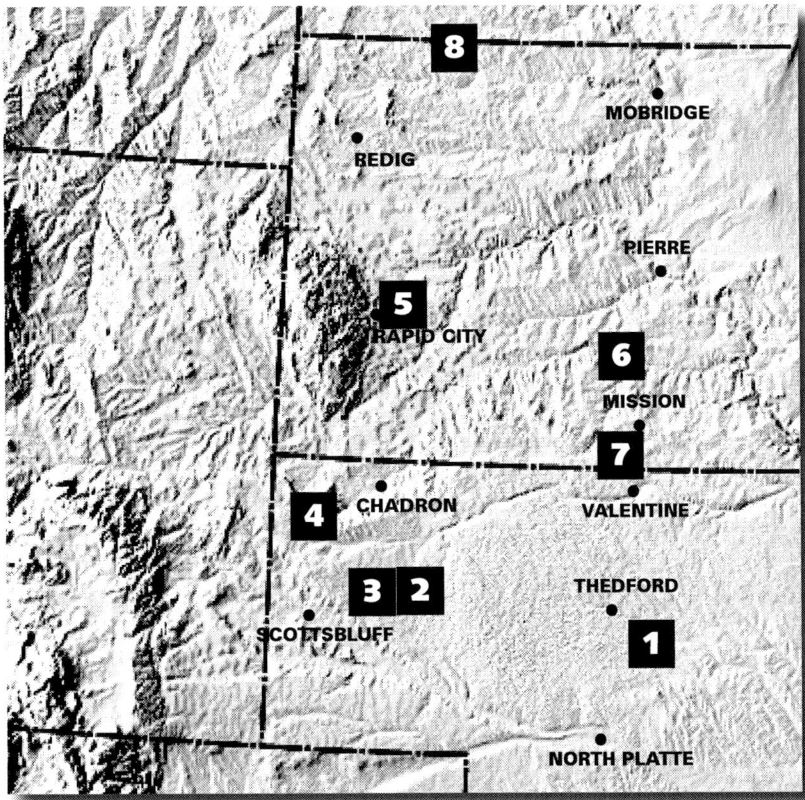

Sand Hills area

1 Nebraska National Forest. Literally an oasis in the desert, a forest looms out of the Sand Hills region west of the town of Thedford. Walking among the pine and cedar, you will feel as if you are high in the Colorado Rockies, but you're only a stone's throw from the Nebraska and Kansas corn belt. The 30 square-mile area is the largest hand-planted forest in the United States [turnout at N41.905 W100.297], created in 1902.

Nebraska Panhandle

2 Antioch ghost town [N42.069 W102.584] is about 14 miles east of Alliance on S.H. 2. During the 1910s, Antioch came into being with the opening of a potash mine, thanks to the area's poor drainage and its alkali lakes that provided rich sources of potassium salts. By the 1920s Antioch was a thriving boomtown with over 2000 residents. The mine ramped production down during the 1930s, and by 1939 only 25 people were left. The remains of old structures can be found along the railroad tracks north of the highway.

3 Sallows Arboretum and Conservatory [N42.106 W102.869] near Alliance features nearly over 100 trees and plants, with special emphasis on adapting your property to work in harmony with vegetation and landscaping. Best of all, there's no charge. Open 7-4:30 weekdays. Located at 11th and Niobrara in Alliance.

4 Belmont ghost town. Located 11 miles south-southeast of Crawford on S.H. 71, and a mile east of the highway, Belmont [N42.550 W103.356] grew in 1889 with the arrival of the railroad. It was a convenient stop for passenger trains plying a scenic spur leading to the Black Hills. Many old buildings are still standing. Walking north along the abandoned railroad grade half a mile, you'll find Belmont Tunnel, 750 ft long and open to exploration. It was Nebraska's only railroad tunnel. Its steep walls along the approach made it a haven for train enthusiasts to watch as the engines struggled against the 1.8% grade. The line was in use until 1976 when Burlington Northern scrapped it as part of a $14 million bypass project.

Southwest South Dakota

5 Museum of Geology [N44.076 W103.207] at the South Dakota School of Mines and Technology features an incredible collection of 250,000 fossils, 6000 minerals, hundreds of dinosaur skeletons, and numerous exhibits. Located just southeast of downtown at 501 E St Joseph St. Hours 8-5 daily (9-4 Sat, 1-4 Sun) tel. 800-544-8162 x 2467. East of Rapid City, the town of Conata [N43.728 W102.188] is located in the Badlands along S.H. 44 due south of Wall. It thrived along the Milwaukee Railroad during the 1900s. A thin agricultural economy, however, was destroyed in the 1930s during the Dust Bowl era, and the town was eventually abandoned by the 1980s. Many structures still remain. The tourist trap of Wall Drug at Wall needs little mention.

6 Okaton ghost town. On Interstate 90, take Exit 183 just west of Murdo for a convenient glimpse at Okaton [N43.886 W100.891], a bizarre ghost town along the Interstate, similar to Texas' Glenrio. It began in the 1900s as an agricultural center along the Milwaukee Railroad. The few residents that still remain survive almost entirely from commerce brought by the Interstate. However you can poke around and uncover a century of historical ruins.

7 Lakeview ghost town [N43.104 W100.748] was a Dutch agricultural town settled in the 1890s. Its economy was destroyed by erosion during the 1930s Dust Bowl. The vast majority of remains consist of old foundations. The ghost town is 2 miles south of Olsonville on U.S. 83 then 7 miles west); a church and school serving the widely dispersed population are nearby.

Northwest South Dakota

8 Petrified Wood Park [N45.938 W102.158] in downtown Lemmon is a free exhibit in the town's municipal park. When Lemmon was being developed agriculturally, so much petrified wood was dredged up out of fields that the town decided to collect it all and fashion it into bizarre buildings, sculptures, and structures.

Topographic maps showing three distinct types of landforms in the High Plains: (Top) Fertile alluvial flats along the Platte River near Gothenburg, Nebraska. (Middle) Hilly shale and sandstone terrain near Winner, South Dakota. (Bottom) Sand Hills near Arthur, Nebraska forming dune topography. (USGS)

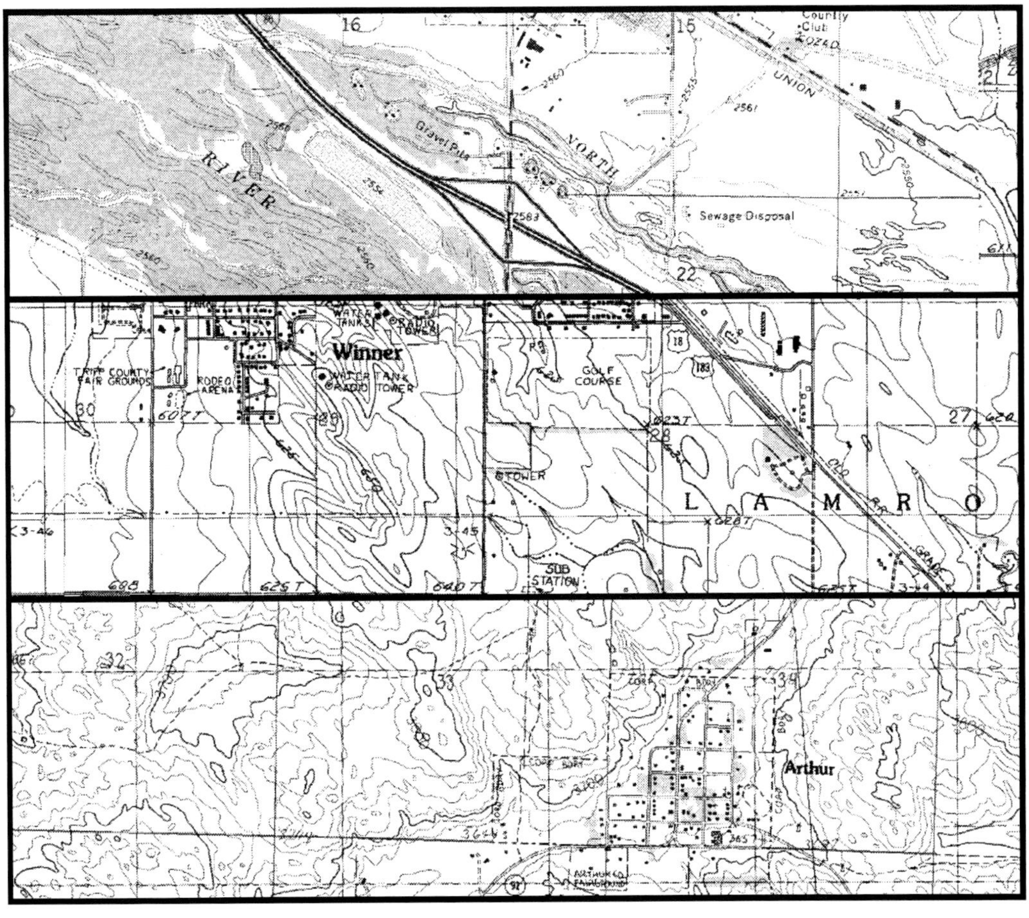

GREAT PLAINS TRAVEL GUIDE

Northern Prairies

The Northern Plains takes the distinction of storm chasing's birthplace. North Dakota and far eastern Minnesota were home to David Hoadley and Roger Jensen, who began chasing this area during the 1950s. The region came into prominence on 20 June 1957, when a powerful tornado swept through Fargo and was intensely studied by Theodore Fujita.

To chasers accustomed to Texas and Oklahoma, with its scenes of ranching, cattle, and feedlots, the Northern Prairies may come as culture shock. Fields here are filled with endless expanses of corn, wheat, oats, and barley. It's often said that the Northern Prairies are the world's bread-basket. There is very little exxageration in this statement. Only the steppes of Russia and Ukraine are comparable in sheer output of wheat and corn. The profitable agricultural industry has served as a stable foundation for the growth of Omaha, Des Moines, and Minneapolis, and has precipitated their offshoot activities such as insurance and commodities. The region's history dates back to the 1850s, when westward expansion of white settlers brought them to a vast fertile prairie. Pioneers staked their claim here with optimism and fierce independence. Scarcity of supplies and food was always present, and there was rampant confrontation with Plains Indian tribes staunchly defending their hunting grounds. Within the political and cultural changes brought by the next few decades, the region developed its firm agricultural roots.

In the Northern Prairies, the agricultural activities pay dividends for storm chasers, as a gridded road network presents infinite targeting options. The only downside, of course, is the agricultural belt's widely dispersed population, which means that slow vehicles and minor traffic congestion may be encountered from time to time and must be planned on.

Thankfully the area is blessed with a fairly rich observation network, good National Weather Service radio coverage, and frequent incidence of surface boundaries, without the chase crowds found in the southern Plains, so here the recipe is always ripe for an enjoyable chase vacation, as long as cool dry polar air is not scouring the region as so often happens!

Plying the Northern Prairies

I can see by my watch, without taking my hand from the left grip of the cycle, that it is eight-thirty in the morning. The wind, even at sixty miles an hour, is warm and humid. When it's this hot and muggy at eight-thirty, I'm wondering what it's going to be like in the afternoon.

In the wind are pungent odors from the marshes by the road. We are in an area filled with thousands of duck hunting sloughs, heading northwest from Minneapolis toward the Dakotas. This highway is an old concrete two-laner that hasn't had much traffic since a four-laner went in parallel to it several years ago. When we pass a marsh the air suddenly becomes cooler. Then, when we are past, it suddenly warms up again.

I'm happy to be riding back in this country. It is a kind of nowhere, famous for nothing at all and has an appeal because of just that. Tensions disappear along old roads like this. We bump along the beat-up concrete between the cattails and stretches of meadow and then more cattails and marsh grass.

ROBERT PIRSIG
Zen and the Art of Motorcycle Maintenance

The famous Roseman Bridge in Madison County, located just southwest of Des Moines, in April 1998. It was photographed hours after the end of events at the 2nd Iowa National Weather Association Severe Weather conference. *(Tim Vasquez)*

Meteorology

At all times of the year, weather on the Northern Plains is heavily influenced by the system of polar fronts that circle the globe. During the cold season, the fronts plunge rapidly southward, while during the warm season, the fronts tend to linger and dwell in the region. Upper-level dynamics tend to follow the mean position of the surface fronts. This means that the Dakotas, Iowa, and Minnesota are on the firing line for strong low-level convergence sources and healthy sources of upper-level lift. June, July, August, and September are peak times for thunderstorms.

Ironically, it is not these strong polar fronts which trigger most of the chaseworthy severe weather events here. Strong fronts have a tendency to produce linear storms and squall lines, and indeed these are very common. Rather, the weaker boundaries that are oriented west-to-east fashion take on greater importance for isolated supercells. These are the boundaries that chasers are interested in.

The Northern Plains are furthest away from elevated terrain than any other chase region in the Great Plains. This means that mid-level capping inversions are usually weak, except when produced by large-scale subsidence. Because of the relatively uncapped air, storms have a tendency to break out in large numbers. Nocturnal mesoscale convective complexes (MCC's), large clusters of hundreds of multicell storms, are very common in this region in the late summer and are responsible for the majority of the beneficial rainfall that occurs here.

The region is near the northern limit of significant influence by the dryline. It does occur with regularity on surface charts, but is much less distinct than those examples found in Texas and Oklahoma. The dryline is strongest when deep frontal systems move west to east across the region. At other times, dryline convergence is weak enough where initiation tends to favor old boundaries, fronts, and pressure troughs.

Iowa

Driving through Iowa, if it were not for the casinos every 50 miles, would rank right up there with the most boring drive on the plains, but I'll give North Dakota the victory for that. I still want to know why Des Moines is as big as it is with 200 miles of corn in every direction. On the contrary, Iowa has been a relative gold mine for tornadoes for myself. You can't beat the terrain/road network combination there.

SCOTT WEBERPAL,
Janesville, WI chaser

Corn!

Which state is most boring to drive through? IOWA! Corn corn corn, house, corn corn corn, Des Moines, corn corn corn, tree, corn corn corn, barn, corn corn corn. You get the picture!

SCOTT WOELM
Minneapolis, MN chaser

Nebraska's austere beauty

Although I love the ocean of sky that roils above all of the Plains, I find Nebraska's austere beauty particularly compelling. I feel as if I'm experiencing what America is all about when I'm parked on a farm road on a gently sloping hill with happily oblivious birds chirping and a huge supercell on the horizon. In Nebraska, when dusty pickup trucks roll by, the farmers driving them always wave.

CHRIS KRIDLER
Indialantic, FL chaser

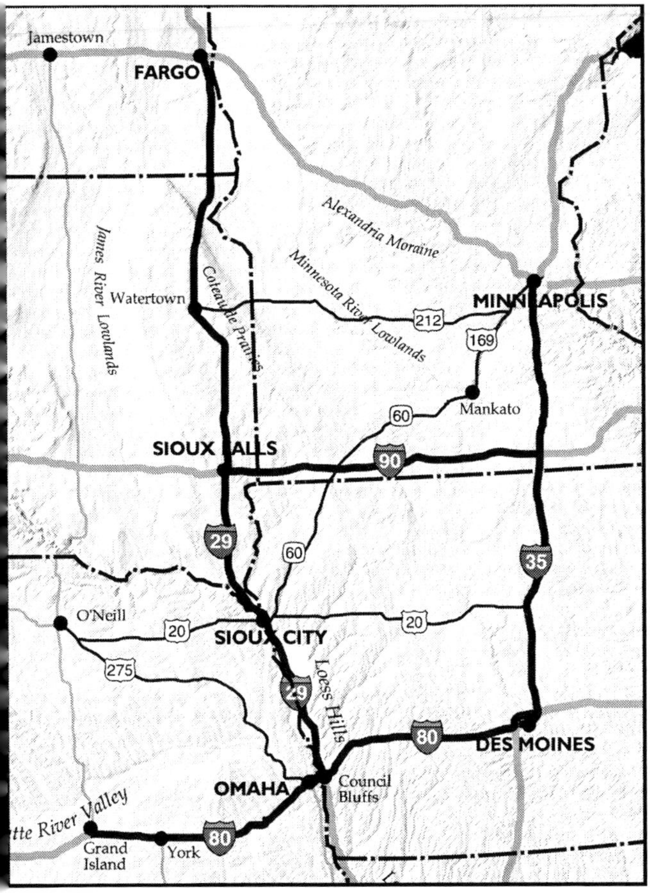

Road Guide

■ Omaha - North Platte NE

Interstate 80 (279 miles; 4.0 hours)

Leaving **Omaha**, the freeway crosses through a system of hills topped with 100-million year old Cretaceous sandstones and shales, which formed an ancient seafloor. On the southwest side of Omaha two miles past the I-680 junction is **Papillon Creek**, where streams have eroded an outcropping of ancient, 300-million year old Pennsylvanian shales on the river slopes. This is also seen along the **Platte River** slopes near **Mile Marker 427**. These are rich with fossils. For a better explanation, see the exhibit a few miles southeast on S.H. 31 at Schramm State Park [N41.026 W96.253]. Past the Platte River plains, the freeway crosses once again through Cretaceous hills, but in the deepest valleys there are again outcrops of Pennsylvanian shales. This part of Nebraska is among one of the third heaviest corn producers in North America. Considerable soy and sorghum is also grown, with a small amount of wheat. Approaching **Seward** and **Milford**, less erosion has taken place, and newer Greenhorn Formation limestones begin appearing as the road ascends onto a flat plateau. Near **York**, Greenhorn limestones are found on the slopes, and a bedrock of shales begins. Approaching **Aurora**, Niobrara chalks and limestones begin dominating rock outcroppings. At **Grand Island** the freeway has entered the vast region of the Ogallala Formation, the wide blanket of erosional sands deposited 5-10 million years ago that makes up most the western Great Plains. However, the road almost completely follows the Platte River and remains on its fertile alluvial plain, and the Ogallala Formation does not visually close in on the scenery for another fifty miles. [See Off the Beaten Path: CRANE MEADOWS NATURE CENTER and HASTINGS MUSEUM] Past **Kearney**, the Ogallala Formation gauntlet closes in on the Platte valley, and its hills can be seen just two miles to the north. These hills become progressively higher as you travel west, revealing the sheer depth of Ogallala deposits which have been carved down in the Platte River valley. You reach the town of **North Platte**.

■ Omaha NE - Council Bluffs IA - Fargo ND

Interstate 29 (304 miles; 5.2 hours)

Leaving **Omaha**'s sister city of **Council Bluffs** the road skirts the loess hills, which loom 320 ft (100 m) above the riverbed. These hills are composed of sediments unloaded by retreating glaciers, and carved down over the years by the Missouri River system. [See Off the Beaten Path: OWEGO] The freeway remains in the flat, highly fertile alluvial plains. It briefly skirts **Sioux City**, whose recent claim to fame was the crash-landing of a United Airlines DC-10 in July 1989. Only in South Dakota north of **Elk Point** does the highway leave the fertile alluvial plain and climb into the loess hills [N42.771 W96.776]. [See Off the Beaten Path: SPIRIT MOUND] Although soy is common in most fields along the route, South Dakota favors hay and oats. The road then reaches **Sioux Falls**, home of computer king Gateway 2000 and its trademark Holstein cow. Here the freeway begins ascending onto an uplifted formation covering most of the eastern state, called the Coteau des Prairies; during the Ice Age it actually split the glaciers into two lobes: the James River and the Des Moines. From **Sioux Falls** to **Dell Rapids**, the highway rides on a bedrock of billion-year old pink quartzite lurking beneath the glacial drift. Past Dell Rapids, the quartzite disappears and the glacial drift becomes many hundreds of feet deep. Near **Mile Marker 123** is the **Big Sioux River**, a major feature which drains the inner Coteau des Prairies. Its flat alluvial plains stretch all the way to **Brookings**. Past **Summit** the freeway crosses the ridgeline of the Coteau des Prairies, well over 2000 ft in elevation, and begins a quick descent to exit its northeast side, losing nearly 800 ft in just ten miles! It is here where the edge of the Coteau des Prairies is the sharpest. The small ridge two miles south of **Sisseton** is a north-south Continental Divide; north of here, streams drain into the Red River and then to Hudson Bay; south of here the streams drain into the Mississippi River, then the Gulf of Mexico. The **South Dakota-North Dakota state line** [N45.935 W96.843] is reached. North Dakota favors wheat and barley (a staple in beer production). The **Fargo** area has the densest concentration of barley, the key fermentation material for beer, in North America.

■ Omaha - Valentine NE

U.S. 275 to U.S. 20 (300 miles; 5.0 hours)

Much of the first half of the trip traverses Cretaceous limestones, which are seen in outcroppings, topped with layers of sand and silt comprising much of the topsoil. **Carlile.** Two miles west of **Pilger** the road begins an ascent into the Ogallala Formation [N42.019 W097.087]; where higher elevations are capped with a sandstone bedrock, the same type that forms the foundation for much of the western Great Plains. It originates from erosional sands weathered off the Rockies during the past 5-10 million years. The German settlement town of **Norfolk** was where talk show host Johnny Carson was raised. The terrain here has been carved down by erosion to the Cretaceous limestone outcroppings. Once outside Norfolk, the road winds in and out of the Elkhorn River's alluvial plains, and the hills become increasingly dominated by the Ogallala Formation. [See Off the Beaten Path: COPENHAGEN] Just 26 miles past Nehigh is the ghost town of **Stafford** [N42.328 W98.447], which in its 1890s glory years had a mercantile, railroad station, Catholic church, and school. **O'Neill** was founded over a two-year period starting in 1874 by an Irishman who wanted to pull his ethnic brothers and sisters out of East Coast coal mine poverty and settle them on a rich agricultural land; the Irish culture still persists today The road leaves the river system near **Bassett** and climbs onto the Ogallala Formation and its loess cover. After crossing the Niobrara River and approaching **Valentine,** you can look across the bluffs on the opposite bank, to the northeast, and see the remains of Fort Niobrara [N42.894 W100.474]. This was the first settlement, established by the Army in 1880 to prevent Indian-settler clashes between here and the Black Hills. It is now a wildlife refuge.

■ Fargo - Bismarck ND

Interstate 94 (192 miles; 2.7 hours)

The entire route is filled with wheat, barley, and soy fields, and is composed entirely of glacial drift, a layer of sediment hundreds of feet deep deposited by the Ice Age glaciers. This largely covers up any interesting rock formations. The farmland begins diminishing driving towards **Jamestown**, replaced by hay fields. **Steele** holds North Dakota's hottest temperature record: 121 deg F in 1936.

■ Sioux City IA - O'Neill NE

U.S. 20 (125 miles; 2.4 hours)

Leaving the ten-mile wide alluvial plain of the Missouri River, the road punches into the Elk Creek draw, then mounts hilly terrain, some of which consists of Pennsylvanian deposits. It then passes through Cretaceous formations. Laurel. At Randolph the road reaches the Ogallala Formation. Osmond. Plainview at the crossroads of the Chicago Burlington & Quincy and Chicago and Northwestern. The road then meets with U.S. 275. Only 1.5 miles southeast of this point is the ghost town of Stafford [N42.328 W98.447], which in its 1890s glory years had a mercantile, railroad station, Catholic church, and school. The road then leads into O'Neill.

■ Watertown - Spearfish SD

U.S. 212 / U.S. 85 (376 miles; 6.0 hours)

Leaving **Watertown**, the ground is almost entirely glacial till, sediments hundreds of feet thick left here by retreating Ice Age glaciers. At an elevation of 1700 ft, the highway brushes by Pelican Lake and Lake Kampeska, beginning its slow ascent into the High Plains. Just 37 miles south of Henry is **De Smet**, the actual townsite of Laura Ingalls Wilder's *Little House on the Prairie*. Six miles west of **Redfield** a 200 ft Niobrara chalk hill can be seen south of the highway: Bald Mountain. It originally was perhaps thousands of feet high, then was worn down by Ice Age glaciers and thick glacial till was deposited around it. About ten miles west of **Faulkton** the road enters stagnation moraine, where a stationary glacier melted with its load of sediment, forming poorly drained topography full of ponds and small lakes. Gettysburg. The road crosses Lake Oahe on the Missouri River, entering rugged terrain comprising an Indian reservation. From here to **La Plant**, the furthest extent of glaciers and their load of large boulders and glacial till is found. This thins out, giving way to vastly older Cretaceous shale outcroppings. Much of it from here to the end of the route contains layers of bentonite, a substance from volcanic ash deposits, which causes the ground to shift, resulting in road imperfections, bumps, and cracks. **Eagle Butte** is home to the Cheyenne River Sioux Agency. Ten miles northeast of **Newell** at the Jug River crossing [N44.784 W103.284] the west face of the valley shows striking slumps, where the brittle Cretaceous shales have slid off the slope in shards as the river cut into the valley. About five miles further are tepee buttes, cones of limestone named after their tepee-like shape. They're rich with clam and snail fossils. **Belle Fourche** thrives on bentonite mined out of the shales, as well as cattle and sheep ranching. At the Interstate 90 junction the elevation is 3500 ft.

■ Des Moines IA - Omaha NE

Interstate 80 (132 miles; 2.0 hours)

The drive west from Des Moines leads into rolling farmland. Rolling terrain punctuates the drive as it crosses the Southern Iowa drift hills, a region of strong erosion through the loess soils. The freeway skirts the northwestern edge of Madison County, site of the Robert James Waller novel and the 1995 film adaptation. Passes Stewart and Adair. The highway often rises and falls 100 ft in a few miles as it crosses north-south eroded drainage. Corn and soy are the crops of choice. Near **Underwood**, the highway leads through the Loess Hills. Roadcuts and outcroppings show Pennsylvanian-era shales and chalky limestones, about 300 million years old. The road abruptly plunges into the Missouri alluvial plain in the heart of **Council Bluffs**.

■ Albert Lea MN - Sioux Falls SD

Interstate 90 (176 miles; 2.6 hours)

Leaving **Albert Lea**, the road heads west across very flat farmland. The area is the single most productive corn and soy region in North America. The freeway enters a long, monotonous glacial till plain. After the retreat of the Ice Age glaciers, much of southern Minnesota was covered by spruce forest, but prairie grasses soon took over and enriched the soil. The freeway skirts Blue Earth. Past **Sherburn** the glacial ponds and lakes begin disappearing, and the freeway starts ascending almost imperceptibly onto the Coteau des Prairies, an uplifted area stretching from northwest Iowa to northeast South Dakota, which split the Ice Age glaciers into two main lobes: the James River and the Des Moines. About 4 miles west of **Worthington**, the freeway is on the highest part of the Coteau des Prairies, reaching an elevation of 1700 ft, and then descends its western slope. Adrian. Skirts Luverne. The **Minnesota-South Dakota state line** is reached [N43.609 W96.453] just after crossing the Great Northern railway. It then reaches the river plains of the Sioux River.

■ Minneapolis MN - Fargo ND (Interstate 94)

Interstate 94 (238 miles; 3.5 hours)

From the northwest Minneapolis suburbs to Monticello, rock outcroppings tend to be composed of extremely old Cambrian sandstone and shale. The road largely follows the Mississippi River, occasionally seen to the northeast. Northwest of **Monticello**, there is a distinct change in the rocks — the sandstone and shale gives way to gneiss and volcanic rocks. These are found for the remainder of the drive. Near **St Cloud**, the freeway begins rolling through some hilly terrain.Past **Alexandria**, the freeway runs past a series of lakes. These continue to **Fergus Falls**. The terrain flattens markedly about four miles north of **Rothsay**. Past **Barnesville** the freeway enters a rich agricultural belt consisting of soy, corn, and wheat. This area was the stomping ground for chase pioneer Roger Jensen, who lived just north in Lake Park. **Moorhead**, **Fargo**'s sister city, holds the all-time record high temperature for Minnesota at 114 deg F, set in 1936.

■ Minneapolis - Des Moines

Interstate 35 (244 miles; 3.6 hours)

This entire route covers terrain that was covered by Ice Age glaciers, which progressively deposited their loads of sediment, providing deep, rich layers of soil called glacial drift. Leaving **Minneapolis**, the highway reaches **Burnsville**, passing through slightly hilly terrain. **Faribault. Owatonna. Albert Lea** is named after an Army explorer who mapped out southern Minnesota in the 1830s. it crosses the glacial **Albert Lea Lake**; Myre State Park lines the north shore and makes a great resting stop. The route crosses some of the richest corn and soy fields in North America, extending for at least a hundred miles. The **Minnesota-Iowa state line** is crossed [N43.450 W93.353]. **Clear Lake** is home to just that: a clear lake, located a mile west of the freeway. **Ellsworth. Story City.** Leading along the South Skunk River valley. The town of **Ames** is home to a meteorology program at Iowa State University. [See Off the Beaten Path: BLOOMINGTON] The highway then reaches **Des Moines**.

■ Central Iowa - Sioux City IA

U.S. 20 (153 miles; 2.3 hours)

Leaving Interstate 35, the road bounds westward across corn and soy fields. **Webster City** is home to Murray McMurray, the largest mail order hatchery in the United States. You then enter the **Fort Dodge** area. Five miles before **Rockwell City**, you skirt by Manson, ten miles to the north, which was the site of the Manson Impact Structure [ground zero at N42.594 W94.558], an impact by a mile-sized meteor impact 74 million years ago. It has been completely covered by glacial till, but the Earth's crust down to a depth of seven miles is violently disturbed over a 12-mile radius. **Lytton** is along the Chicago Milwaukee & St Paul line. Sac City is along the North Raccoon River. Seven miles further, you must then head north for 3.5 miles before continuing west. Just two miles past Holstein, the road descends into the eroded Bacon Creek valley, descending from 1450 ft to 1350 ft MSL. Along the Sioux River is **Correctionville**; several miles north on S.H. 31 is the tiny town of Washta, which recorded Iowa's tied all-time record low of -47 deg F, set in 1996. The road then traverses a series of hills. Moville. Tiny town of Lawton. Arrives at Sioux City.

■ Minneapolis MN - Sioux City IA

U.S. 169 / S.H. 60 (267 miles; 4.6 hours)

Meandering along the alluvial flats of the Minnesota River, the highway reaches the town of **Shakopee**. It then remains in the alluvial flats, past **Jordan**. At **Belle Plaine** over a five-mile stretch, it ascends the southern bank, gradually rising from 750 to 1000 ft MSL, but drops once again into the flats at **Le Sueur** to cross to the western banks. Bluffs towering to 250 ft loom over the west side of the road, harboring the Minnesota prairie. The city of **Mankato** is reached. Here the highway departs the river's southern bank and aims southwest to cross the prairie. The first prairie town is **Lake Crystal**. Past **Madelia** the road begins slowly ascending the Coteau des Prairies, an uplifted area extending from northwest Iowa to northeast South Dakota; it split the glaciers into two main lobes: the James River and the Des Moines. The road leads around the south side of **St. James**. Here it picks up the Chicago & Northwestern railroad. The railroad junction of The road then leads through **Worthington**, reaching the uppermost point of the Coteau des Prairies. It skirts the one-square-mile Okabena Lake. Just past **Bigelow** the state line [N43.500 W95.694] is crossed. [See Off The Beaten Path: HIGHEST POINT IN IOWA] Past **Sheldon** the terrain becomes progressively hilly and the road begins a long, 300 ft descent into an eroded river valley. At the large town of **LeMars** the road reaches the flat alluvial plains of the Floyd River valley, following it southward to **Sioux City**.

■ Minneapolis MN - Watertown SD

U.S. 212 (210 miles; 3.4 hours)

Leaving the town of **Chaska** in the flat alluvial Minnesota River plain, the highway aims west, loosely following the Milwaukee St Paul & Pacific line. You reach the town of **Cologne**. Norwood's sister city of **Young America** should ring a bell for anyone who's filled out sweepstakes entry forms: they're processed here by the Young America Corporation (you pass by the building, seen to the northwest after crossing the railroad tracks). [See Off the Beaten Path: SPRINGERVILLE] About five miles past **Sacred Heart** the road crosses a series of deep, eroded streams, arriving in a 100 ft deep valley carved out by the Minnesota River, and populated by **Granite Falls**. The road follows the river's alluvial flats upstream to **Montevideo**, then continues west across the prairie. About 19 miles past **Dawson** is the state line [N44.936 W96.451], and the road shifts southwest to accomodate a new range-township system. The road arrives at **Watertown** and the junction of **I-29**.

Off the beaten path

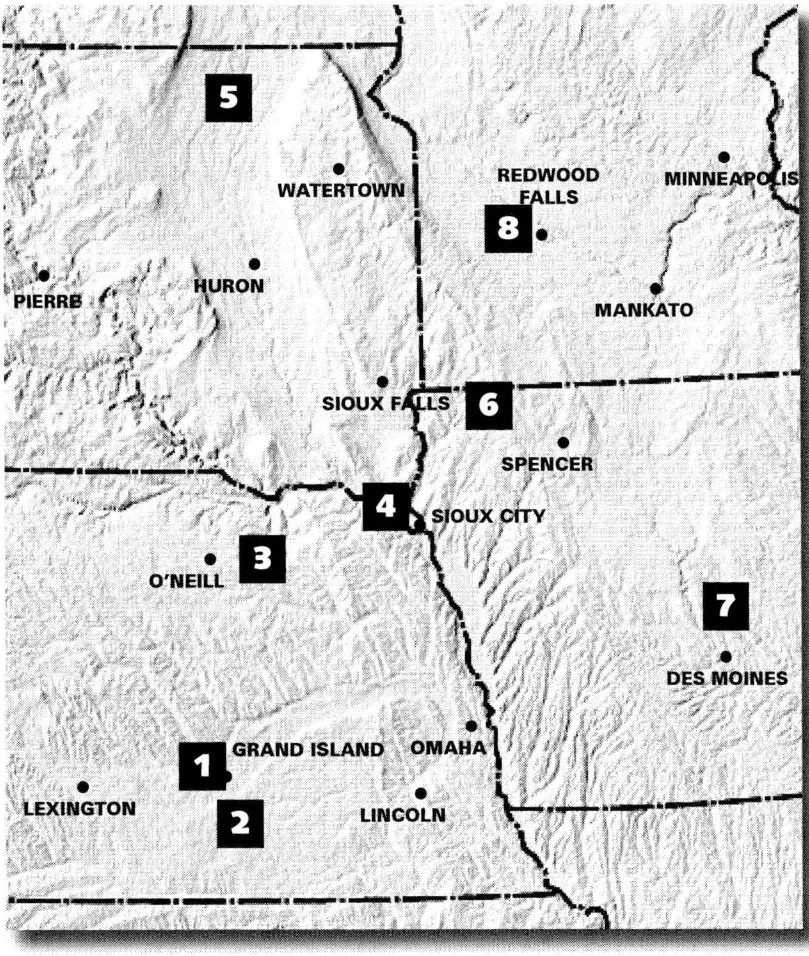

Southeast Nebraska

1 Crane Meadows Nature Center [N40.795 W98.493] is located immediately south of the I-80 Exit 305 interchange just west of Grand Island. It's a 250-acre park with self-guided tours, nearly 8 miles of trails, and a visitor center stocked with nature and geology exhibits. Open 8:30-5:30 daily; Sunday 1-5. Nominal admission.

2 Hastings Museum [N40.600 W98.391] is the smallest venue to have an IMAX theater. When time is short, check out the three floors dedicated to the Great Plains. And if you need a break from the Plains, there's a Kool-Aid exhibit (the inventor lived in Hastings). Located on U.S. 281 on the north side of town. Open 9-5 (Sun 11-5).

Northeast Nebraska

3 Copenhagen ghost town [N42.337 W97.893] is an easy detour for those plying the Norfolk and O'Neill region. It was settled in 1878 by farmers moving here from Crawford County, Iowa, and grew along the Chicago Burlington & Quincy railroad. It reached a population of nearly 100 before dwindling in the 1900s and 1910s, leaving only one original residence. A trackside grain elevator is still used here. It suffered from a major fire in April 1996 which burned $5 million worth of grain over the course of 3 weeks, however it soon returned to service. Copenhagen is 5 miles west of the edge of Plainview, then 1 mile south at the railroad track.

Southeast South Dakota

4 Spirit Mound [N42.874 W96.959] rises 100 ft over the flat terrain. It was visited in August 1804 by the explorers Lewis & Clark and nine men. The Sioux Indians believed it was haunted by small demons which would kill anyone that came near. The hill is open for climbing. Located along S.H. 19 six miles north of Vermilion.

Northeast South Dakota

5 Storybook Land. How can you go wrong when there's no admission and it's within easy access to chase routes in all directions? Located in the city's Wylie Park [N45.489 W98.516], Storybook Land is a curious collection of exhibits, buildings, and landscaping dedicated to fairy tales. And since it holds the Land of Oz, it's a must-see for chasers! Located about 3 miles northwest of downtown Aberdeen. The town of Winfield [N45.923 W98.518] is an easy stop when travelling U.S. 281 between Aberdeen SD and Jamestown ND. Winship came into being in 1889 as an agricultural stop on a spur of the new Chicago Milwaukee & St Paul railroad. In the 20th century it relied on traffic patronizing its large general store and gas station from U.S. 281. This dwindled when the route was adjusted west of town. Winship fell into ghost town status during the 1970s. It is located exactly 1 mile south of the state line about a quarter mile east of the highway.

Northwest Iowa

6 Hawkeye Point. It's hard to believe that there is a highest point in Iowa, but it does exist: Hawkeye Point [N43.460 W95.709] on Sterler Farm. It rises to the Alpine height of 1,670 ft MSL. What is unusual about this stop is that the landowners are actually tickled about their distinction and love to have visitors. Enjoy some Iowan hospitality and leaf through their guest book! Located on S.H. 60 five miles northeast of Sibley and 2.5 miles south of the state line

Central Iowa

7 Bloomingtown ghost town. Just northeast of Ames is the ghost town of Bloomington [N42.056 W93.587]. It lies on a ridge near the South Skunk River. The town dates back to 1857 in anticipation of the new railroad, which was instead routed into what is now Ames. The town was largely abandoned by the 1900s, and only some collapsed ruins are left. Half a mile to the southeast is the National Animal Disease Center, opened in 1961, which conducts research into minimizing livestock and poultry losses.

Southwest Minnesota

8 Springerville ghost town [N44.627 W95.191] was the nucleus of a Minnesota gold rush in 1894, leading to the creation of a town and a 120 ft deep gold mine. The site was on the shores of an oversized pond dubbed Gold Mine Lake, which now serves as a local swimming hole. The town thrived but the gold could not be extracted economically, so the mine suspended operations only after two years. The town was largely abandoned by 1897. Ruins and the old mine are still there. Go 1.5 miles east from Delhi then north 1.3 miles. Before reaching the river bridge, turn northwest. The lake is one mile.

Classic Minnesota moraine about 10 miles west of Alden along Interstate 90. The random, rounded hills were formed when deposits of sediment were unloaded by retreating glaciers. *(USGS)*

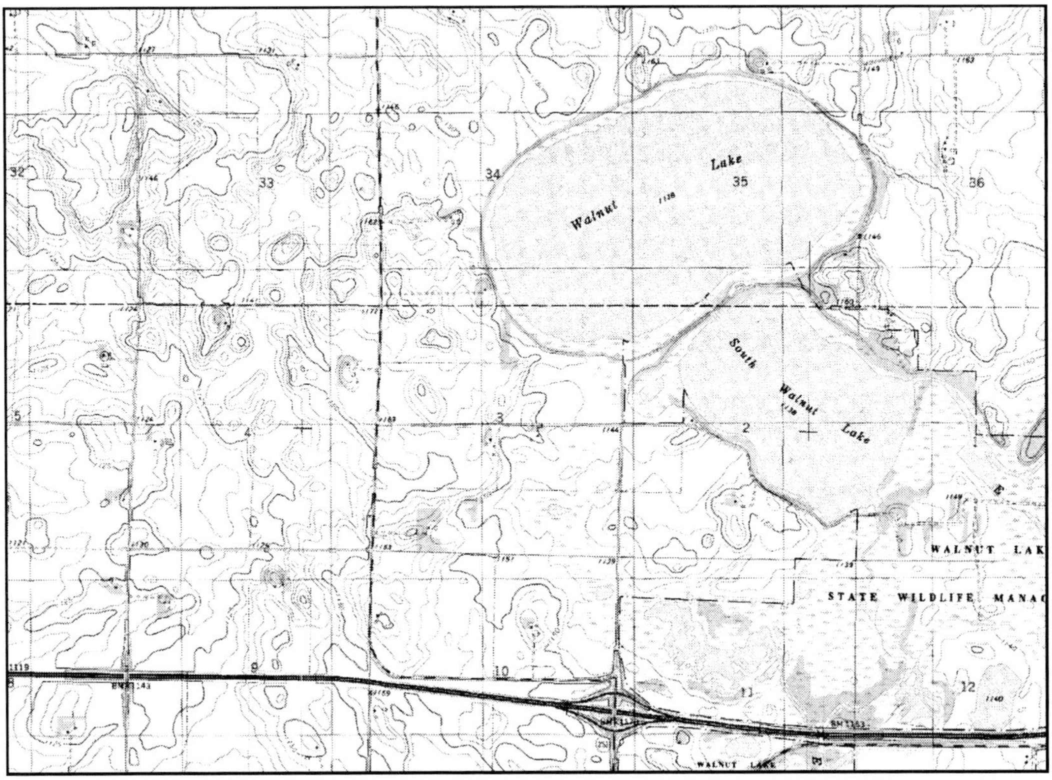

GREAT PLAINS TRAVEL GUIDE

Canada

When mid-June arrives, there is often a grand finale chase event on the traditional Great Plains. Then chasers seem retire into their dens for the long, hot summer, dreaming about next season. Certainly a lot of chasers are drained and must go back to their day jobs. However the chase season continues! As many Minneapolis-based chasers know, the entire Northern Plains opens wide for all types of chase possibilities, and by mid-July the Canadian Prairies and border regions are often sparking with large supercell storms. Fortunately, Canada has a thriving, prosperous agricultural belt that rivals that of Nebraska and Kansas. And this, of course, means plenty of roads.

The main advantage of chasing the Northern Plains is that there is much less of a chase crowd. Here you are likely to be the only chaser watching a storm. The negatives? Distances are vast and there are more data gaps. There's no Storm Prediction Center intensely monitoring the action, there's no Level 2 WSR-88D data to back up your mesoscale work, and there's no mesonet available to refine that important outflow boundary. Slant angles from GOES satellites are higher, so fine-scale visible imagery is a little more difficult to use. The chaser must know their stuff, increase their fuel budget, and allocate more vacation time. The right ingredients combine over a much broader area, shifting radically in location from day to day.

The western extent of Canadian chase action is bounded by the Rocky Mountains in far west Alberta. The eastern boundary of chase action is in eastern Manitoba about 40 miles east of Winnipeg, where farmland quickly transitions to boreal forest. The northern chase zones do not extend into the northern parts of Alberta, Saskatchewan, or Manitoba due to the disappearance of the farming belt and the lack of roads, even though strong storms do occur in these areas in July and August.

Meteorology

The system of polar jets and fronts tend to form a swath across the Dakotas and Montana in June, and in the Canadian provinces in July. They have an enormous influence on defining storm chase target areas, and chasers find theirselves playing a game of finding the best moisture and instability that don't involve a wall of forcing. Old boundaries

The Canada experience

Chasing in Canada can be quite challenging. You really need to be up on your forecasting skills because there is simply nothing else available that will guide you to the storms in time to see them, unless of course you're extremely lucky to have one in your backyard.

Southern Manitoba can offer quite a few opportunities to see isolated storms due to it's wide open prairie landscape and lack of heavy forestation. The road network is generally laid out well in a grid format, however a good paper map or program is essential since you can find yourself in some dead-end situations, particularly in the south-east part of the province due to some marshlands.

The best advice I can give someone who is interested in storm-chasing here in Manitoba would be to be very patient, do your homework, and don't wait for Environment Canada to warn of an impending storm. You pretty well need to be in position by mid-afternoon or you'll be out of play.

JOHN ERWIN, VE4WX
Winnipeg, Manitoba chaser

Canada offers a lot of late-season chase opportunities in Alberta, Saskatchewan, and Manitoba. The only cost is time and patience. *(Tim Vasquez)*

Canadian paydirt

Once I owned my first vehicle at the age of 18, that's when the chasing took off. I've chased pretty much every local event in and around Southern Manitoba, and I've chased some bigger severe weather set-ups in the USA. June 22, 2007 was the day of the Elie, MB F5 tornado. I tracked that weather system while working at the Prairie Arctic Storm Prediction Center as a co-op student. I left work that day with no sign of convective initiation. As I entered the suburbs of the city, I could see huge towers going up. I parked about a mile south of Elie, MB as a wall cloud emerged. And the real tornado show began.

I was in a trance when it was all over. I had been chasing for years and seen nothing!

JUSTIN HOBSON
Winnipeg, Manitoba chaser

and warm fronts present the best opportunities. Although there can be distinct moisture gradients across the Northern Plains, the dryline, by definition, rarely makes appearances at these northern latitudes.

Major routes

It must be noted that most U.S.-Canada border crossings close at 9 or 10 pm. Chasers driving at night must plan their border crossings accordingly. A few key stations on the Plains are open 24 hours: Sweetgrass, MT (I-15); Raymond, MT (S.H. 16); Portal, ND (U.S. 52); Dunseith, ND (U.S. 281); Pembina, ND (I-29); and Warroad, MN (S.H. 313).

Effective 1 June 2009 new security requirements mandate a passport for land re-entry into the U.S. from any country, including Canada and Mexico. Therefore it will pay to plan ahead and apply for a passport now if you have plans to chase in Canada in 2009. If you are bringing a child you may be required to present documentary evidence of relationship. Any firearms must be declared; if an item is prohibited you will be given the opportunity to turn around or store the item.

Visitors from foreign countries should contact their consulate for accurate information and requirements, since tightened immigration policies following the wake of the September 11 disaster has made border crossings quite difficult for those who aren't North American citizens.

Canada's first F5 tornado on record touched down 22 June 2007 near Elie, Manitoba. It was witnessed by storm chaser Justin Hobson (pictured), a University of Manitoba student. The southern Manitoba and Saskatchewan regions are becoming a popular destination for American chasers in July. *(Justin Hobson)*

APPENDIX

Great Plains dining

Chasing does not often offer the luxury of relaxing in a full-service restaurant, since storm events occur right at dinnertime and continue past closing times. However on slower chase days or chase busts, a visit to a good restaurant is a chance to refresh and feast on a quality meal.

Only *quality restaurants* are listed here. To find them, I've sifted through my own experiences and that of others. The goal is to find *a high-quality meal well known by locals*. The restaurant with the biggest crowd is not an ideal choice, because in many cases crowded local restaurants are simply offering average-quality food for a cheap price, which not coincidentally draws large numbers of patrons. Most "feeding troughs" and buffets fall into this category. Well-known chain restaurants are likewise omitted since many chasers already know what to expect.

Keep in mind that the food served by legendary restaurants are usually the same across a region. Texas listings will have a lot of Tex-Mex, except where local consumer spending allows expensive barbecue operations to thrive. In the central and northern Plains, local flavor usually consists of steak with a few scatterings of barbecue pits and Italian food. In eastern locales, a legendary restaurant is often a brewpub and grill!

The phone number for each restaurant is provided so that you can call ahead and check on the hours. Someplaces in smaller towns do close quite early. A final word — if you think you've found a local legend, or if you've found that a certain restaurant is a disgrace to this section, send it in for consideration for future editions!

Colorado

COLORADO SPRINGS

Red Hot & Blue BBQ [N38.894 W104.758] is located on the far northeast side of town on CO 83 (4290 N. Academy Blvd, 719-592-0300).

LA JUNTA

Felicias [N37.989 W103.565] serves great Mexican food, and it's darn cheap (27948 Frontage Rd, phone # unavailable)

Kansas

ARLINGTON

While on the long stretch between Hutchinson and Pratt, check out a great home-style restaurant and bakery run by a Mennonite lady: Carolyn's Essenhaus [37.897 W98.175] (104 E. Main St; 620-538-4711).

DODGE CITY

For amazing fajitas, friendly staff, affordable prices, and nearby WiFi, stop in at Casa Alvarez [37.753 W100.038] (1701 W. Wyatt Earp Blvd (U.S. 400); 620-225-7164).

HAYS

Recommended is Al's Chickenette [N38.864 W99.317] (700 Vine St; 785-626-7414).

KANSAS CITY

* WEST SIDE: Good digs southwest of Kansas City? Big Bubba's BBQ [N38.855 W94.779] (16695 West 151st, 913-390-0007). Zarda Bar-B-Q [N38.971 W94.725] just off I-35 at W 87th (11931 W 87th St)

LIBERAL

Great steaks are at the Cattleman's Cafe [N37.032 W100.912] (744 E Pancake, 620-626-5553).

PAOLA

Awards from the Kansas City BBQ Society were lauded on We B Smokin [N38.535 W94.926] 2.5 miles north-northeast of Osawatomie; no dinner Sunday (32580 Airport Rd; 913-755-0175).

PRATT

Donald's Serva-Teria [N37.646 W98.727] is a retro 50s local buffet with great fried chicken and other country foods (1123 E 1st St (U.S. 400); 620-672-5341).

SALINA

A Kansas favorite is the Amarillo Grill [N38.794 W97.612] (2601 Market Place; 785-827-3599).

WICHITA

* EAST SIDE: On the far northeast side of town, take the KS 96 exit for the Amarillo Grill [N37.743 W97.244] (3151 N Rock Rd, 316-684-1861)
* WEST SIDE: Right off U.S. 400 is the Amarillo Grill [N37.674 W97.432] (600 S Holland, 316-722-5666).

Iowa

AMES

Battles BBQ [N42.023 W93.651] is a local favorite (112 Hayward Ave; 515-292-1670) along with the gourmet Great Plains Sauce

& Dough Co [N42.025 W93.611] (129 Main St; 515-232-4263).

DES MOINES

Finding a truly good dining experience in the area can be a challenge. West of town on I-80 at Exit 117 is Rube's Steakhouse [N41.561 W93.881] (3309 Ute Ave, Boonville).

Minnesota

ST CLOUD

Granite City Brewery [N45.550 W94.206] is in the downtown area (3945 S 2nd St; 320-203-9000).

Missouri

SPRINGFIELD

James River Grill [N37.160 W93.279] located in the heart of town makes a mean BBQ (1155 E Battlefield St; 417-890-0024).

Nebraska

HASTINGS

Barrel Bar Lounge [N40.582 W98.366] is a local favorite (1200 E South; 402-463-9158).

MILLIGAN

Located 25 miles southeast of York, Frosty Mug [N40.500 W97.389] has been a fierce competitor for best burger in Nebraska; its 11 pm closing hours (1 am weekends) make it a definitive pit stop after a chase (602 Main; 402-629-4280).

NORTH PLATTE

A local favorite is Merrick's Ranch House [N41.134 W100.749] just east of downtown (1220 E 4th; 308-532-8200). Also try La Casita's excellent Mexican fare [N41.134 W100.741] (1911 E 4th; 308-534-8077).

OMAHA

There are no legendary restaurants in Omaha. One regional favorite is Louie M's Burger Lust in southern downtown [N41.234 W95.939] (1718 Vinton St; 402-449-9112). South of town and an easy jaunt from I-29 is Uncle Ernie's [N41.048 W95.922] offering legendary BBQ in a funky atmosphere (20300 Hwy 75, Plattsmouth; 402-298-7483)

PAXTON

A regional legend is Ole's Big Game Steakhouse [N41.123 W101.356] at I-80 Exit 145 with super steak and the biggest collection of mounted animals (113 N Oak St; 308-239-4500).

STRANG

Located 30 miles south of York, Jan's Strang Tavern [N40.413 W97.586] features a great hamburger; open late (304 Main; 402-759-4834).

YORK

Try Chances R [N40.866 W97.593] for steaks (124 W 5th; 402-362-7755).

New Mexico

EUNICE

Just 18 miles south of Hobbs is Diana's Cafe [N32.437 W103.158]; the chiles rellenos are legendary (1210 Ave J; 505-394-2266).

Oklahoma

GUTHRIE

Granny Had One [N35.193 W101.742] offers healthy sandwiches, soups and other light fare in a beautiful Victorian building (113 W. Harrison at U.S. 77; 405-282-4482).

LAWTON

In a town of culinary mediocrity, El Zarape [N34.596 W98.403] offers good Tex-Mex square in downtown (1015 SW Park; 353-3610). If you head north of the mountains near Meers, the Meers Store is legendary in SW Oklahoma for its longhorn burgers, though its cleanliness is slightly debatable.

MCALESTER

Legends here are built on Italian food, of all things. And the legend name is Pete's Place [N34.927 W95.727] just a short jaunt north up U.S. 69 (120 SW 8th, Krebs; 918-423-2042).

NORMAN

Norman's definition is chains with little local flavor. For a few exceptions, try The Mont [N35.211 W97.436], an outdoor cafe near the old OU weather school (1300 Classen; 405-329-3330); or Coaches Brewpub [N35.220 W97.444] (102 W Main; 405-360-5726).

OKLAHOMA CITY

There's not much outstanding local flavor. Best bets are in the trendy Bricktown area [N35.465 W97.510] on the east edge of downtown at dives such as Abuelo's, Chelino's, Bricktown Brewery, and Spaghetti Warehouse.

PONCA CITY

One restaurant in Ponca City stands ahead of the crowd: Enrique's [N36.729 W97.101] in the city's airport terminal (405-762-5507).

TULSA

The situation in Tulsa as nearly the same as OKC: lots of average restaurants but none that lead the pack. Two exceptions. Polo Grill [N36.133 W95.963] on the southeast side of Tulsa outside the loop (2038 Utica Square; 918-744-4280). India Palace [N36.062 W95.957] south of I-44 east of the river (6963 South Lewis Avenue, 918-492-8040).

VINITA

The best BBQ in the region is said to be Big Bill's [N36.643 W95.152] (359 N Wilson; 918-256-4024).

South Dakota

BADLANDS

While you're there, seek out the Cuny Table Cafe [N43.513 W102.641] said to have some of the best Indian tacos in the region.

MITCHELL

For great burgers, steaks, wings, and WiFi in a railroad-themed atmosphere, try The Depot Pub & Grill [N43.706 W98.025] (210 S. Main St.; 605-996-9417).

MOUND CITY

Calico's Steakhouse [N45.725 W100.069] in the Mobridge region offers home-style cooking with a German influence (125 Main St. N.; 605-955-3535).

RAPID CITY

Recommended is Art's Southern Smokehouse [N44.081 W103.227] with blues entertainment (609 Main St; 605-348-5499).

Texas

ABILENE

Try the legendary Joe Allen's BBQ [N32.435 W99.728] just south of downtown Abilene. It's so good you'll see the locals loading up food in coolers. Chasers report it's still great (1185 China St. near S. 12th and S.H. 36; 325-672-9948).

AMARILLO

The Big Texan Steakhouse [N35.194 W101.748] is iconic for its offer of a free meal if you can eat a 4.5-pound steak with all the trimmings. It tends to be a chaser magnet (7701 E. Interstate 40 (near Exit 75 east of the city), Amarillo TX 79118).

ATHENS

If you can handle a 36-mile diversion to the east of Corsicana, try Danny's Smokehouse Bar-B-Que [N32.204 W95.842], not quite a Texas legend but pretty darn good nevertheless (850 E Corsicana St; 903-675-5238).

AUSTIN

There's too much good cooking in Austin. But one legend worth visiting is in downtown Austin: Stubb's BBQ [N30.268 W97.736] is an offshoot of a famous Lubbock operation that at one time had the best BBQ in the state (801 Red River, 512-480-0203).

BIG SPRING

Try a regional favorite: Al & Sons BBQ [N32.237 W101.472] just south of downtown (1810 Gregg St; 915-267-8921).

BRADY

Lone Star BBQ [N31.116 W99.335] has great local flavor; be sure to try the cobbler! On the main drag south of town (2010 S. Bridge, 915-597-1936).

DEL RIO

Culinary quality is generally dull in Del Rio. An exception is Carmelita's Restaurant [N29.350 W100.912] in the downtown district (1501 Las Vacas St; 830-774-5171).

FORT STOCKTON

Try the Camphouse [N30.894 W102.891] on the main drag, just west of downtown (1216 N Hwy 285; 915-336-9791). Sarah's Cafe is a local gem [N30.885 W102.880] (106 N Nelson; 915-336-7700).

GAINESVILLE

Before heading into Oklahoma, be warned that BBQ fare there is quite average. For a final pit stop, stop at the Smokehouse II [N33.641 W97.136] just east of downtown (1040 E Hwy 82; 940-665-8691).

HILL COUNTRY

Highly recommended is the upscale Hill Top Cafe about halfway between Fredericksburg and Mason [N30.397 W98.968] serving Cajun, Tex-Mex, and Greek (830-997-8922). If you can swing east from Mason or Fredericksburg, the legendary Coopers Pit BBQ [N30.758 W98.680] vies for the absolute best BBQ in Texas, period, among BBQ lovers; it's in downtown Llano (505 W. Dallas, 915-247-5713).

HUNTSVILLE

If you're in an adventurous mood, try searching for the Mount Zion Baptist Church BBQ, easily the best between Houston and Dallas. We haven't tried it and are not even sure where it is, so an address and GPS coordinates are not available here.

JUNCTION

The regional favorite is Come N Git It [N30.504 W99.778] between I-10 and downtown (2341 N Main; 915-446-4357).

KERRVILLE

Mi Ranchito [N30.022 W99.126] near Schreiner University (2523 Memorial Blvd; 830-257-4010).

LUBBOCK

The only local legend, Stubbs BBQ, closed in 1999. Seasoned locals now fall back on Goodfella's [N33.570 W101.909], a great Italian place on the west inner side (2608 Salem; 806-687-0240); and the chain County Line BBQ [N33.645 W101.841] on the far north side (FM 2641 west of I-27; 806-763-6001).

MARATHON

At Marathon try the stunning Gage Hotel Restaurant [N30.207 W103.247] on the west side of town along U.S. 90 (888-991-6749).

MIDLAND-ODESSA

Head to Odessa for Tex-Mex at Mi Casa [N31.847 W102.391] between I-20 and downtown (1301 N County Rd W; 432-580-3014).

PAMPA

Highly recommended is Dyer's Bar-B-Que Hwy 60 W (806-665-4401) . Chasers report it was still great even in 2007. If you can make it over to Borger, try Monkey's Bar B Que Pit and Sutphen's Bar-B-Q, both on Cedar St.

PECOS

Tex-Mex prevails, with La Nortena Tortilla Factory [N31.426 W103.494] square in downtown a regional favorite (212 E 3rd; 915-445-3273).

QUANAH

Medicine Mound Depot is a regional favorite for its BBQ [approx. N34.285 W99.706] (1802 Hwy 287 East; 940-663-5619).

SAN ANGELO

The Old Time Pit Bar-B-Que [N31.443 W100.442] looks like a cheap fast food joint but looks are deceiving: it's an authentic Texas pit BBQ. Located on U.S. 277 south of downtown (1805 S. Bryant; 915-655-2771)

SNYDER

For the ultimate West Texas meal, try a mini-steakhouse at a dude ranch north of Snyder: the Wagon Wheel Ranch [N32.867 W100.989]. It's 1.5 miles east of the tiny town of Dermott.

WACO

Waco is nearly devoid of anything outstanding or legendary. Exceptions are Diamond Back's restaurant [N31.557 W97.127] (217 Mary Ave; 254-757-2871) and Buzzard

Billy's cajun food [N31.559 W97.127] (208 S. University Parks Dr; 254-753-2778).

WICHITA FALLS

The area is short on legendary food but these Mexican dives will please: Sevi's Burritos [N33.902 W98.508] in downtown along U.S. 281 (907 Denver St; 817-766-4905); and El Mejicano [N33.904 W98.530] just west of downtown (3148 9th; 817-322-1846).

Wyoming

CHEYENNE

Sanford's Grub 'n Pub [N41.134 W104.814] is a regional chain but is said to have great burgers & brew (115 E 17th; 307-634-3381).

Travel time map

Distances are in miles. Travel times assume a brisk, no-stop trip average of 65 mph and serves as an initial estimate only.

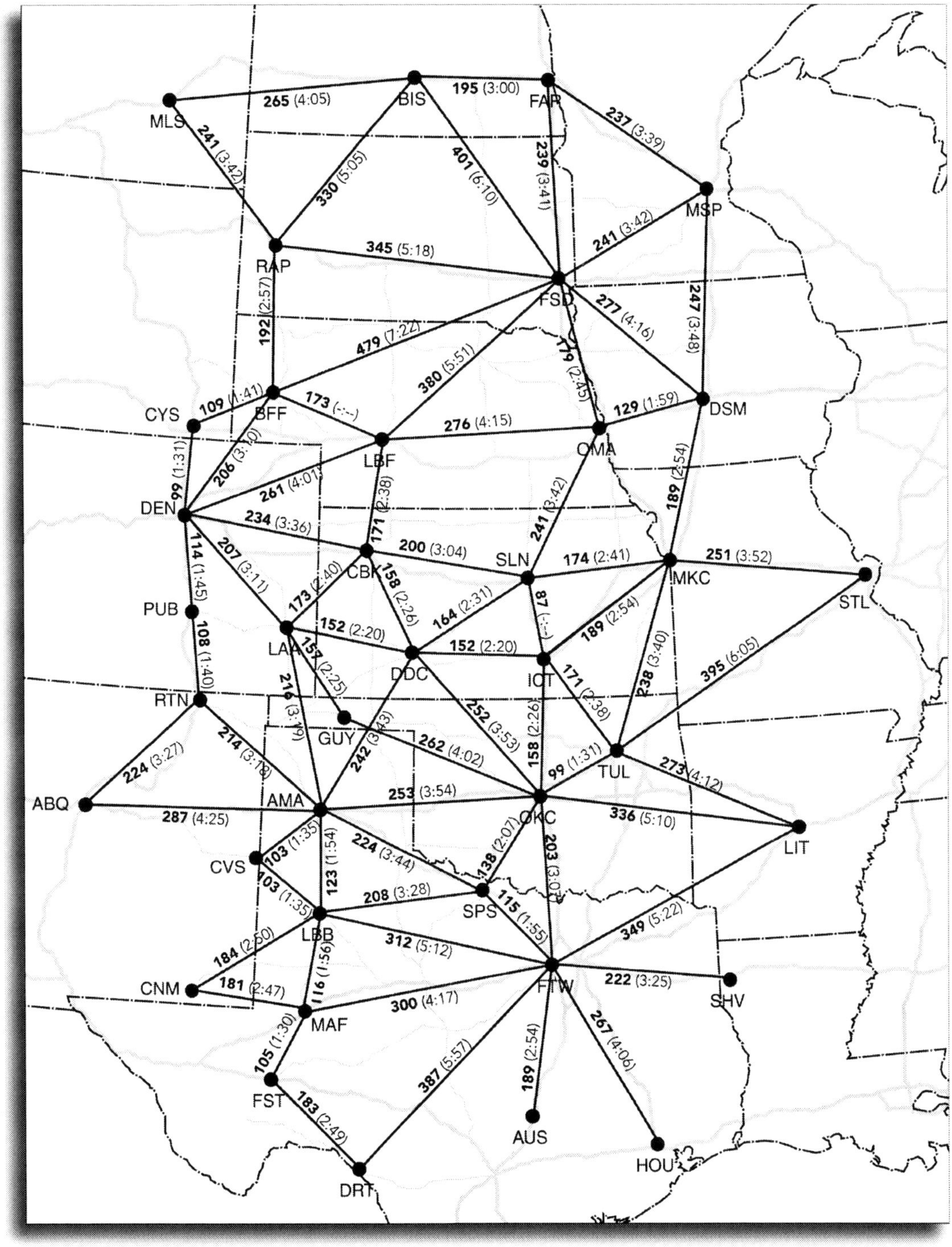

NWS telephone numbers

The following maps identify each NWS office's policy regarding chaser reports and their preferred phone numbers for this purpose. Simply use the county outlines below to identify which office is responsible for the event, then use the number *only* for reporting severe weather (hail at least 3/4", penny size, winds over 58 mph, or tornado activity). The top number is the primary contact number. Other listed numbers are backups in case you can't contact the primary number. Spotters should use designated reporting procedures for the location rather than these maps. See the "Strategy" chapter for information on how to make an effective report.

Prefix and meaning

p = This is the published public number. No response received at press time. Also try 911.

c = Designated number for use by storm chasers.

i = Office expressly asks that chasers identify theirselves as chasers.

e = Office expressly monitors eSpotter.

s = Expressly monitors SpotterNetwork site.

w = You may also use this office's NWS website to submit a report.

d = Office asked for post-storm reports, images, and video from chasers for training/verification.

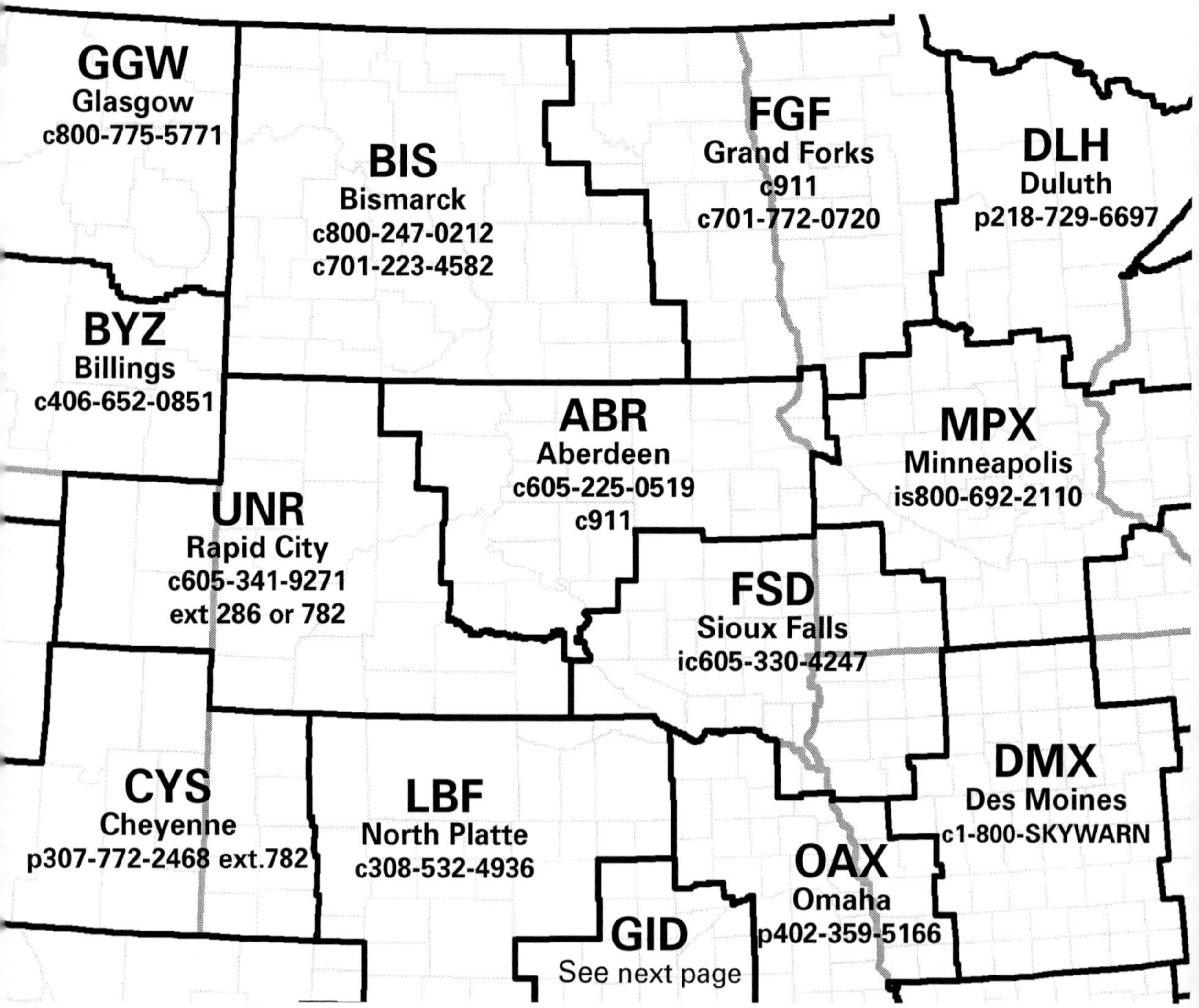

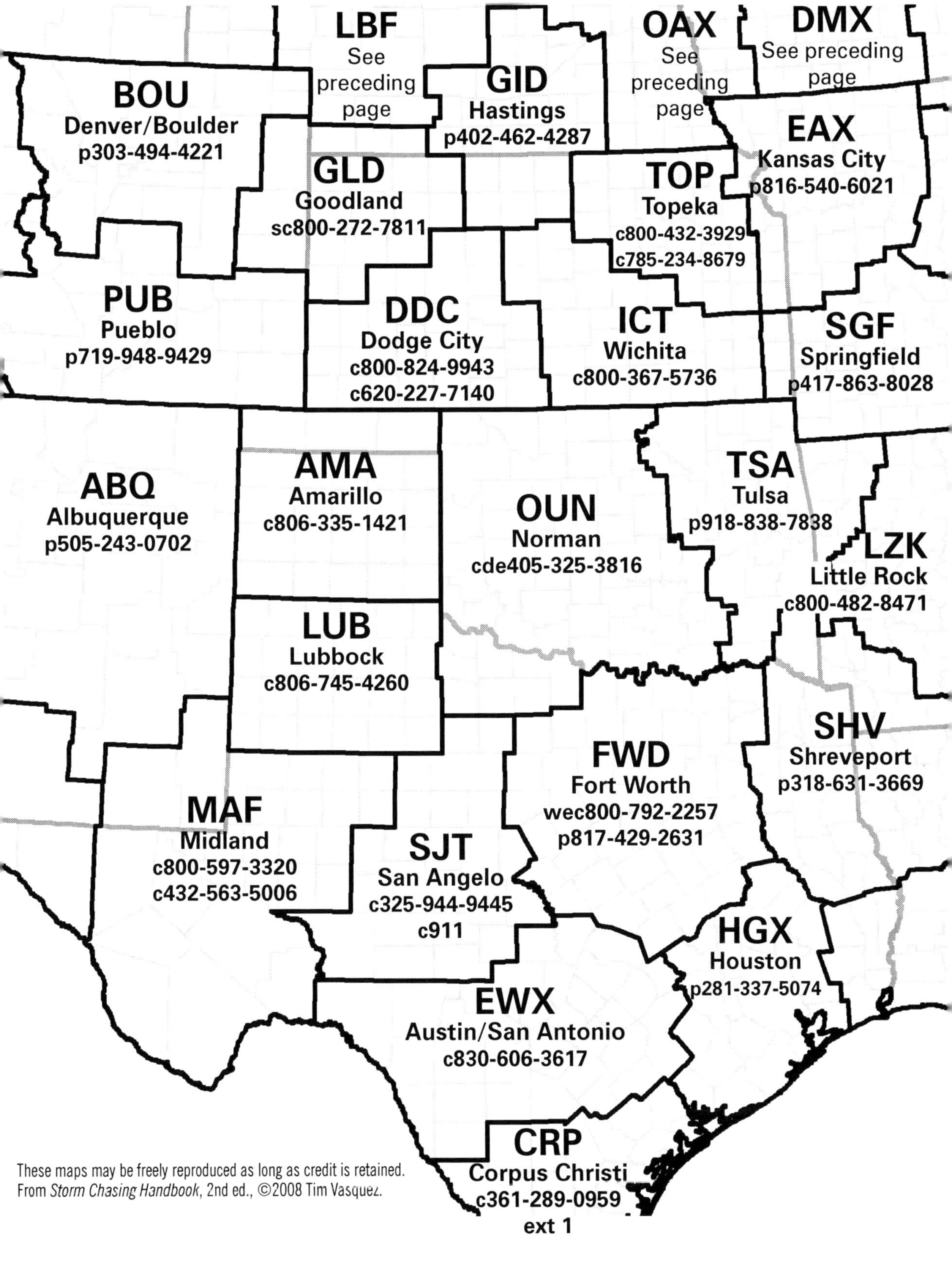
LBF
See preceding page
OAX
See preceding page
DMX
See preceding page
BOU
Denver/Boulder
p303-494-4221
GID
Hastings
p402-462-4287
EAX
Kansas City
p816-540-6021
GLD
Goodland
sc800-272-7811
TOP
Topeka
c800-432-3929
c785-234-8679
PUB
Pueblo
p719-948-9429
DDC
Dodge City
c800-824-9943
c620-227-7140
ICT
Wichita
c800-367-5736
SGF
Springfield
p417-863-8028
AMA
Amarillo
c806-335-1421
TSA
Tulsa
p918-838-7838
ABQ
Albuquerque
p505-243-0702
OUN
Norman
cde405-325-3816
LZK
Little Rock
c800-482-8471
LUB
Lubbock
c806-745-4260
SHV
Shreveport
p318-631-3669
FWD
Fort Worth
wec800-792-2257
p817-429-2631
MAF
Midland
c800-597-3320
c432-563-5006
SJT
San Angelo
c325-944-9445
c911
HGX
Houston
p281-337-5074
EWX
Austin/San Antonio
c830-606-3617
CRP
Corpus Christi
c361-289-0959
ext 1

NOAA Weather Radio

The U.S. National Weather Service and Environment Canada operate a dense network of plain-language weather broadcasts on the 162 MHz band. In the United States it is called NOAA All Hazards Weather Radio, and in Canada it is known as Weatheradio Canada. These services are identical, providing the public with important regional weather information as well as government emergency messages.

Unfortunately these broadcasts lack detailed information on the mesoscale progression of the afternoon events, and the automation of the sites has diluted the availability of informal remarks about the situation recorded by NWS meteorologists, which were actually quite common through the early 1990s and were sometimes ad-libbed. Radar summaries, which were useful for finding out what was going on across a target area, have disappeared from the lineup. However a skilled chase forecaster will be able to read between the lines and piece together clues from the broadcasts, such as trends in wind direction at a certain station, the pattern of severe thunderstorm warnings that have been issued, and changes in forecast thinking.

To receive National Weather Service radio, you will need a specially-designed weather radio, which can be bought for as cheap as $20. Unfortunately, the manufacturers usually pay little atttention to the antenna design, and such radios struggle to get a reception distance of beyond 25 miles. Most chase locations are quite some distance from NWS Radio transmitters, so a dedicated external antenna can be a vital piece of equipment. If your budget permits, it's a good idea to get an amateur radio scanner, most of which have weather radio reception built in and are more suited to receive antennas. Under ideal conditions with a properly matched VHF antenna, this will allow broadcasts 70 miles away to be heard.

Some automobiles such as BMW, Range Rover, and Saab come standard with NOAA Weather Radio tuning in their factory-installed radio. For those without this luxury, most electronics superstores sell vehicle radios and CD players equipped with the weather bands. The range reception will not be as good as a scanner/external antenna combination, but the convenience factor can't be beat.

In summary the radio frequencies used by the NOAA Weather Radio network are as follows:

Chan #	Frequency (MHz)
1	162.400
2	162.425
3	162.450
4	162.475
5	162.500
6	162.525
7	162.550

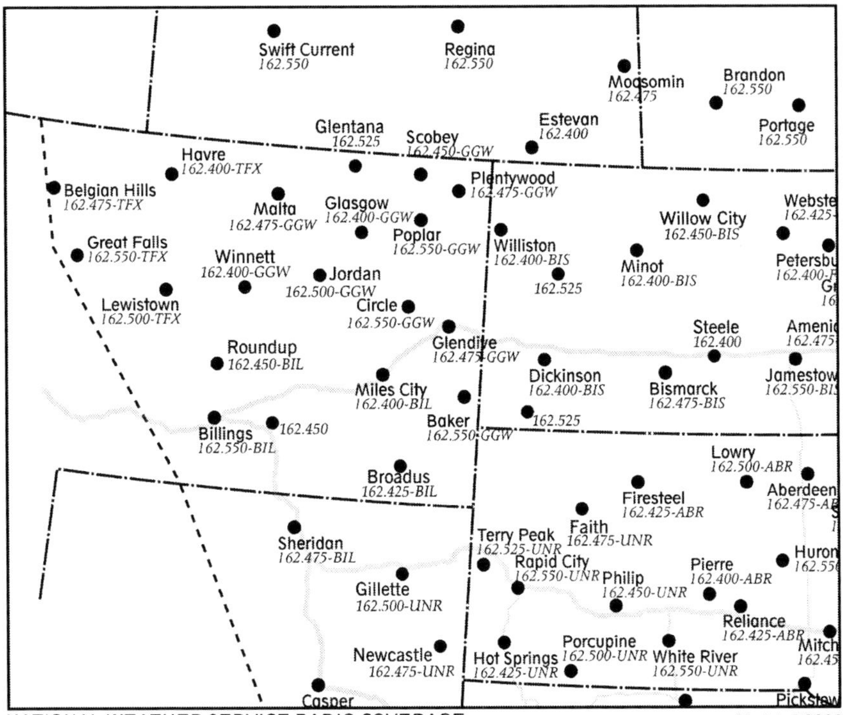
Swift Current
162.550
Regina
162.550
Moosomin
162.475
Brandon
162.550
Portage
162.550
Estevan
162.400
Glentana
162.525
Scobey
162.450-GGW
Havre
162.400-TFX
Plentywood
162.475-GGW
Belgian Hills
162.475-TFX
Malta
162.475-GGW
Glasgow
162.400-GGW
Poplar
162.550-GGW
Willow City
162.450-BIS
Great Falls
162.550-TFX
Winnett
162.400-GGW
Jordan
162.500-GGW
Williston
162.400-BIS
162.525
Minot
162.400-BIS
Lewistown
162.500-TFX
Circle
162.550-GGW
Steele
162.400
Roundup
162.450-BIL
Glendive
162.475-GGW
Dickinson
162.400-BIS
Bismarck
162.475-BIS
Miles City
162.400-BIL
162.525
Baker
162.550-GGW
Billings
162.550-BIL
162.450
Lowry
162.500-ABR
Broadus
162.425-BIL
Firesteel
162.425-ABR
Aberdeen
Sheridan
162.475-BIL
Terry Peak
162.525-UNR
Faith
162.475-UNR
Rapid City
162.550-UNR
Philip
162.450-UNR
Pierre
162.400-ABR
Gillette
162.500-UNR
Reliance
162.425-ABR
Newcastle
162.475-UNR
Porcupine
162.500-UNR
Hot Springs
162.425-UNR
White River
162.550-UNR
Casper

NATIONAL WEATHER SERVICE RADIO COVERAGE Updated 2008

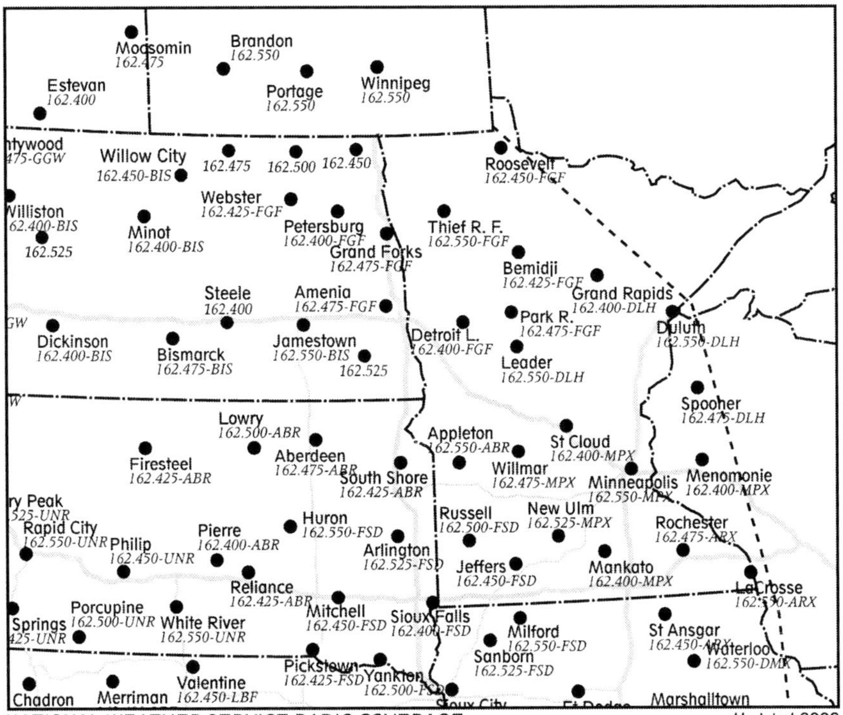
Moosomin
162.475
Brandon
162.550
Estevan
162.400
Portage
162.550
Winnipeg
162.550
Willow City
162.450-BIS
162.475
162.500
162.450
Roosevelt
162.450-FGF
Webster
162.425-FGF
Minot
162.400-BIS
Petersburg
162.400-FGF
Grand Forks
162.475-FGF
Thief R. F.
162.550-FGF
162.525
Bemidji
162.425-FGF
Grand Rapids
162.400-DLH
Steele
162.400
Amenia
162.475-FGF
Park R.
162.475-FGF
Duluth
162.550-DLH
Dickinson
162.400-BIS
Bismarck
162.475-BIS
Jamestown
162.550-BIS
162.525
Detroit L.
162.400-FGF
Leader
162.550-DLH
Spooner
162.475-DLH
Lowry
162.500-ABR
Appleton
162.550-ABR
St Cloud
162.400-MPX
Firesteel
162.425-ABR
Aberdeen
162.475-ABR
South Shore
162.425-ABR
Willmar
162.475-MPX
Minneapolis
162.550-MPX
Menomonie
162.400-MPX
Rapid City
162.550-UNR
Philip
162.450-UNR
Pierre
162.400-ABR
Huron
162.550-FSD
Russell
162.500-FSD
New Ulm
162.525-MPX
Rochester
162.475-ARX
Arlington
162.525-FSD
Jeffers
162.450-FSD
Mankato
162.400-MPX
Reliance
162.425-ABR
LaCrosse
162.550-ARX
Porcupine
162.500-UNR
White River
162.550-UNR
Mitchell
162.450-FSD
Sioux Falls
162.400-FSD
Milford
162.550-FSD
St Ansgar
162.450-ARX
Sanborn
162.525-FSD
Waterloo
162.550-DMX
Pickstown
162.425-FSD
Yankton
162.500-FSD
Valentine
162.450-LBF
Chadron
Merriman
Marshalltown

NATIONAL WEATHER SERVICE RADIO COVERAGE Updated 2008

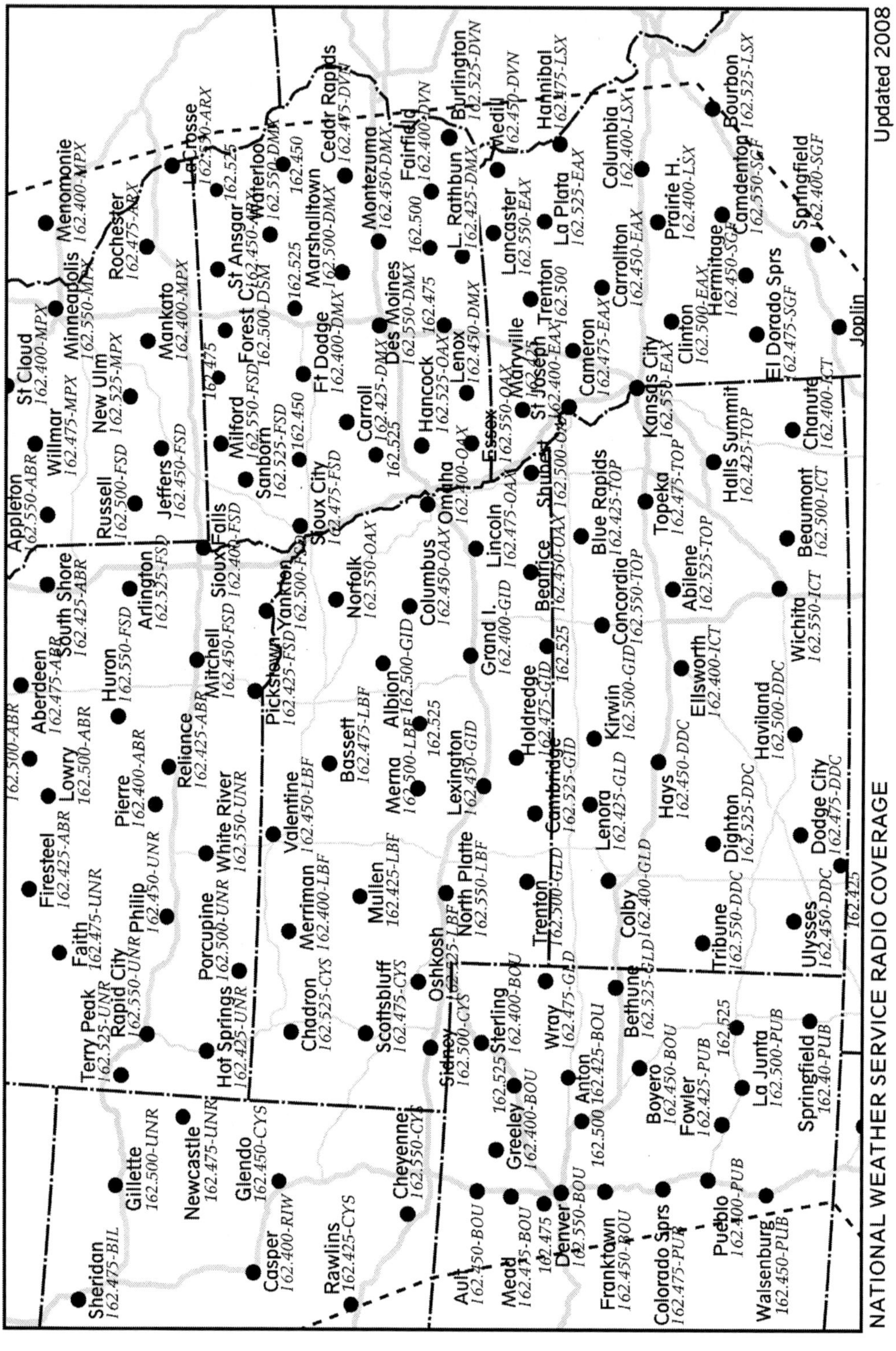
NATIONAL WEATHER SERVICE RADIO COVERAGE
Updated 2008
Sheridan 162.475-BIL
Gillette 162.500-UNR
Newcastle 162.475-UNR
Casper 162.400-RIW
Glendo 162.450-CYS
Rawlins 162.425-CYS
Cheyenne 162.550-CYS
Terry Peak 162.525-UNR
Rapid City 162.550-UNR
Hot Springs 162.425-UNR
Faith 162.475-UNR
Philip 162.450-UNR
Porcupine 162.500-UNR
Firesteel 162.425-ABR
Lowry 162.500-ABR
Aberdeen 162.475-ABR
162.500-ABR
Pierre 162.400-ABR
Reliance 162.425-ABR
White River 162.550-UNR
Huron 162.550-FSD
Mitchell 162.450-FSD
South Shore 162.425-ABR
Arlington 162.525-FSD
Appleton 162.550-ABR
Willmar 162.475-MPX
St Cloud 162.400-MPX
Russell 162.500-FSD
New Ulm 162.525-MPX
Minneapolis 162.550-MPX
Jeffers 162.450-FSD
Mankato 162.400-MPX
Rochester 162.475-ARX
Menomonie 162.400-MPX
La Crosse 162.550-ARX
Sioux Falls 162.400-FSD
Chadron 162.525-CYS
Merriman 162.400-LBF
Valentine 162.450-LBF
Scottsbluff 162.475-CYS
Mullen 162.425-LBF
Bassett 162.475-LBF
Pickstown 162.425-FSD
Yankton 162.500-FSD
Norfolk 162.550-OAX
Sioux City 162.475-FSD
Sidney 162.500-CYS
Oshkosh 162.425-LBF
North Platte 162.550-LBF
Merna
Lexington 162.450-GID
Albion
Columbus 162.450-OAX
Grand I. 162.400-GID
Omaha 162.400-OAX
Lincoln 162.475-OAX
Holdredge 162.475-GID
Beatrice 162.450-OAX
Shubert 162.500-OAX
Trenton 162.500-GLD
Cambridge 162.525-GID
Milford 162.550-FSD
Sanborn 162.525-FSD
Carroll 162.425-DMX
Ft Dodge 162.400-DMX
Forest C. 162.500-DSM
St Ansgar 162.450-ARX
Waterloo 162.550-DMX
Marshalltown 162.500-DMX
Cedar Rapids 162.475-DVN
Des Moines 162.550-DMX
Hancock 162.525-OAX
Lenox 162.450-DMX
Montezuma 162.450-DMX
Fairfield 162.400-DVN
L. Rathbun 162.425-DMX
Burlington 162.525-DVN
Medill 162.450-DVN
Hannibal 162.475-LSX
Maryville
St Joseph 162.400-EAX
Lancaster 162.550-EAX
La Plata 162.525-EAX
Trenton 162.500
Cameron 162.475-EAX
Carrollton 162.450-EAX
Columbia 162.400-LSX
Kansas City 162.550-EAX
Prairie H. 162.400-LSX
Clinton 162.500-EAX
Hermitage 162.450-SGF
Camdenton 162.550-SGF
Bourbon 162.525-LSX
El Dorado Sprs 162.475-SGF
Springfield 162.400-SGF
Joplin
Ault 162.450-BOU
Mead 162.475-BOU
Denver 162.550-BOU
Greeley 162.400-BOU
Sterling 162.400-BOU
Wray 162.475-GLD
Anton 162.425-BOU
Franktown 162.450-BOU
Colorado Sprs 162.475-PUB
Boyero 162.450-BOU
Bethune 162.525-GLD
Colby 162.400-GLD
Lenora 162.425-GLD
Kirwin 162.500-GID
Concordia 162.550-TOP
Blue Rapids 162.425-TOP
Topeka 162.475-TOP
Pueblo 162.400-PUB
Fowler 162.425-PUB
La Junta 162.500-PUB
Walsenburg 162.450-PUB
Springfield 162.40-PUB
Tribune 162.550-DDC
Dighton 162.525-DDC
Hays 162.450-DDC
Ellsworth 162.400-ICT
Abilene 162.525-TOP
Halls Summit 162.425-TOP
Ulysses 162.450-DDC
Dodge City 162.475-DDC
Haviland 162.500-DDC
Wichita 162.550-ICT
Beaumont 162.500-ICT
Chanute 162.400-ICT

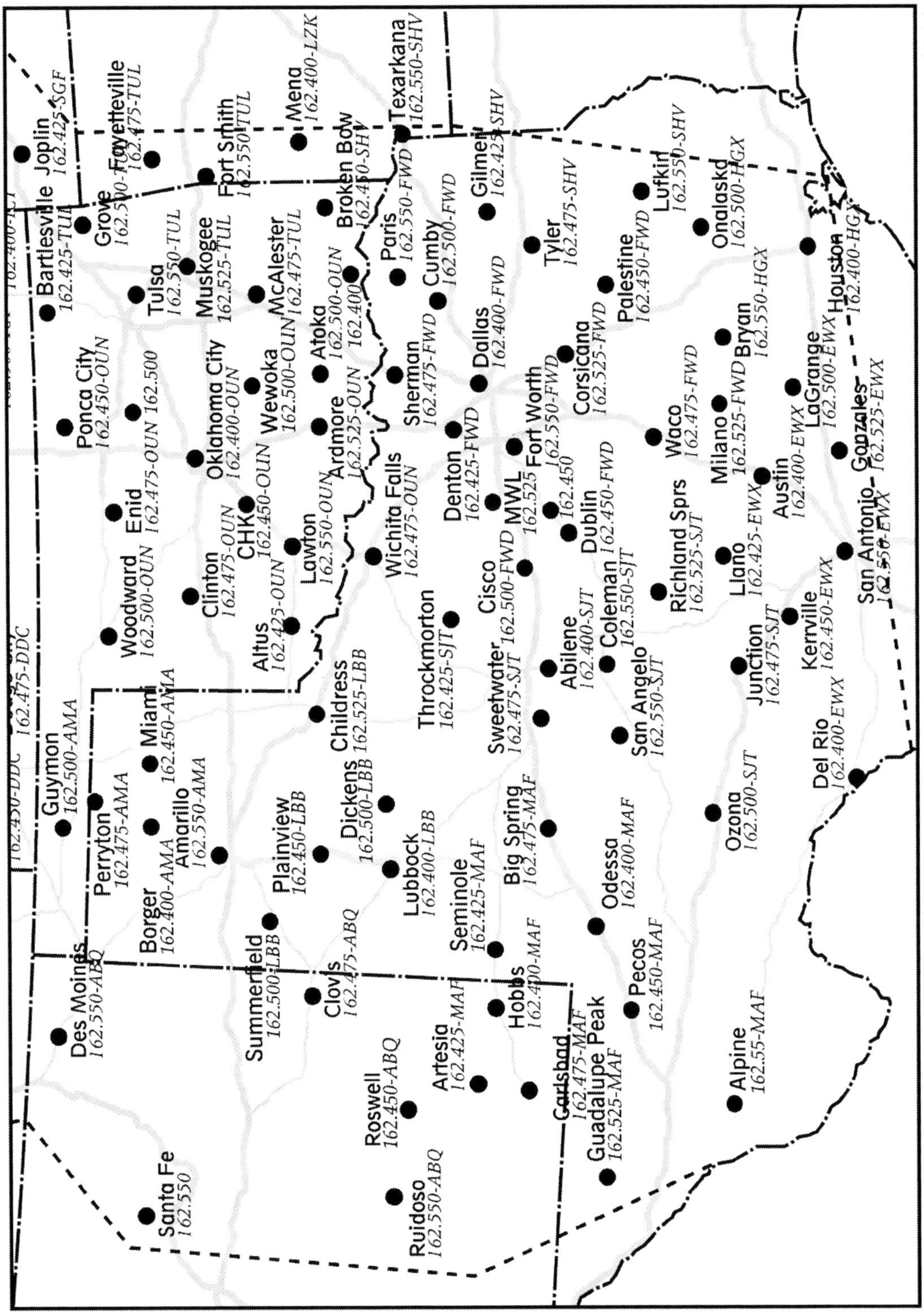
Joplin 162.425-SGF
Fayetteville 162.475-TUL
Mena 162.400-LZK
Texarkana 162.550-SHV
Bartlesville 162.425-TUL
Grove
Fort Smith 162.550-TUL
Broken Bow 162.450-SHV
Gilmer 162.425-SHV
Lufkin 162.550-SHV
Onalaska 162.500-HGX
Tulsa 162.550-TUL
Muskogee 162.525-TUL
McAlester 162.475-TUL
Paris 162.550-FWD
Cumby 162.500-FWD
Tyler 162.475-SHV
Palestine 162.450-FWD
Houston 162.400-HGX
Ponca City 162.450-OUN
162.500
Enid 162.475-OUN
Oklahoma City 162.400-OUN
Wewoka 162.500-OUN
Atoka 162.500-OUN
162.400
Sherman 162.475-FWD
Dallas 162.400-FWD
Corsicana 162.525-FWD
Bryan 162.550-HGX
Ardmore 162.525-OUN
Denton 162.425-FWD
Fort Worth 162.550-FWD
Waco 162.475-FWD
Milano 162.525-FWD
LaGrange 162.500-EWX
Gonzales 162.525-EWX
Woodward 162.500-OUN
Clinton 162.475-OUN
CHK 162.450-OUN
Lawton 162.550-OUN
Wichita Falls 162.475-OUN
MWL 162.525
162.450
Dublin 162.450-FWD
Richland Sprs 162.525-SJT
Austin 162.400-EWX
Llano 162.425-EWX
San Antonio 162.550-EWX
Altus 162.425-OUN
Throckmorton 162.425-SJT
Cisco 162.500-FWD
Abilene 162.400-SJT
Coleman 162.550-SJT
Kerrville 162.450-EWX
Junction 162.475-SJT
162.450-DDC
162.475-DDC
Guymon 162.500-AMA
Miami 162.450-AMA
Perryton 162.475-AMA
Amarillo 162.550-AMA
Childress 162.525-LBB
Sweetwater 162.475-SJT
San Angelo 162.550-SJT
Del Rio 162.400-EWX
Borger 162.400-AMA
Plainview 162.450-LBB
Dickens 162.500-LBB
Lubbock 162.400-LBB
Seminole 162.425-MAF
Big Spring 162.475-MAF
Odessa 162.400-MAF
Ozona 162.500-SJT
Des Moines 162.550-ABQ
Summerfield 162.500-LBB
Clovis 162.475-ABQ
Hobbs 162.400-MAF
Pecos 162.450-MAF
Artesia 162.425-MAF
Carlsbad 162.475-MAF
Guadalupe Peak 162.525-MAF
Alpine 162.55-MAF
Roswell 162.450-ABQ
Ruidoso 162.550-ABQ
Santa Fe 162.550

NATIONAL WEATHER SERVICE RADIO COVERAGE

Updated 2008

AM/FM radio chase maps

AM/FM radio chase maps are expected to be removed from the next edition of this book. Although live programming from various towns was quite common through the mid-1990s, this has been pre-empted at many stations by large blocks of national syndicated programming and restrictive corporate oversight. As a result, many stations are unable or unwilling to provide severe weather coverage. Given the other alternatives for gathering information, AM/FM stations should be a last resort! These maps have not been updated since our 2002 edition.

The technique of using AM/FM radio for weather tidbits was often used by chasers before the advent of mobile Internet data. After all, broadcasts are free and provide local entertainment and flavor. At least during the 1970s and 1980s, local stations were somewhat dependable for relaying weather warnings and providing clues about the local weather.

Stations which in 2002 were known to be using syndicated or centralized programming are indicated with an asterisk (*) following the frequency. This is to alert you that the programming could be centrally produced, originating from places like Clear Channel, ABC, Jones Radio Network, or Westwood One. We have no way of determining how much local programming is inserted, if at all. News/talk formats are automatically assumed to carry heavy syndicated content and are not marked with the asterisk.

ABBREVIATIONS

A	Adult contemporary
B	R & B / Hip-hop
C	Country & western
I	Tribal
J	Christian rock
N	News (likely to be syndicated)
O	Oldies
P	Pop / Top 40
R	Rock
S	Standards
T	Talk
V	Variety
*	Syndicated/centralized

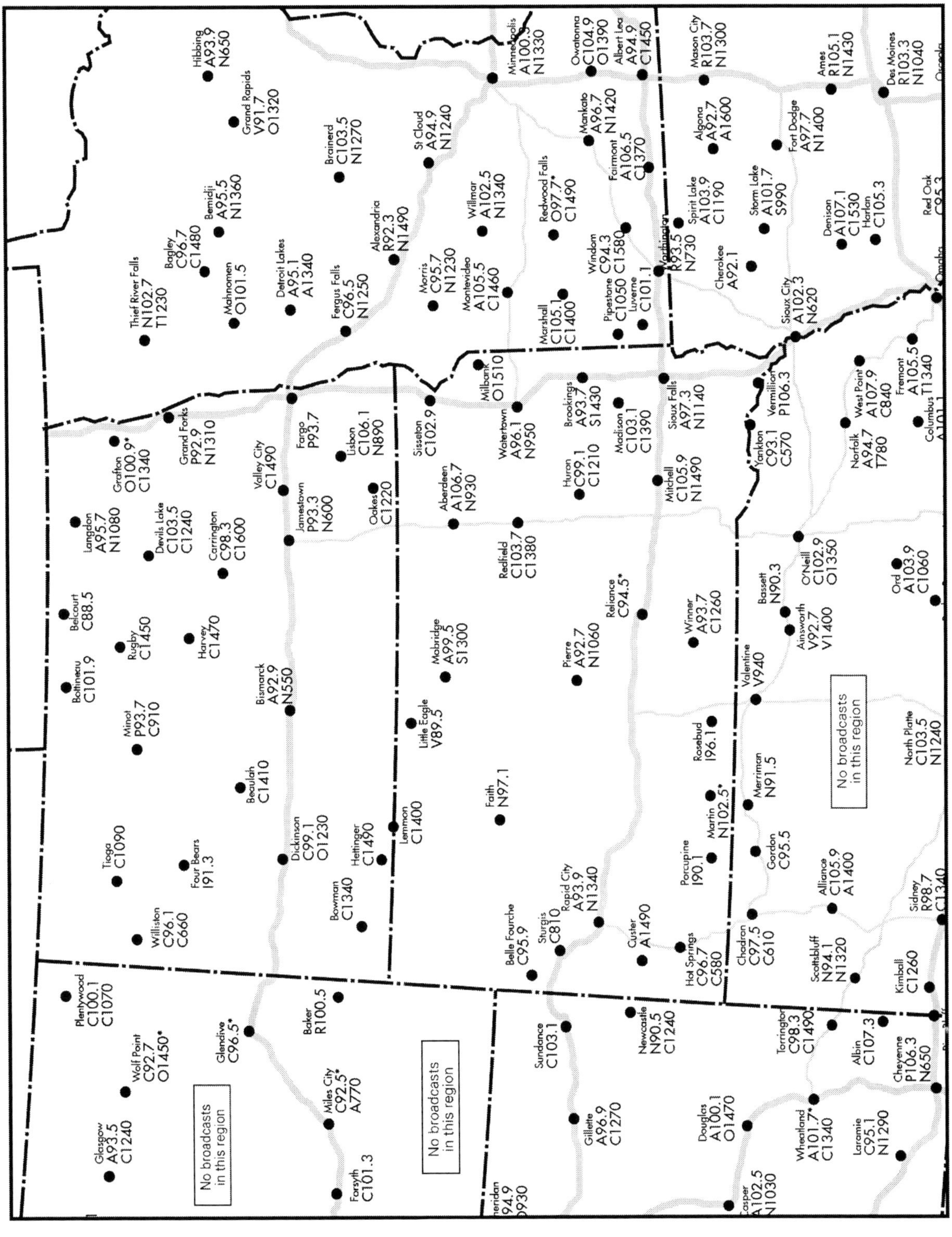

STORM CHASE - AM/FM Broadcast station reference map

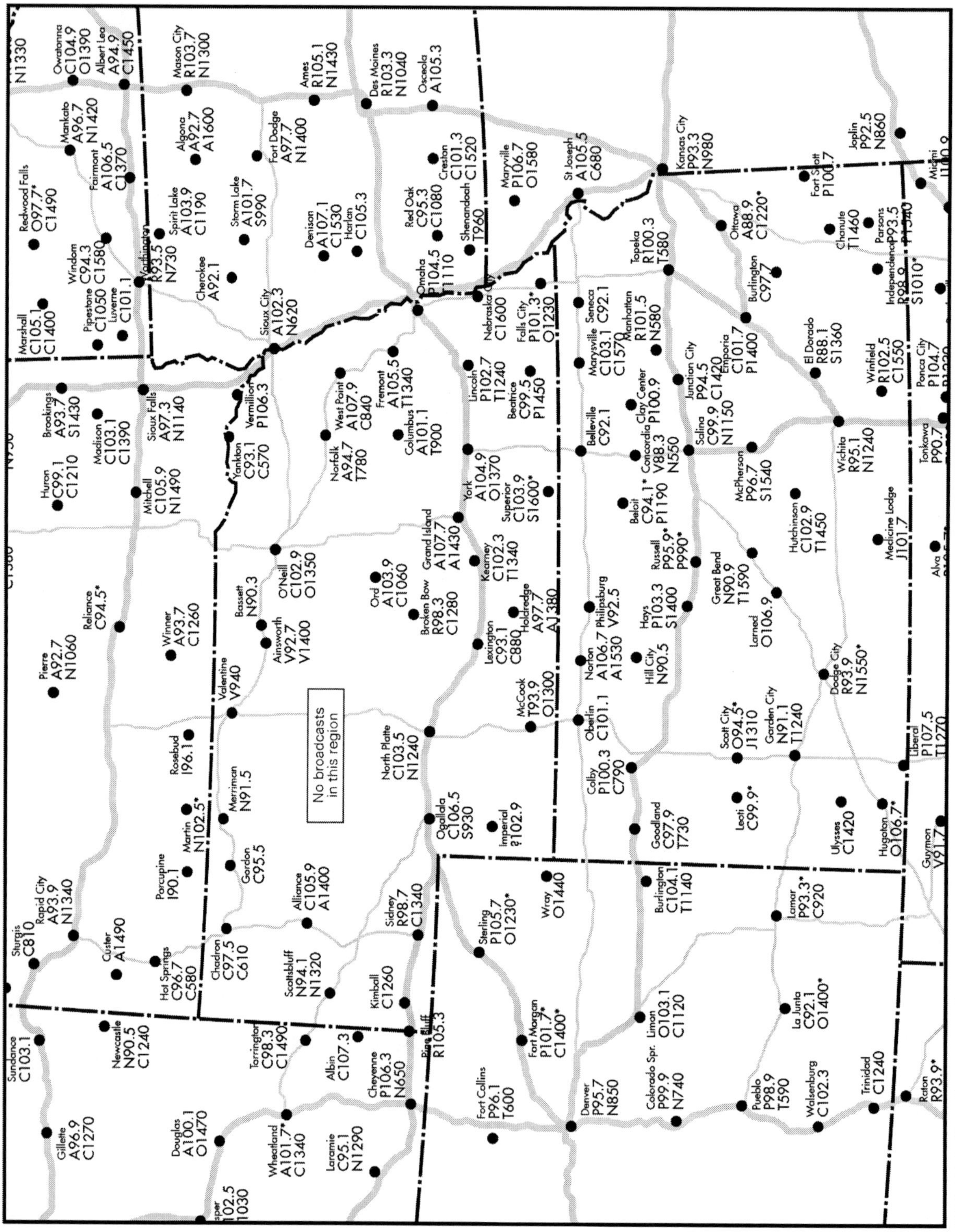

STORM CHASE - AM/FM Broadcast station reference map

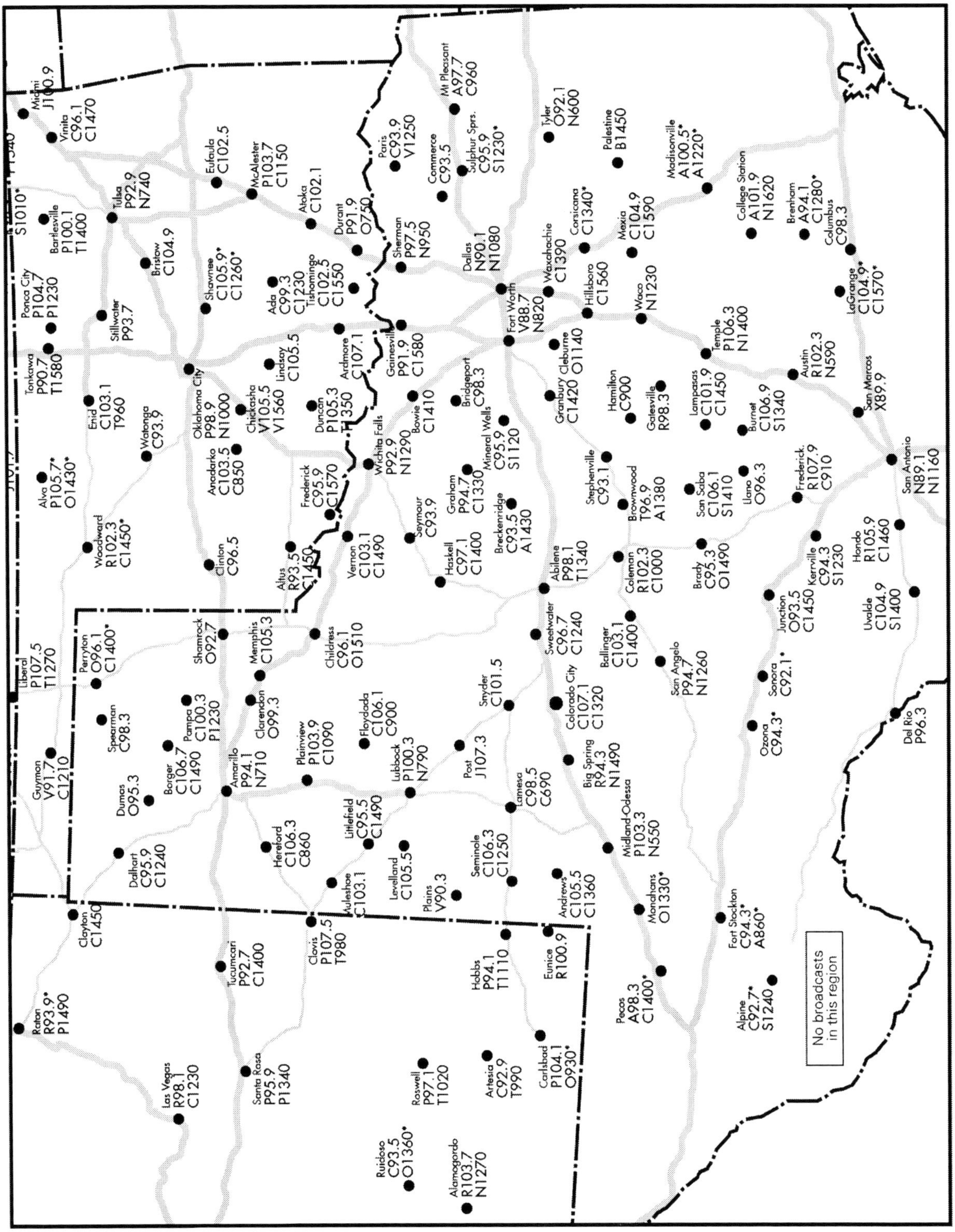

STORM CHASE - AM/FM Broadcast station reference map

Annual chase digest

Ratings of "good", "poor", etc, indicate the relative likelihood that an average chaser will successfully intercept a severe storm on any given spring day. They are not biased by the inevitable one or two days of excellent chasing. Major events by date are listed here are ranked according to "chaseworthiness", not newsworthiness. El Nino/La Nina cycle state and teleconnection indices are listed to give a general idea of the large-scale patterns which shaped the chase season, and are provided for reference only. Their impact on any given season is unclear and a subject of much debate. For further information see the Outlooks chapter.

The early years

- **June 9, 1971**. Long-lived, almost stationary cylinder tornado near Sunray, TX takes on a legendary status. The period of June 5-13 was quite similar to June 2-9, 1995.
- **May 24, 1973**. The Union City, OK tornado, intercepted by NSSL chase teams, was the first to undergo major documentation and research.
- **April 10, 1979**. A violent tornado moves through Wichita Falls, TX. It is among NSSL's first significant tornado intercepts.
- **May 22, 1981**. A big storm year, culminating in the Binger, OK violent tornado. It yielded a massive dataset for NSSL that would be studied for over a decade.

1982

It was an excellent chase year, of such a caliber that it would not be repeated until thirteen years later. A weak El Nino episode was developing, with a +NAO index that became -NAO in June.

- **April 2, 1982**. Tornado outbreak hits Paris, TX and Broken Bow, OK.
- **May 9, 1982**. Picturesque tornado at Dawn, TX.
- **May 11, 1982**. Tornado at Altus, OK.
- **May 19, 1982**. A massive supercell produced a violent tornado that grazed Pampa, TX. The storm itself is still talked about with awe by seasoned veterans.
- **June 5, 1982**. Tornado at Borger, TX is spawned by a strikingly beautiful storm that showed LP characteristics.

1983

This season is generally regarded as a poor chase year. Too many late-season polar outbreaks shut out most chase days, though the Gulf Coast was very active. The spring was within the weakening phase of a strong El Nino, with a -AO and -PNA index.

- **May 13, 1983.** At least 30 tornadoes in southeast OK and northeast TX.
- **March 3, 1983**. Surprise tornadoes near Clarendon TX.

1984

The season turned into a disappointing mess due to a series of very deep lows that emerged into the Plains in much of April and May. The moisture supply and instability never got a chance to recharge. A weak La Nina was occurring, slowly tapering off, and a +PNA index was dominant.

• **April 26, 1984**. An LPish storm occurred near Guthrie, OK.

1985

This marginal chase season brought lots of action on the Plains, but much of it was weak or non-tornadic. The best action centered around Colorado and the northern Plains. A weak La Nina was slowly tapering, and a weak -PNA index was dominant.

• **May 10, 1985**. Tornadic storm near Agra KS.

• **May 31, 1985**. The worst tornado outbreak in the U.S. since 1974 occurred, but was not generally chased by hobbyists. There were 76 fatalities in Niles OH alone.

• **June 2, 1985**. Large hail from a supercell near Mountain View, OK breaks chaser Jim Leonard's windshield, yielding a legendary piece of footage for its time.

1986

In all respects it was an average year. A neutral El Nino/La Nina pattern gave way to a weak El Nino by summer, and indices showed +NAO, +AO, and -PNA throughout the spring.

• **May 7, 1986**. A long-lived tornado touched down near Canadian, TX, yielding the biggest chase day of 1986.

• **May 14, 1986**. A spectacular supercell near Windthorst and Archer City, TX provided a great experience for storm-deprived chasers.

• **July 18, 1986.** A KARE-TV (NBC Channel 11) helicopter from Minneapolis aired live footage of a tornado taking place in the northern suburbs of the city. It's perhaps the very first aerial, non-research storm chase.

1987

It was a bad chase year, second only to 1988. A stable long wave pattern persisted across the northern hemisphere with a ridge covering the Great Plains. The best prospects were in Colorado, which recorded a few excellent landspout events. A moderate El Nino was gradually developing, and a +NAO +AO index was dominant.

• **May 22, 1987**. A tornado strikes Saragosa in the far west Texas. Many chasers caught off guard.

• **July 31, 1987**. Large tornadoes from Red Deer to Edmonton, Alberta, Canada. Again, no chasers around.

1988

This was a bad season, known as the year of the Death Ridge, and it's considered the worst of all chase years. Very few chasers had any success. Several photogenic storms were able to get going in Colorado. A moderate El Nino was waning to neutral, and a -AO +PNA pattern was dominant.

• **March 28, 1988**. The chase season struggles into gear with modest chase opportunities in SW Oklahoma.

• **May 2, 1988**. A tornado near Ardmore, OK provides one of the year's only chase opportunities.

• **June 15, 1988**. A photogenic tornado touched down in the Denver, CO suburbs.

1989

It was an average year, but for those who had weathered the 1987-88 doldrums it was considered a godsend. Texas was a hot spot for chasing. It was also the year of the record North Texas derecho of May 4 (?).

A strong La Nina was weakening, and indices showed +NAO, +AO, and -PNA.

• **May 4, 1989**. One of the biggest derechos in southern Plains history steamrolls from Amarillo, TX to Houston, TX in ten hours. Millions of dollars in damage affected the Fort Worth area westward.

• **May 13, 1989**. Tornado north of Abilene TX near Hodges contributes to what is perhaps the biggest chase day of 1989. It was also the day Jim Leonard filmed the softball-sized hail shredding trees by the swimming pool.

• **June 3, 1989**. Surprise tornado near Muleshoe TX.

• **June 6, 1989**. Tornado near Plainview TX.

1990

Things just kept getting better as 1990 emerged. Spectacular footage from the March 13 tornadoes began to stir the public's interest. Most of the action this year was found in Colorado, Kansas, and Nebraska. A long wave trough prevailed on the west coast, with a ridge on the east coast. There was no El Nino or La Nina pattern, and a strong +NAO, strong +AO, and

weak -PNA pattern existed.
- **March 13, 1990**. A tornado outbreak in Nebraska and Kansas; Hesston KS was hardest hit.
- **May 25, 1990**. Great Bend KS wedge tornado.
- **May 31, 1990**. Tornado outbreak near Spearman TX.
- **June 1, 1990**. Iraan TX tornado.
- **May 18, 1990**. Wheeler TX mothership LP supercell.
- **August 28, 1990**. Plainfield IL tornado, chased by a few individuals but visibility was poor.

1991

It was a model chase year. A weak Hudson Bay vortex was a key factor in allowing for numerous chase days. A weak El Nino was slowly strengthening, and a +AO pattern was dominant.
- **April 12, 1991**. A good chase season opener with tornadoes near Glen Rose, TX and in Grant County, OK.
- **April 26, 1991**. Kansas-Oklahoma tornado outbreak (Andover KS and Red Rock OK) April 26.
- **May 10, 1991**. Lazbuddie and Pep TX tornadoes (often referred to as Lazbuddie I).
- **May 15, 1991**. An very active day in Oklahoma with 5 tornadoes in the northwestern state, and a strong one near Laverne, OK that carved out a 12-mile track.
- **May 16, 1991**. Clearwater, KS tornado was the first one filmed by an IMAX crew.
- **May 26, 1991**. Tornadoes near El Dorado, KS; Ulysses, KS; and Woodward, OK.
- **July 18, 1991**. A violent downburst flattened part of a forest in far western Canada near Pakwash, Ontario. The event was caught on video. The term Pakwash is now applied to HP supercells that produce severe wind damage.

1992

Overall it was an average chase year with a few nice surprises. The best chase action was in the northern Plains. A strong El Nino was in effect, and indices showed +AO, +PNA, and strong +NAO.
- **1992 May 11**. Paydirt in the jungles of SE Oklahoma. Chaser convergence near Kingston, OK.
- **1992 June 2**. Big tornado outbreak in the Midwest. This ranks as the second biggest chase event of 1992.
- **1992 June 15**. A massive HP supercell spawns a series of tornadoes in north central Kansas, near Beloit and Plainville. It was the biggest chase event of 1992.

1993

1993: Good. Aside from a shutdown during the late spring, there was plenty of summer chasing on the northern Plains. A weak El Nino was slowly strengthening, and a -NAO, -AO, and +PNA was dominant.
- **April 24, 1993**. Rain-wrapped tornadoes move through the Tulsa area and endanger several chasers.
- **May 5, 1993**. Tornadoes in the Oklahoma Panhandle and southwest Kansas. Guymon, OK was a hot spot. It was the biggest chase day of 1993.
- **June 7, 1993**. Tornadoes in the Sioux Falls, SD area with a wedge near Colton, SD.
- **July 21, 1993**. Last Chance CO tornado.
- **October 12, 1993**. Spectacular autumn supercell outbreak in the San Angelo and Abilene, TX region.

1994

1994: Good. The dryline was poorly defined most of the season. In this year the famous Lahoma OK storm of 8/17/94 brought devastating hail and winds to a small swath, but few chasers were near it. It was a neutral lull between El Nino episodes, and +NAO, +AO, and +PNA was dominant.
- **April 25, 1994**. A supercell moves into the Dallas-Fort Worth area and produces an after-dusk tornado near Lancaster, TX.
- **April 26, 1994**. A large tornado moves through the Gainesville, TX area.
- **May 29, 1994**. Albany, TX and Newcastle, TX tornadoes are spawned by northwesterly flow supercells.
- **August 17, 1994**. An isolated, violent HP supercell (Pakwash-type storm) occurred near Lahoma, OK. Incredible wind readings were observed at Oklahoma mesonet stations.

1995

It was an excellent chase year, perhaps the best since 1982. The first week of June brought the best string of chase days in many years. A weak Hudson Bay vortex kept things looking bright on the Plains. An El Nino pattern was occurring which diminished to neutral by late spring, and a

-AO and slight +PNA pattern was dominant.

- **May 7, 1995**. Ardmore, TX is grazed by a tornado. Significant damage occurred at the Uniroyal tire plant.
- **May 16, 1995**. Tornadoes near Garden City, KS and Hanston, KS provide a significant target for VORTEX.
- **June 2, 1995**. A week of big tornadoes kicked off, with the day's action near Dimmit, Friona, and Tulia, Texas.
- **June 4, 1995**. A spectacular multiple landspout event occurred at Lazbuddie, TX (often referred to as Lazbuddie II). Other great storms occurred near Lamesa, TX.
- **June 8, 1995**. A large tornado grazed Pampa, TX, providing stunning video footage. Further south, a violent tornado occurred near Kellerville, TX and Allison, TX. It was the biggest chase day of 1995.

1996

It was a slow season that paid dividends for Colorado and Kansas only. Early June brought northwesterly flow events. A weak La Nina was weakening, and indices were -NAO and -AO.

- **May 10, 1996**. The Warner Brothers film Twister is released theatrically, with a $41 million gross on its opening weekend.
- **May 23, 1996**. Upslope produces Last Chance CO storm.
- **May 26, 1996**. Sublette, KS tornado.
- **May 30, 1996**. Numerous tornadoes near Elba, CO. It's perhaps the biggest chase day of 1996.
- **May 31, 1996**. Ness City KS tornado.

1997

It was an average year that got off to a slow start due to a cold, cloudy April. A developing El Nino was occurring, with a -NAO, +AO that reverted to negative in mid-May, and +PNA.

- **May 7, 1997**. Big HP supercells north of Amarillo, TX.
- **May 25, 1997**. Central OK and south Kansas tornadic storms (near Ellsworth KS). The "Dillo-Cam" was successfully deployed in front of a tornado.
- **May 26, 1997**. Eastern OK tornadic storms.
- **May 27, 1997**. Jarrell TX: Violent tornado moves SW.

1998

It was an marginal year, complicated by extensive haze from Mexican crop burning and the strange "CAPE robber" phenomenon. The season managed to squeak out a few memorable events. A strong El Nino was weakening, with a +AO, -PNA, and slight -NAO.

- **May 24, 1998**. Tornadoes near Lamont, OK.
- **May 30, 1998**. Spencer, SD tornado.
- **June 13, 1998**. Oklahoma City, OK tornado.
- **October 4, 1998**. The biggest chase event of 1998, with one of the most photogenic tornadoes on record: long-lived and slow-moving.

1999

A few predictable outbreaks bump this otherwise moderate season up into the "good" category. Arizona chasers report it was an outstanding monsoon season with countless lightning opportunities. A strong La Nina was weakening, and a -NAO (+NAO after mid May), +AO, and -PNA pattern existed.

- **May 3, 1999**. In central Oklahoma one of the most prolific tornado outbreaks in history occurred; the largest hit Moore OK and Midwest City OK.
- **May 15, 1999**. Tornado near Norton, KS.
- **May 31, 1999**. The Sitka KS tornado showed highly dynamic, fast-paced evolution.
- **June 3, 1999**. Almena KS.
- **June 5, 1999**. Big tornadoes in Chase County, NE.

2000

The 2000 season was generally regarded as difficult for most chasers, which characterizes it as marginal. A moderate La Nina was weakening, with a +NAO, +AO, and +PNA.

- **March 28, 2000**. A tornado hits downtown Fort Worth after business hours, captured by a few lucky chasers. It was a mild reminder to city governments of their need for an urban preparedness plan.
- **April 23, 2000**. Rare classic chase day unfolds across NW Louisiana, and is enjoyed by dozens of chasers.
- **April 30, 2000**. Supercells near Crowell & Olney, TX.
- **May 11, 2000**. At least six tornadoes touched down near Waterloo, IA.
- **May 17, 2000**. A large tornado touches down near Brady, NE. It occurred among a line of northward-moving supercells. Only the skilled and the lucky were spectators.

2001

Overall it was a fairly good chase season, with chasers enjoying a number of mini-outbreaks in different parts of the Great Plains. A weak La Nina was weakening, and a -NAO, +AO, and -PNA pattern was dominant.

- **May 5, 2001**. Picturesque mini-supercell tornado near Cordell.
- **May 6, 2001**. Chaser and media circus in Norman, OK with the real tornadoes in the Arbuckle Mountains.
- **May 20, 2001**. Lake Eufaula tornado; many chasers.
- **May 27, 2001**. Large derecho sweeps eastward across Kansas, producing a haboob.
- **May 29, 2001**. Classic and HPish storms rake the Texas Panhandle. Tornado near Panhandle, TX.
- **June 13, 2001**. Tornado outbreak occurred across eastern Nebraska. It was perhaps the second biggest chase event of 2001.
- **October 9, 2001**. A close analogy of October 4, 1998, this date was perhaps the biggest chase event of 2001. A dozen tornadoes in western Oklahoma.

2002

It was a poor chase season with significant cap and moisture problems. There were some definitive LP supercell photo opportunities though. The El Nino/La Nina was neutral, and a strong +NAO, +AO, and strong -PNA pattern existed.

- **May 5, 2002**. Among several supercells in the Texas Panhandle, one produced the Happy, TX tornado.
- **May 7, 2002**. Numerous tornadoes were observed in southwest Kansas. It is generally considered the biggest chase event of 2002.
- **June 23, 2002**. Tornadoes near Brown County, SD.

2003

The year 2003 was regarded as a good chasing season but soured by fast moving systems and a lot of down days. It was a La Nina season, with a neutral NAO, -AO transitioning to +AO, and +PNA over the winter transitioning to -PNA.

- **May 4, 2003**. A tornado outbreak hit southwestern Missouri.
- **May 15, 2003**. Twenty-six tornadoes hit the TX/OK panhandles, breaking the record set on June 8, 1995.
- **June 24, 2003**. Major tornado outbreak in South Dakota with a noteworthy event near Manchester SD.

2004

A major tornado year, with a record 1,819 confirmed tornadoes in the United States and chasers reporting a magical season with great success, particularly in Kansas. The El Nino/La Nina was neutral with, +NAO, -AO, and a fairly neutral PNA.

- **May 12, 2004**. Significant tornado outbreak in Kansas, with a significant tornado in Attica.
- **May 22, 2004**. Large Nebraska and Iowa outbreak, with derecho into Iowa. Hallam NE was hard-hit.
- **May 24, 2004**. At least 53 tornadoes were reported in northern Kansas and southern Nebraska.
- **May 29, 2004**. More tornadoes in northern Kansas, with tornadoes near Belleville and Jamestown KS.
- **June 12, 2004**. A tornado hit Mulvane KS.
- **September 15-17, 2004**. A total of 117 tornadoes across the Southeast were associated with Hurricane Ivan.

2005

The record tornado year of 2004 gave way to a record hurricane year. It was regarded as a marginal tornado year with slim pickings. But a record 28 named Atlantic storms developed, forcing NHC to go to the Greek alphabet for the first time since 1970. It was a La Nina season, with strong -NAO, +AO during the winter transitioning to -AO, and a strong +PNA.

- **April 10, 2005.** Tornadoes in southwest Kansas.
- **April 15, 2005.** Tornadoes hit Neosho County KS.
- **May 12, 2005.** Tornadoes and hail in the Plainview TX area. Some chasers had serious hail damage to their cars.
- **June 9, 2005.** The best chase day of the year with action in west Kansas and a large tornado near Floydada TX.
- **November 12, 2005.** A rare fall outbreak hits Iowa.

2006

The year had a good start in March and April but it went on to produce a lot of garbage in May and June. Many chasers reported a string of busts during their scheduled chase vacations. Weak El Nino, with -AO and neutral NAO/PNA.

• **April 15, 2006**. Large tornado near Beatrice NE.
• **June 9, 2006.** Tornadoes touched down in the Hill City KS area.

2007

A drastic improvement from the poor chase prospects of 2005-2006, but like 2006 the good chases were early in the season. Neutral El Nino/La Nina, with +AO, +NAO, and +PNA.

• **March 28, 2007**. Tornadoes in the Texas Panhandle.
• **April 21, 2007**. Damaging tornadoes touch down near Tulia and Dumas TX.
• **May 4-5, 2007**. Tornadoes across much of western Oklahoma during OU finals week.
• **June 23, 2007**. Tornadoes swept through ND and MB, making for an international Great Plains outbreak.

2008

The 2008 season was another banner year for chasers. An El Nino episode was underway, with high +AO becoming high -AO by late spring, +NAO becoming strong -NAO by late spring, and neutral PNA.

• **February 5, 2008**. The Super Tuesday outbreak brought at least 35 confirmed tornadoes in a broad band from much of AR into TN and KY.
• **April 7, 2008**. Tornadoes touched down southeast of Vernon TX. They occurred early in the storm's life cycle, causing many chasers to miss the action.
• **May 22, 2008**. Numerous tornadoes occurred in northern Colorado and western Kansas.
• **May 23, 2008**. Another Kansas tornado day, with a big event right on Interstate 70 near Quinter, KS.
• **May 25, 2008**. Tornadoes touched down near Parkersburg, Iowa, producing one F5 wedge.
• **June 11, 2008**. F2 tornado near Spencer, IA.

Top ten mistakes
made by new chasers

10. **Bragging and telling tall tales**. Humility is one of the finest virtues in chasing, and you'll find good company among many experienced chasers who are happy to discuss their failures. Failure is meteorology's fountain of insight. While it's only human to be ashamed about a tactical error, exaggeration and falsification should be avoided at all costs. Not only does it go against the spirit of science; it may create false conclusions about an important event.

9. **Starting chase teams**. It's common for newcomers to start a formal chase team to establish credibility. Even the author felt compelled to do it! Just *chase for fun or for personal enlightenment!* As you get experience and build your reputation, you don't want a pseudonym earning all the accolades.

8. **Parking hazardously underneath a storm**. Some beginners and yahoos park on the road because they see others doing it: even academic chase teams. See the Safety chapter.

7. **Rating tornados visually**. The size of a funnel does not always correlate with damage. Other aspects of the tornado's behavior must be examined. Only a damage survey or short-wave radar measurements can conclusively establish the tornado's intensity.

6. **Abusing models**. Numerical models, and in particular forecast soundings, can be highly suspect on severe weather days. By late morning most of your emphasis should be on surface, profiler, radar, satellite, and sounding data, not on models.

5. **Expecting tornadoes right away**. New chasers often go for a couple of years without seeing a tornado. But so do some highly experienced chasers! There is no "tornado club" in storm chasing. Getting on the right storm and making good forecast decisions counts for much more than whether you saw a tornado or not.

4. **Not preparing for the unexpected**. You're having lunch somewhere. The clouds slowly wither away, then suddenly storms appear to the east. The dryline slipped past! Be alert, and cultivate a sense for hour-to-hour changes in wind direction, temperature, and humidity.

3. **Not fueling up by afternoon**. When a severe storm knocks out the power grid, you will be stranded if your gas tank is empty. This can be a serious mistake.

2. **Chasing weather warnings**. Most "local yokels" chase the weather warnings, but by the time a warning is issued it's too late to get into position. A wise chaser is already ahead of the game, and the warning tells what's on the way, not where to go.

1. **Assuming a tornado warning means a tornado is on the ground**. It's true that many chasers groan when they hear a tornado warning for a distant cell. Others may abandon their chase and move to the warned storm. However, many times such a warning is for a dubious "radar-indicated" tornado that never materializes. Never jump ship because of a warning on another storm unless you have good reason to think that your storm will fail.

Hail size

Description	Decimal Diameter	Fractional Diameter	Metric Diameter
Pea	0.25″	1/4″	5-6 mm
Marble	0.50″	1/2″	10-13 mm
Dime/penny	0.75″	3/4″	19 mm
Nickel	0.88″	7/8″	21 mm
Quarter/Loonie	1.00″	1″	24-27 mm
Twoonie (Canada)	1.13″	1 1/8″	29 mm
Half dollar	1.25″	1 1/4″	32 mm
Ping-pong/walnut	1.50″	1 1/2″	40 mm
Golf ball	1.75″	1 3/4″	45 mm
Hen egg	2.00″	2″	50 mm
Tennis ball	2.50″	2 1/2″	65 mm
Baseball	2.75″	2 3/4″	70 mm
Tea cup	3.00″	3″	75 mm
Grapefruit	4.00″	4″	100 mm
Softball	4.50″	4 1/2″	110 mm

All hail sizes of 0.75″ or greater constitute severe criteria in the U.S.
Bold fonts indicate descriptors recognized by U.S. forecasting and emergency management agencies. Non-bold descriptors are for reference only.

MacGyver techniques

If you have no ruler or prefer not to use the one on the right margin of this page, look around in your car for any standard 8½ x 11 piece of photocopier, laser, or laserjet paper. This is commonly found in home printouts, correspondence, grass-roots newsletters, and memos from your workplace. Wrap it around the hailstone to help estimate its diameter.

- The short side envelops a diameter of **2.7 inches** (baseball size).
- The long side envelops a diameter of **3.5 inches** (grapefruit size).

For smaller hailstones, fold the paper in half on either axis.

- A folded short side envelops a diameter of **1.4 inches** (ping-pong ball size).
- A folded long side envelops a diameter of **1.75** inches (golf ball size).

A dollar bill measures 6.1″ x 2.6″, enveloping a diameter of **2 inches** on its long side and **0.8 inches** (dime size) on its short side.

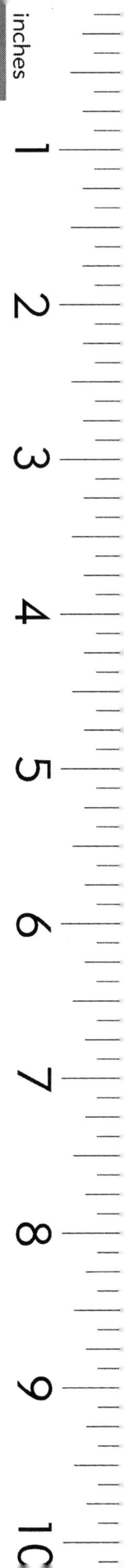

Fujita damage (F) scale

The Fujita scale was first published by Theodore Fujita in 1971. This classification was published to help provide a way to estimate wind speeds based on damage to wood-frame houses. Accurate damage assessment can be an incredibly difficult engineering problem because of inconsistencies in building codes, structure age, and worksmanship. Furthermore, damage may unknowingly be caused by debris, such as a lofted automobile or a whole tree that falls onto a house. From a chasing and forecasting standpoint, tornado intensity can best be described as simply "weak", "strong", and "violent" without any set guidelines.

Though the original Fujita damage scale was phased out in the United States starting February 1, 2007, it is still in use elsewhere in the world.

Rating	Wind speed	Damage
F0	40-72 mph	Some damage to chimneys; breaks branches off trees; pushes over shallow-rooted trees; damages sign boards.
F1	73-112 mph	The beginning of hurricane wind speed; peels surface off roofs. Mobile homes pushed off foundations or overturned. Moving autos pushed off the roads; attached garages may be destroyed.
F2	113-157 mph	Considerable damage. Roofs torn off frame houses. Mobile homes demolished. Boxcars pushed over. Large trees snapped or uprooted. Light object missiles generated.
F3	158-206 mph	Roof and some walls torn off well constructed houses. Trains overturned. Most trees in forest uprooted.
F4	207-260 mph	Well-constructed houses leveled; structures with weak foundations blown off some distance. Cars thrown and large missiles generated.
F5	261-318 mph	Strong frame houses lifted off foundations and carried considerable distances to disintegrate. Automobile sized missiles fly through the air in excess of 100 meters. Trees debarked. Steel re-inforced concrete structures badly damaged.

Enhanced Fujita (EF) scale

For decades it was known that the original Fujita scale was insufficient for standardizing tornado damage in the United States. The new Enhanced Fujita scale distinguishes between different types of construction, accounts for construction quality, and improves upon ambiguous definitions. It was developed in the early 2000s and the specification was frozen in 2006. Use of it for United States damage surveys began on February 1, 2007. The first EF5-ranked tornado was the Greensburg KS event of May 4, 2007.

Rating	Wind speed	Damage
EF0	65-85 mph	Surface peeled off some roofs. Some damage to gutters or siding. Branches broken off trees. Shallow-rooted trees pushed over. Confirmed tornadoes with no reported damage (i.e. those that remain in open fields) are always rated EF0.
EF1	86-110 mph	Roofs severely stripped. Mobile homes overturned or badly damaged. Loss of exterior doors. Windows and other glass broken.
EF2	111-135 mph	Roofs torn off well-constructed houses. Foundations of frame homes shifted. Mobile homes completely destroyed. Large trees snapped or uprooted. Light-object missiles generated. Cars lifted off ground.
EF3	136-165 mph	Entire stories of well-constructed houses destroyed. Severe damage to large buildings such as shopping malls. Trains overturned. Trees debarked. Heavy cars lifted off the ground and thrown. Structures with weak foundations blown away some distance.
EF4	166-200 mph	Well-constructed houses and whole frame houses completely leveled. Cars thrown and small missiles generated.
EF5	201+ mph	Strong frame houses leveled off foundations and swept away. Automobile-sized missiles fly through the air in excess of 100 m (109 yd). High-rise buildings have significant structural deformation. Incredible phenomena will occur.

Named storms and tornadoes

Many legendary severe weather events are referred to by date or place name. This can leave quite a few newcomers stumped. Here we have included primarily the ones that were noteworthy from a storm chasing or storm forecasting perspective. Asterisked storms are usually the primary storm of reference.

STORMS BEARING A PLACE NAME

Allison, TX tornado — June 8, 1995.
Alma, NE tornado — June 16, 1990.
Altus, OK tornado — May 11, 1982.
Andover, KS tornado — April 26, 1991.
Beloit, KS tornadoes — June 15, 1992.
Benkelman, NE tornado — May 22, 1996
Binger, OK tornado — May 22, 1981.
Brady, NE tornado — May 17, 2000.
Bridge Creek, OK tornado — May 3, 1999.
Canadian, TX tornado — May 7, 1986.
Dunkerton, IA tornado — May 11, 2000.
Edmonton, AB tornado — July 31, 1987.
Fargo, ND tornado — June 20, 1957.
Fort Worth, TX tornado — March 28, 2000.
Gainesville, TX tornado — April 26, 1994.
Grand Island, NE tornado — June 3, 1980.
Greensburg, KS tornado — May 4, 2007
Happy, TX tornado — May 5, 2002.
Hesston, KS tornado — March 13, 1990.
Hodges, TX tornado — May 13, 1989.
Hugoton, KS tornado — May 5, 1993.
Jarrell, TX tornado — May 27, 1997.
Kellerville, TX tornado — June 8, 1995.
Lahoma, OK storm — August 17, 1994.
Lancaster, TX tornado — April 25, 1994.
Laverne, OK tornado — May 15, 1991.
Lazbuddie (I), TX tornado — May 10, 1991.
Lazbuddie (II), TX multiple landspouts — June 4, 1995.
Lela, TX tornado — June 11, 1997.
Limon, CO tornado — June 6, 1990.
Lubbock, TX tornado — May 11, 1970.
Moore, OK tornado — October 4, 1998; May 3, 1999*; May 8, 2003.
Mulvane, KS tornado — June 12, 2004
Newcastle, TX tornado — May 29, 1994.
Oakfield, WI tornado — July 18, 1996.
Pakwash, ON derecho — July 18, 1991.
Pampa, TX tornado — 5/19/82*; 6/8/95.
Paris, TX tornado — April 2, 1982.
Quinter, KS tornado — May 23, 2008
Red Rock, OK tornado — April 26, 1991.
Saragosa, TX tornado — May 22, 1987.
Sitka, KS tornado — May 31, 1999.
Snyder, OK tornado — May 14, 1986.
Spearman, TX tornado — May 31, 1990
Spencer, SD tornado — May 30, 1998.
Sunray, TX tornado — June 9, 1971.
Tulia, TX tornado — April 21, 2007.
Tulsa, OK tornado — April 24, 1993.
Vernon, TX tornado — April 10, 1979.
Waco, TX tornado — May 11, 1953.
Wichita Falls, TX tornado — April 10, 1979.
Windthorst, TX supercell — May 14, 1986.

STORMS BEARING A DATE NAME

May 3rd — May 3, 1999; central OK.
Mayfest — May 5, 1995; Fort Worth TX severe hailstorm.
October 4th — October 4, 1998; central OK.
Palm Sunday tornadoes:
— April 11, 1965; Indiana, Illinois, Ohio. Ambiguous use usually refers to this event.
— March 27, 1994; north Alabama and north Georgia. Sometimes called "Palm Sunday II".

Storm troubleshooter

■ The storm is high-based. It looks a lot like what I've seen in Arizona.

The storm may be drawing inflow that has low relative humidity (such as in summer) or insufficient dewpoint and insufficient depth. It is certainly possible that the dewpoints were excellent earlier in the day, but the moisture depth was too shallow and ended up being mixed out during the afternoon. In any case, moisture-starved storms tend to weaken and die, especially towards sunset.

■ The storm is producing cold outflow.

The storm is outflow-dominant, which commonly occurs during the cool season and with weak instability and poor moisture. Symptoms are cold, gusty outflow, linear updraft bases, and squall line structures. Sometimes these storms may transition into a balanced state.

■ The storm has an odd structure, with an updraft base on the north side.

You may be chasing a left-split, which is a mirror image of a storm further southeast. These storms often weaken and dissipate, though brief anticyclonic tornadoes are not unheard of. If you don't like what you see, you should head south and seek out the right split, or find a right split on another storm further north (if one exists).

■ The storm is not producing a tornado.

The science of meteorology still does not have an explanation for this. However, check all of the other trouble spots first. Does the storm have strong, backed inflow? This is necessary to maximize the storm-relative helicity available to the cell. Has the storm had sufficient time to organize? Most supercells need at least two hours before they can produce their first tornadoes.

■ The storms are moving too quickly.

This indicates that the average tropospheric wind speeds are quite high, are concentrated from a certain direction, or both. Your only options are to make less stops and use extreme vigilance when planning your intercept. If storms have not yet developed, remain well downstream from where you expect initiation.

■ The storms are becoming hidden in rain.

There are usually two reasons for this: (1) rain is being drawn cyclonically into the updraft area by the mesocyclone, or (2) the storm is being seeded by other storms upstream, usually southwest or west. In the first case, the solution is to get more east than south of the updraft; in this area the updraft tends to draw in dry air from the east (i.e. you will be seeing into the "notch"). In the second case, the best solution is often to drop down to the next storm upstream.

Chase tours

Going out for a week with a chase tour is a major expense: a few week's wages for most individuals. The tour operator has a huge influence on what kind of memories you will bring back and whether you'll see anything. Choose your company and spend wisely according to these tips:

■ **Does the chase tour literature introduce the staff openly and sincerely?** Tours that are anonymously run or post vague biographies are, by far, the best indicator of poor experience.

■ **Does the tour operator have a good reputation among the storm chase community?** Word of mouth is valuable. Experienced chasers will quickly recognize tour operators who haven't paid their dues in the hobby. Check with regulars on Internet chase communities. Ask chasers you know personally.

■ **What happens during the down days?** When the Great Plains is ridged out, how does the tour operator intend to entertain their customers? Will you be left to "chill out" at the hotel, taken to fun "tourist traps" and malls, or will you get to look at cultural or historical points of interest? *What do you want to do?* Think about it, and pick a chase tour that coincides with your preferences.

■ **Does the literature confirm that chasing is often dull and you may not see any tornadoes?** This is a good sign that the tour operator is putting profits on the line by being open and honest. A chase tour guaranteeing success will likely involve reckless driving, a hurried agenda, and a very testy tour staff.

■ **Does the tour operator ask for an excessive deposit?** An unknown tour operator asking for a lot of money up front may be a scammer. A standard advance deposit is about $500 per person.

■ **Does the tour operator boast about its technology?** In some cases, tour operators rely heavily on equipment to compensate for inexperience. Successful, experienced tours will make a balanced effort to address their own experience and skill, and will be happy to explain their forecasting methodology.

■ **Statistics don't mean anything.** Shady tour operators will distort their record, and a few even post false stastistics. Think about it: how can any of it be proven? The author has even seen an instance of a tour operator claiming 20 years of experience; upon further investigation, the math implied that he began chasing at age seven! When pondering a tour operator's statistics, ask an experienced chaser to help out and see if they can weed through the hype.

References

This book cannot possibly cover all aspects of thunderstorm meteorology and storm chasing. Check out some of these interesting publications and papers.

Books

Tornado Alley: Monster Storms of the Great Plains, Howard B. Bluestein, 1999. Oxford University Press, 192 pp. ISBN 0195105524. The finest piece of literature on storm chasing, detailing the history of chase research, the current state of the art, and thoughts on tornadogenesis with vivid color photos. This is the next logical step after this book.

Significant Tornadoes: 1680-1991, Thomas P. Grazulis, 1993, Environmental Films, 1340 pp., ISBN 1879362031, out of print. With this book, Tom Grazulis established himself as the nation's authority on tornado history. This book is nearly 3 inches thick!

In the Shadow of the Tornado, Richard Bedard, 1996, 170 pp., Gilco Publishing, ISBN 0-9649527-1-8, out of print. This book created a positive stir among storm chasers when it was released. In three parts, it recounts the Woodward, OK tornado of 1947, explores Oklahoma's relationship with tornadoes in the mid-90's, and acquaints us with several chasers of the era.

Storm Chaser: In Pursuit of Untamed Skies, Warren Faidley, 1996, Weather Channel, 182 pp., ISBN 1888763000. A popular coffee-table book written by a storm chasing journalist under a partnership with the Weather Channel. It's a non-technical book that unfolds the atmosphere's grandeur in large color photographs.

Techniques of Natural Light Photography, Jim Zuckerman, 1996. Writer's Digest Books, 137 pp., ISBN 0-89879-716-0. A great book that focuses on elements of outdoor photography.

Under The Whirlwind, Everything You Need To Know About Tornadoes, Arjen and Jerrine Verkaik, 2001. Whirlwind Books, 224 pp. ISBN 0968153747. There's information on tornado formation, forecasting, safety and a detailed personal account of a damaging tornado. The photos are awesome with images of storm structure, clouds and tornadoes.

Storm Chaser: A Photographer's Journey, Jim Reed, 2007. Abrams Books, 192 pp., ISBN 0810993929. This is a beautiful art book of storm, tornado, hurricane and other extreme weather images by Jim Reed. Although the focus is on the photos, the text is very interesting with descriptions of his storm chases and journal entries.

Adventures in Tornado Alley: The Storm Chasers, Mike Hollingshead and the late Eric Nguyen, 2008. Thames & Hudson, 192 pp., ISBN 0500287376. This book is a collection of amazing storm chase images, accounts and commentary organized by chase day along with a small section on the science of storms by Charles Doswell.

The Tornado: Nature's Ultimate Windstorm, Thomas P. Grazulis, 2003. University of Oklahoma Press, 304 pp., ISBN 0806135387. The author of the Tornado Project covers tornado forecasting, formation, historical events, myths and storm chasers.

Hurricane Katrina: Through the Eyes of Storm Chasers, Jim Reed and Mike Theiss.

Farcountry Press, 96 pp., ISBN 1560373776. A nice book of powerful images by two well-known storm chasers after their intense encounter with Hurricane Katrina in Mississippi. They show both the intensity of the storm and the human element.

Storm Chasers! On the Trail of Twisters, Jon Davies and Jessica Solberg, 2007. Farcountry Press, 48 pp., ISBN 1560374071. For children and even adults, this is a wonderful and engaging book that ties the science of storm formation to the excitement of storm chasing. The artwork, photos and diagrams are accurate and clear.

Tornado Hunter: Getting Inside the Most Violent Storms on Earth, Tim Samaras and Stefan Bechtel, 2009. National Geographic, 272 pp., ISBN 1426203020. Set for release May 19, 2009.

Hunting Nature's Fury: A Storm Chaser's Obsession with Twisters, Hurricanes, and Other Natural Disasters, Peter Bronski and Roger Hill, 2009. Lyons Press, 272 pages, ISBN 1599213052. Set for release March 3, 2009.

Publications

Stormtrack (newsmagazine), David Hoadley and Tim Marshall, 1977-2001. This publication was printed every two months, covering important topics of interest to chasers, along with summaries and educational articles. It's no longer in print, but the magazine's 25 years of articles are available on CD-ROM from Tim Marshall, along with many other great educational resources. Visit www.stormtrack.org !

A Comprehensive Glossary of Weather Terms for Storm Spotters, Michael L. Branick, 1993, NOAA Technical Memorandum SR-145. A monumental collection of severe weather terms and their meaning. Available online at www.srh.noaa.gov/oun/severewx/branick2.html

Videos

Storms of (2004/2005/2006/2007/2008). This series of DVDs was started with The Storms of 2004 by Greg Stumpf and Jim Ladue as a charity project to raise money for storm victims. Each DVD is a compilation of donated storm video organized by major chase day.

Tornado Video Classics, Tom Grazulis (Tornado Project), 1992, 3-part set. This is the single best collection of tornado video in existence. *<tornadoproject.com>*

The Chasers of Tornado Alley, Martin Lisius, 1996. During the 1995 chase season, Lisius shows us the human side of storm chasing, and what makes us tick. *<tempest-tours.net>*

The Art of Storm Chasing, Tim Vasquez and Shannon Key (Weather Graphics Technologies), 1999, 60 min. An introduction into storm chase strategy and safety, produced by this book's own author. It's becoming somewhat dated, but is still an engaging introduction. *<weathergraphics.com>*

Stormwatcher, Gene Rhoden, 1992, 40 min. This professionally-produced video is an exceptional introduction to understanding visual features of thunderstorms. *<weatherpix.com/shop>*

Driven by Passion, Tim Samaras, includes amazing tornado footage including video from inside a tornado. The 2003 beautiful Manchester, SD tornado is featured. *<thunderchase.com>*

Tornado Glory, a PBS program by filmmaker Ken Cole. This program profiles

Joel Taylor and Reed Timmer during the 2003 season, covering their aggressive style during a wild chase season. <*www.shoppbs.org*>

Extreme Storms, Nature At Her Worst, by Scott McPartland, Dave Lewison and Jim Edds. Chase accounts narrated with thoughts and strategies. Includes the famous Attica, KS tornado. <*www.extremestorms.com*>

Eastern Fury: Tornadoes of the Eastern United States, Bill Hark. A compilation of over two hours of extremely rare eastern tornado video by amateurs, media and storm chasers from 1953 to 2006. Many of the videos are close-up views of large tornadoes with flying debris that are as intense as tornadoes across the Plains. <*harkphoto.com*>

Internet sites

This section is reserved for web sites which have exceptionally unique content related to storm chasing. These also serve as perfect launching points to take you to countless other storm chasing sites, tornado photos, data and much more.

Stormtrack, the largest collection of chase discussion, news, and educational articles from the original chaser magazine.
www.stormtrack.org

Jon Davies, creator of the EHI index and a resident expert in Kansas storms, has a web page with excellent papers and photos.
www.jondavies.net

Roger Edwards Home Page, a large collection of writings, commentary, and insight from a veteran chaser and longtime SPC forecaster.
www.stormeyes.org/tornado

Chaser Convention, the February get-together every year in Denver, is a meeting of storm chasers, spotters, researchers and weather enthusiasts with lectures, vendors, and the traditional video night.
www.chaserconvention.com

Sam Barricklow's Storm Chase Homepage, loaded with chase accounts dating back to 1989, and devoted to amateur radio as it relates to chasing.
www.k5kj.net

Charles Doswell's home page, a vast collection of formal writings, essays, and outspoken rants from NOAA's most prolific severe weather researcher.
www.cimms.ou.edu/~doswell
www.flame.org/~cdoswell

Gene Moore has been chasing since the 1970s, hails from the San Antonio area, and has a highly informative website.
www.chaseday.com

Mike Geukes has perhaps the most exhaustive list of links related to storm chasing, in itself an noteworthy original work.
geukesweather.blogspot.com

Technical

To start with the true building blocks of storm knowledge, go straight to the journal papers that introduced these new findings!

Bluestein, Howard B., 1999: *A History of Severe-Storm-Intercept Field Programs.* Weather and Forecasting, Vol. 14, No. 4: 558-577. A fantastic overview of the history of research chasing.

Brooks, Harold E., Charles A. Doswell, and Robert B. Wilhelmson, 1994: *The role of midtropospheric winds in the evolution and maintenance of low-level mesocyclones.* Monthly Weather Review, Vol. 22, pg. 126-136. Explored possibilities for mechanisms that support a low-level mesocyclone, and the importance of the right storm-relative mid-level winds.

Doswell, Charles A. III, 1982: *The Operational Meteorology of Convective Weather, Volume 1: Operational Mesoanalysis.* NOAA Technical Memorandum NSSFC-5. A cornerstone paper on mesoscale analysis. Available online at: *www.weathergraphics.com/dl*

Doswell, Charles A. III, 1985: *The Operational Meteorology of Convective Weather, Volume 2: Storm Scale Analysis.* NOAA Technical Memorandum ERL ESG-15. Provides a succinct summary of the state of knowledge on storms during the mid-1980s.

Doswell, Charles A. III, Alan R. Moller, and Ron W. Przybylinski, 1990: *A unified set of conceptual models for variations on the supercell theme.* Preprints, 16th Conf. Severe Local Storms (Kananaskis Park, Alberta), AMS, 40-45.

Doswell, Charles A., Alan R. Moller, and Harold E. Brooks, 1999: *Storm Spotting and Public Awareness since the First Tornado Forecasts of 1948.* Wea. Forecasting, Vol. 14, 544–557.

Doswell, Charles A. III, 2000: *Severe Convective Storms — An Overview.* Chapter 1, Severe Convective Storms. Available online at: www.cimms.ou.edu/~doswell/Monograph/Overview.html

Fujita, Theodore, 1960: *A detailed analysis of the Fargo tornadoes of June 20, 1957.* U.S. Weather Bureau Research Paper 42. A hallowed pioneer work of tornado and storm structure, defining the wall cloud and many other features.

Galway, Joseph G., 1985: *J.P. Finley: The first severe storms forecaster.* Bulletin of the American Meteorological Society, Vol 66, No. 11: 1389-1395, and No. 12: 1506-1510.

Galway, J. G., 1989: *The Evolution of Severe Thunderstorm Criteria within the Weather Service,* Wea. Forecasting, Vol. 4, 585–592.

Galway, Joseph G., 1992: *Early severe thunderstorm forecasting and research by the United States Weather Bureau.* Weather and Forecasting, Vol. 7, 564-587.

Gropper, Daniel R., 1996: SKYWARN Net Control Operations Manual – National Edition. Washington, D.C.

Johns, Robert H. and William D. Hirt, 1987: *Derechos: widespread convectively induced windstorms.* Weather and Forecasting, Vol. 2, pp. 32-49.

Klemp, Joseph B. and Robert B. Wilhelmson, 1978: *Simulations of right- and left-moving storms produced through storm splitting.* Journal of the Atmospheric Sciences, Vol. 35, pg. 1097-1110. One of the first numerical simulations of a supercell.

Klemp, Joseph B. and Richard Rotunno, 1983: *A study of the tornadic region within a supercell thunderstorm.* Journal of the Atmospheric Sciences, Vol. 40, pg. 359-377.

Lemon, Leslie R. and Charles A. Doswell, 1979: *Severe thunderstorm evolution and mesocyclone structure as related to tornadogenesis.* Monthly Weather Review, Vol. 107, pg. 1184-1197. This is an extremely important paper that forms the foundation for visual aspects of the tornado's life cycle, as well as the behavior of the supercell itself.

Lilly, Douglas K., 1986: *The structure, energetics, and propagation of rotating convective storms.* Journal of the Atmospheric Sciences, Vol. 43, No. 2, pg. 113-140.

Moller, Alan R., Charles A. Doswell, and Ron W. Przybylinski, 1990: *High-precipitation supercells: a conceptual model and documentation.* Preprints, 16th Conf. Severe Local Storms (Kananaskis Park, Alberta), AMS, 52-57.

Moller, Alan R., Charles A. Doswell, Michael P. Foster, and Gary R. Woodall,

1994: *The operational recognition of supercell thunderstorm environments and storm structures.* Weather and Forecasting, Vol. 9: 327-347.

Rotunno, Richard, and Joseph B. Klemp, 1985: *On the rotation and propagation of simulated supercell thunderstorms.* Journal of the Atmospheric Sciences, Vol. 42, No. 3, pg. 271-292.

Schaefer, Joseph T., 1974: *The life cycle of the dryline.* Journal of Applied Meteorology, Vol. 13, pg 444-449. A fundamental paper on the dryline, its roots, and its behavior.

Schaefer, Joseph T., 1986: *Severe thunderstorm forecasting: a historical perspective.* Weather and Forecasting, Vol. 1, pg. 164-189. A great historical overview.

Schultz, David M., Katharine M. Kanak, Jerry M. Straka, Petra M. Klein, Robert J. Trapp, Brent A. Gordon, Dusan S. Zrnić, George H. Bryan, Adam J. Durant, Timothy J. Garrett, and Douglas K. Lilly, 2006: *The Mysteries of Mammatus Clouds: Observations and Formation Mechanisms.* J. Atmos. Sci., Vol. 63, 2409–2435. One of the first major modern studies of mammatus clouds.

Tegtmeier, Steve A., 1974: *The role of the surface sub-synoptic low pressure system in severe weather forecasting.* M.S. thesis, Univ. of Okla. One of the first papers to look at small-scale factors as causes of severe weather production.

Weisman, Morris L. and Joseph B. Klemp, 1984: *The structure and classification of numerically simulated convective storms in directionally varying wind shears.* Monthly Weather Review, Vol. 112, pg. 2479-2498.

Glossary

ACCAS. See *altocumulus castellanus*.
accessory *n.* Any secondary feature, such as a shelf cloud as distinguished from a large updraft base.
Allsup's *n.* Chain of convenience stores found in many small towns in the southern Plains.
altimeter setting *n.* Barometric pressure reduced to sea level, not corrected for any temperature trend, and usually expressed in inches of mercury ("in Hg"). Compare with *sea-level pressure*.
altocumulus castel-lanus *n.* Turreted or vertically-shaped altocumulus clouds, often seen in the hours before storm development, signifying mid-level instability.
anvil *n.* Upper portion of a thunderstorm, usually glaciated, fibrous, and in the shape of an anvil.
anvil crawlers *n.* Long flashes of lightning that appear to "crawl" within the anvil of the thunderstorm. It is quite pronounced within severe thunderstorms.
anvil zits *n.* Brief, very short flashes of lightning that occur within the anvil. They often appear to crawl around one another like bees in a hive.
arcus cloud *n.* Linear, horizontal cloud that tends to form along outflow boundaries.
backbuild *v.* To grow new updraft towers on the upshear side of a storm (usually to the southwest).
back *v.* 1. For a wind to change direction in a counterclockwise sense on the compass, such as from south to east, either with height or with time. The opposite of *veer*. 2. The nocturnal retreat of a dryline into the drier air.
backshear *n.* Tendency of an anvil to spread upshear, signifying a strong updraft or weak upper level winds.
bag *v. (Slang)* To intercept successfully.
barber pole *n.* An updraft tower which is wrapped with *helical bands*.
baroclinic *adj.* Quality of there being a horizontal temperature gradient across a given area, such as across a front.
barotropic *adj.* Quality of there being a lack of a horizontal temperature gradient across a given area.
bear's cage *n.* Rain-free area in updraft of HP supercell nearly surrounded by rain wrapped into mesocyclone.
blue box *n.* Severe thunderstorm watch box.
boundary *n.* Interface between two air masses. Includes fronts, drylines, and outflow boundaries.
bounded weak echo region *n.* Vaulted region of weak radar reflectivities in the upper portions of a very strong updraft; not readily resolvable with conventional radar products.
bow echo *n.* Radar echo showing a bowed appearance; indicative of high winds.
broken *adj.* Sky or cloud layer which is 60 to 90 percent filled with cloud material.
bubble high *n.* Strong high with bubble appearance on maps, usually formed by a large pool of outflow air from previous thunderstorms and surrounded by an outflow boundary.
bust *n.* Storm chase in which no storm was intercepted.
BWER See *bounded weak echo region*. Pronounced BEE-wahr.
cap *n.* Layer of warm air, often at a height of 2,000 to 10,000 feet above the ground, which tends to supress thunderstorm activity.
CAPE See *convective availability of potential energy*.
CAPE robber *n. (Slang)* Any unusual layer of warm air above 500 mb which significantly diminishes CAPE values. Quite prominent during the 1998 season.
Central Plains *n.* That part of the Great Plains covering central and northern Kansas, Colorado, and Nebraska.
cheesenado *n. (Slang)* Small, weak tornado of dubious nature.
CIN *See convective inhibition.*
CINH See *convective inhibition*.
clear *adj.* Absent of clouds.
clear slot *n.* Relatively cloud free area upwind of a storm (usually to the west) that wraps into the storm's circulation.
cloud tag *n.* Piece of *scud*; used in context of determining cloud motion and flow.
cone *n., adj.* Refers to a tornado which resembles a cone, but does not appear wider than it is tall.
confluence *n.* Tendency of *streamlines* to converge on a weather map. May indicate *convergence*. Opposite of *difluence*.
convective availability of potential energy (CAPE) *n.* Convective availability of potential energy; the total instability integrated throughout the depth of the cloud.
convective inhibition (CIN, CINH, -BE) *n.* Convective inhibition; the total stability that must be overcome for an updraft to reach its *level of free convection*.
convective temperature (T_c) *n.* The temperature which the atmosphere must be warmed to eliminate all *convective inhibition*. Storms often form well before the air temperature reaches the convective temperature.
convergence *n.* Process of air coming together on a horizontal plane. Low-level convergence usually results in upward motion; upper-level convergence usually results in downward motion.

core *n.* Portion of thunderstorm which contains the heaviest concentrations of hail and rain (highest radar reflectivity).
core punch *v.* Act of driving through a *core* or through any part of the storm where visibility is restricted.
cumulus *n.* Puffy clouds which represent buoyant, rising air.
cumulonimbus *n.* A *cumulus* cloud whose top contains characteristics of an *anvil*.
cyclogenesis *n.* Deepening of a low pressure area. Opposite of *cyclolysis*.
cyclolysis *n.* Weakening of a low pressure area. Opposite of *cyclogenesis*.
dewpoint *n.* Temperature at which condensation will occur; directly proportional to amount of moisture in air.
dewpoint depression *n.* Difference in degrees between the air temperature and the *dewpoint*. The larger the value, the drier the air.
derecho *n.* A *mesoscale convective system* which contains widespread severe weather; it often appears bow-shaped on radar. Pronounced da-RAY-show.
difluence *n.* Tendency for *streamlines* to spread apart. May indicate *divergence*. Opposite of *confluence*.
dig *v.* Process of an upper-level low to moving southward, producing an intensification of the weather pattern. Opposite of *lift*.
divergence *n.* Process of air moving apart on a horizontal plane. Low-level divergence usually results in downward motion; upper-level divergence usually results in upward motion.
downburst *n.* A strong *downdraft*.
downdraft *n.* The region of sinking air and precipitation within a thunderstorm. It is the counterpart to the *updraft*.
downshear *adj.* Downwind, as determined by the average winds through the troposphere rather than the wind at one given level. In a typical atmosphere, this is to the east or northeast.
dryline *n.* Boundary that separates moist, tropical air from warm, dry continental air.
dryline bulge *n.* Discontinuity along a dryline which expands unusally far into the moist air mass.
dry slot *n.* Region of dry air which surges into or over a frontal system, usually from the west.
earth mover *n.* Very strong tornado.
echo *n.* Area of radar reflectivity which indicates the presence of precipitation, dust, or other matter.
EHI *n.* See *energy-helicity index*.
energy-helicity index (EHI) *n.* Ratio between instability and low-level shear. Higher values are conducive to tornado development.
FFD *n.* See *forward flank downdraft*.
flanking line *n.* Line of cumulus towers, usually upwind of and attached to a storm, which represent the process of *backbuilding*.
forward flank downdraft *n.* The main downdraft area of a supercell which occurs downshear of the updraft; as differentiated from the *rear flank downdraft*.
gorilla hail *n. (Slang)* Large hail; typically baseball-sized or larger.
grinder *n. (Slang)* Large, slow-moving tornado.
grunge *n. (Slang)* See *grunge*.
gunge *n.* Low stratus or stratocumulus which interferes with chase navigation and observation. Common north of a warm front.
gust out *v.* Surge of outflow away from a storm, cutting it off from inflow (fuel).
gustnado *n.* Brief vortex that occurs along a fresh outflow boundary, not directly connected to the cloud.
hail *n.* Frozen sphere of ice which contains alternating layers of rime and clear ice.
hallucinado *n. (Slang)* False tornado report.
heat burst *n.* Unusual downdraft which contains warm air, sometimes up to 90 deg F. A typical episode occurs at night during the warm season.
helical bands *n.* Striations in the side of an updraft tower which are oriented upward and to the right. Indicative of a mesocyclone.
helicity *n.* The sum of the shear in the vertical through a column of air.
hodograph *n.* Diagram in which wind values at all heights above a station are plotted on an azimuth-range grid; allows shear and storm-relative motion to be easily visualized.
knuckles *n.* Knuckle-like protrusions from the side of a rock-hard anvil cloud which suggest a very strong updraft.
inflow *n.* Air which enters the storm; becomes part of the *updraft*.
instability *n.* Condition in which the air temperature cools rapidly with height; making strong vertical motions possible.
isentropic *adj.* Relating to the estimation of large-scale vertical motion by assuming that air parcels follow surfaces of equal potential temperature.
isobar *n.* Line connecting points of equal pressure.
isodrosotherm *n.* Line connecting points of equal dewpoint.
isotherm *n.* Line connecting points of equal temperature.
jet streak *n.* Localized area of very strong upper-level winds.
junkus *n. (Slang)* Weak thunderstorms, often those north of boundaries which are ingesting cold air.
landspout *n.* Weak tornado which is often spawned without the presence of a mesocyclone.
level of free convection *n.* Height at which a developing updraft no longer must pass through a layer of warmer air (thus accumulating negative buoyancy).
LFC See *level of free convection*.
lift *v.* 1. Upward motion. 2. The northward movement of an upper-level low, resulting in a weakening of the weather pattern; opposite of *dig*.
LLJ See *low level jet*.
low level jet *n.* A current of winds, usually at a height of 1 to 2 km,

which generally blows from south to north. It is important in transporting moisture to a threat area and increasing low-level shear.
mammatus *n.* Rounded bumps that form on the underside of an *anvil*. They bear no real indicator of storm strength.
meridional *adj.* State in which the net upper-level flow across a large region flows perpendicular to latitude lines rather than flowing with them. A south-to-north flow is meridional. Opposite of *zonal*.
mesocyclone *n.* Cyclonic circulation, measuring one to ten miles in diameter, which occurs within strong thunderstorms. Not to be confused with *mesolow*.
mesolow *n.* Cyclonic circulation measuring tens to hundreds of miles in diameter and may reflect small-scale processes occurring aloft which are acting on the atmosphere. Not to be confused with *mesocyclone*.
microburst *n.* An extremely localized *downburst*, usually measuring only a few miles in diameter or less.
mixing ratio *n.* Expression of the amount of moisture in the atmosphere; calibrated in grams of water vapor per kilogram of air.
model *n.* 1. A numerical model forecast, usually produced by a computer. 2. Any man-made representation of the real atmosphere, such as a conceptual model or a statistical model.
moisture *n.* The amount of water vapor in the air. While this technically does include liquid water, chasers usually are referring to water vapor, which contributes to latent heat, and thus, instability.
National Oceanic and Atmospheric Administration (NOAA) *n.* Executive agency which has general oversight of all official civilian weather efforts in the U.S. It falls under the Department of Commerce and is the parent organization of the National Weather Service.
National Severe Storms Laboratory (NSSL) *n.* Government agency based in Norman, Oklahoma. It specializes in severe weather research efforts and works cooperatively with the University of Oklahoma.
National Weather Service (NWS) *n.* Government agency which is tasked to produce operational weather forecasts and warning services for the United States.
negative tilt *adj.* Describing a trough whose axis extends northwest-southeast.
NOAA See *National Oceanic and Atmospheric Administration*.
NSSL See National Severe Storms Laboratory.
Northern Plains *n.* That part of the Great Plains covering the Canadian Prairie, Montana, and the Dakotas.
northwest flow *n., adj.* Referring to storms which develop in a region dominated by average tropospheric flow that moves from northwest to southeast. It results in unexpected storm orientations and movement.
nuclear cap *n.* An extremely strong *cap*.
NWS See *National Weather Service*.
outflow *n.* The pool of cool, dense air which is produced by the *downdraft*.
outflow boundary *n.* Interface which demarcates the edge of an area of rain-cooled air.
overcast *n., adj.* Sky or cloud layer completely filled with clouds.
parcel *n.* Imaginary bubble of air.
PFJ See *polar front jet*.
polar front jet (PFJ) *n.* A current of air, usually ringing the globe through temperate latitudes, and lying above or just north of polar fronts at the surface. It is important in increasing bulk shear and providing mechanisms which create imbalances or sets the atmosphere into motion.
positive tilt *adj.* Of a trough whose axis extends northeast-southwest.
pulse storm *n.* Storm which develops in high instability and very weak upper-level winds; strong and short-lived.
rear flank downdraft *n.* Area of downward motion and outflow upshear of a supercell updraft.
red box *n.* Tornado watch box.
road option *n.* One of a set of routes available to a chaser at any given time which allow an intercept or an escape. A chaser must know their road options at all times.
RFD See *rear flank downdraft*.
ridge *n.* 1. Elongated area of high barometric pressure. 2. An elongated area of high geopotential height, such as a long wave ridge; generally it is found where contours are deformed in a way that points poleward.
roll cloud *n.* A horizontal, tubular low cloud often associated with outflow-dominant storms.
rope out *v.* Evolution of a tornado into a thin rope shape in the decaying stage of its life cycle.
scattered *adj.* Sky or cloud layer which is 10 to 50 percent filled with cloud material.
scud *n.* Ragged stratus fragments hanging underneath an updraft base; indicative of strong outflow.
scudnado *n. (slang)* Collection of scud cloud material which yields the false appearance of a tornado.
SDS See *storm deprivation syndrome*.
sea level pressure *n.* Barometric pressure, reduced to sea level, and corrected for temperature trends over the past 12 hours; usually expressed in millibars. Compare with *altimeter setting*.
severe thunderstorm *n.* 1. (United States) Storm which produces 3/4-inch diameter hail or 50 kt (58 mph) winds. 2. (Australia) Storm which produces 2 cm hail, 90 km/h winds, flash floods, or tornadoes.
shear *n.* Measure of the change in the wind vector (speed and direction) over a given distance, usually in the vertical.
shelf cloud *n.* Horizontal, linear, laminar cloud often associated with squall line updraft bases.
short wave trough *n.* A small-scale trough reflected in the middle levels of the troposphere. Indicates a disrupted balance of wind forces in the atmosphere.

sidewinder *n.* Nonsensical term used in the film *Twister*.
sister *n.* Nonsensical term used in the film *Twister*.
sloshing *v., adj.* Of a dryline which moves back and forth predictably across a given area from one day to the next.
sheriffnado *n. (Slang)* Scud reported as a tornado by law enforcement, often triggering a false tornado warning.
Southern Plains *n.* That part of the Great Plains covering West Texas, Western Oklahoma, and the southern border areas of Kansas.
South Plains *n.* The southern portion of the Texas Caprock Escarpment, including Lubbock and Lamesa. (Not to be confused with *southern Plains*)
squeegee squall line *n. (slang)* Squall line which thoroughly scours out all moisture and instability.
SPC See *Storm Prediction Center*.
split *n.* 1. Condition in which a storm divides into two storms, one moving left and one moving right of the mean tropospheric flow. 2. Any portion of a storm that splits. —*v.* The act of splitting
spotter *n.* A person whose objective is to report the occurrence of severe weather.
squall line *n.* A highly linear thunderstorm, often measuring hundreds of miles long.
STJ See *subtropical jet*.
stogie *n. (slang)* Roll cloud.
storm deprivation syndrome (SDS) *n. (slang)* Imaginary ailment, often manifested by depression, which is caused by the lack of chase opportunities.
Storm Prediction Center *n.* A NOAA facility located in Norman, Oklahoma which is responsible for all severe and hazardous weather watches and outlooks in the United States.
storm-relative *adj.* Measured relative to the motion of a storm.
streamline *n.* Line on a weather map drawn parallel to the wind flow.
striations *n.* See *helical bands*.
subsidence *n.* Downward motion of air.
subtropical jet (STJ) *n.* A jet stream which tends to originate from latitudes equatorward of 30 degrees. It is not associated with strong surface air mass contrasts. The subtropical jet is always equatorward of the polar front jet.
supercell *n.* Large storm which contains a deep, persistent mesocyclone.
synoptic *adj.* Having a scale of several hundred to thousands of miles, or a lifecycle of days.
tag See *cloud tag*.
tornado *n.* A violently-rotating column of air in contact with the ground and the cloud base. It originates within a *mesocyclone*.
transverse *adj.* Perpendicular to the flow of air.
triple point *n.* The intersection of two boundaries, usually a dryline and a warm front.
trough *n.* 1. Elongated area of low barometric pressure. 2. An elongated area of low geopotential height, such as a short wave trough; generally it is found where contours are deformed in a way that points equatorward.
turkey tower *n. (Slang)* Vertical cumulus clouds which become sheared apart by upper-level winds, briefly taking on the appearance of turkey heads.
TWC See *Weather Channel*.
updraft *n.* The region of rising motion and cumuliform towers within a thunderstorm. The counterpart to the *downdraft*.
upflow *n.* Nonsensical term used in the film *Twister*.
upshear *adj.* Upwind, as determined by the average winds through the troposphere rather than the wind at one given level. In a typical atmosphere, this is to the southwest or west.
upslope (flow) *n.* Condition in which air flows from lower to higher terrain. Lift of the lower atmosphere is forced by the terrain.
veer *v.* The changing of winds in a clockwise sense on the compass, such as from east to south, either with height or with time. The opposite of *back*.
vortex *n.* Any rotating column of air.
vorticity *n.* A property of air in which rotation occurs around an axis.
wall cloud *n.* A marked lowering of an updraft base; often associated with intensification and tornadic development.
watch box *n.* Geographic area covered by an official weather watch.
weak echo region (WER) *n.* Region of weak radar reflectivities overlain by strong reflectivities in an intense updraft; not readily resolvable with conventional radar products.
Weather Channel, The (TWC) *n.* Cable/satellite television service providing 24-hour weather information. Starting in 1982, it is owned by Landmark Communications and has operated continously from Atlanta, Georgia.
wedge *n., adj.* Tornado which appears wider than it is tall.
wind direction *n.* Direction in which the wind is originating from.
WER See *weak echo region*.
worked over *adj.* Condition in which an air mass has been stabilized by outflow air. Typically occurs within a bubble high.
zonal *adj.* Tendency for the net upper-level flow across a large region to flow parallel to latitude lines rather than crossing them. A west-to-east flow is zonal. Opposite of *meridional*.

Index

K

L

M

N

O

P

R

S

T

U

V

W

X

Y

Z

I recall one evening in a small, dirt-road town in western North Dakota, when I excitedly stopped to photograph an approaching squall line. It was wrapped in green and purple, above a rolling wall of dust --and I locked the keys in the car!

I ran to the nearest house for help. An old Swedish couple greeted me at the door and said the storm was too close and to come in and have dinner. The retired farmer said he would loan me a hammer to break the vent window after the storm passed. Then, while it raged outside with wind, rain and hail, his wife filled the dinner table with an absolute banquet. I don't recall all the condiments, but do remember her meat loaf was wonderfully seasoned and the pecan pie, hot from the oven, was the best I ever ate.

The storm subsided; I got the hammer and got the keys. After thanking them again for dinner --and as they waved from the doorway, I drove away into the night to my Bismarck home. We knew we would probably never see each other again, but that didn't matter.

Then it occurred to me how infrequently they probably had out-of-town guests of any kind, with children and grandchildren long gone. There I was at their door, a young boy with an interesting hobby and just starting his life. They couldn't hear enough about who I was, and what I wanted to become. Only then came the realization that I may have given them as much as they gave me. That night taught me how important it is to share with others, and what an impact each of us can have, that may leave behind a world that's a little better.

DAVID HOADLEY

Chase Logs

This section can be used to log basic information about the chase day, odometer readings, expenses, etc.

All chase log pages may be photocopied from this book and reproduced without restriction.

CONTACTS & PHONE NUMBERS

Chase Log

YEAR —

March 1

March 2

March 3

March 4

March 5

March 6

March 7

March 8

March 9

March 10

March 11

March 12

March 13

March 14

March 15

March 16

March 17

March 18

March 19

March 20

March 21

March 22

March 23

March 24

March 25

March 26

March 27

March 28

March 29

March 30

March 31

CHASE LOG

YEAR —

April 1

April 2

April 3

April 4

April 5

April 6

April 7

April 8

April 9

April 10

April 11

April 12

April 13

April 14

April 15

April 16

April 17

April 18

April 19

April 20

April 21

April 22

April 23

April 24

April 25

April 26

April 27

April 28

April 29

April 30

CHASE LOG

YEAR —

May 1

May 2

May 3

May 4

May 5

May 6

May 7

May 8

May 9

May 10

May 11

May 12

May 13

May 14

May 15

May 16

May 17

May 18

May 19

May 20

May 21

May 22

May 23

May 24

May 25

May 26

May 27

May 28

May 29

May 30

May 31

Chase Log

YEAR —

June 1

June 2

June 3

June 4

June 5

June 6

June 7

June 8

June 9

June 10

June 11

June 12

June 13

June 14

June 15

June 16

June 17

June 18

June 19

June 20

June 21

June 22

June 23

June 24

June 25

June 26

June 27

June 28

June 29

June 30

YEAR —

July 1

July 2

July 3

July 4

July 5

July 6

July 7

July 8

July 9

July 10

July 11

July 12

July 13

July 14

July 15

July 16

July 17

July 18

July 19

July 20

July 21

July 22

July 23

July 24

July 25

July 26

July 27

July 28

July 29

July 30

July 31

NOTES

CHASE LOG

YEAR —

March 1

March 2

March 3

March 4

March 5

March 6

March 7

March 8

March 9

March 10

March 11

March 12

March 13

March 14

March 15

March 16

March 17

March 18

March 19

March 20

March 21

March 22

March 23

March 24

March 25

March 26

March 27

March 28

March 29

March 30

March 31

CHASE LOG

YEAR —

April 1

April 2

April 3

April 4

April 5

April 6

April 7

April 8

April 9

April 10

April 11

April 12

April 13

April 14

April 15

April 16

April 17

April 18

April 19

April 20

April 21

April 22

April 23

April 24

April 25

April 26

April 27

April 28

April 29

April 30

Chase Log

YEAR —

May 1

May 2

May 3

May 4

May 5

May 6

May 7

May 8

May 9

May 10

May 11

May 12

May 13

May 14

May 15

May 16

May 17

May 18

May 19

May 20

May 21

May 22

May 23

May 24

May 25

May 26

May 27

May 28

May 29

May 30

May 31

CHASE LOG

YEAR —

June 1

June 2

June 3

June 4

June 5

June 6

June 7

June 8

June 9

June 10

June 11

June 12

June 13

June 14

June 15

June 16

June 17

June 18

June 19

June 20

June 21

June 22

June 23

June 24

June 25

June 26

June 27

June 28

June 29

June 30

CHASE LOG

YEAR —

July 1

July 2

July 3

July 4

July 5

July 6

July 7

July 8

July 9

July 10

July 11

July 12

July 13

July 14

July 15

July 16

July 17

July 18

July 19

July 20

July 21

July 22

July 23

July 24

July 25

July 26

July 27

July 28

July 29

July 30

July 31